AGEING

AGEING

THE BIOLOGY OF SENESCENCE

by

Alex Comfort

HOLT, RINEHART AND WINSTON, INC
New York . Chicago . San Francisco

First published in 1956 as
THE BIOLOGY OF SENESCENCE

This revised and reset edition
published 1964 as
AGEING: THE BIOLOGY OF SENESCENCE

Library of Congress Catalog Card Number: 64-15946

Printed in Great Britain
21526-0214

To the question propounded . . ., I can make only one answer: yes, it is useful to prolong human life.

ILYA METCHNIKOFF (1907)

PREFACE TO THE FIRST EDITION

THIS book is a compilation. It was written as an aid to my own research, in a subject where it is difficult to know where to begin, but I hope that the references, at least, will be useful to others.

The denunciation of a subject and its current theoretical basis as 'unsatisfactory' is a relatively easy exercise—dealing with it satisfactorily is quite another matter. No biological treatment of senescence can hope to be satisfactory in the absence of a great deal of factual information which at present is not there. I have attempted to collect as much of this information as possible: since most of it comes from fields in which I have no experience, there are bound to be errors both of fact and of deduction in such a survey, and I hope that they will be pointed out to me.

I am deeply grateful to Professor Peter Medawar, F.R.S., under whom I have worked, to Professor J. B. S. Haldane, F.R.S., for kindly drawing my attention to a number of references I would not otherwise have seen, and to many colleagues whom I have molested for information or criticism, and whose help and advice has been invaluable, though they bear no responsibility for the result. I am also profoundly indebted to the Nuffield Foundation for several years' financial support, to Dr. Harrison Matthews, Director of the London Zoo, for access to its records, and to Miss Rosemary Birbeck and Miss Jane Henderson for much help in preparing the manuscript and bibliography.

ALEX COMFORT

December 1954

PREFACE TO THE REVISED EDITION

IT is a cheering fact for age studies that this second edition has to be effectively a new book. The rate of advance in gerontology has been slow initially, but fast enough to enable us to give answers where in 1954 we asked questions—about the presence or absence of senescence in fish, for example. About one-third of the text is wholly new, including the sections on radiation and somatic mutation, and a large part of the bibliography. It seems a reasonable hope that the process will repeat itself, so that the questions asked in this edition may be answered ten years from now—this is one of the functions of compilatory textbooks such as mine.

ALEX COMFORT

October 1963

CONTENTS

Contents

Contents

FIGURES

Figures

Figures

xiv

Figures

—Ah quanta spes est, Lapidem sperare Sapientium! What a hope that is, to have the Philosopher's Stone! Yet what shall it profit him if meanwhile he that has it sickens? if he groans in the torments of pain? if he rots in a merciless corruption? if wasting and the regiment of fevers contrive his death? To him that has riches and desires to have more, this is a most bitter fate . . . Yet none of these need the Chymist fear. His hope is fixed in the sufficiency of that secret in which he rejoices . . . For not only has this noble Medicine the virtue of combatting all the embattled forces of disease—it sustains the very vitals, nourishes the breath, and so conserves the natural heat that perfusing the whole body and entering all the limbs it ingenders and maintains there a constant motion and vigour . . . O Alchymist's hope, how you charm our minds, and with what promise you comfort us! To hold to an unfailing bodily health, a constant vigour and tranquillity of mind, to preserve these into a green and rugged old age, until, without a struggle or any sickness, soul and body dissever . . . The old granddam regains a merry suppleness, the long dry juice of her youth returns, as source and witness of her renewed fruitfulness. Grey hairs fall, and young curls appear; her teeth are renewed—new fingernails grow and the old are shed. The wrinkles of her brow fill and level, she straightens and she shines . . . Even old moulted fowls feather and lay eggs again. . . .

Yet alas for that fortunate hope: the nearer they win to it, so much more does the possession threaten present dangers to them that all but have it. And how these may be avoided I do not know. . . .

Abram Kaau von Boerhaave, *Declamatio academica de Gaudiis Alchemistarum.* 1737.

INTRODUCTION

0·1 *Introductory and Historical*

IF we kept throughout life the same resistance to stress, injury and disease which we had at the age of ten, about one-half of us here today might expect to survive in 700 years' time. The reason that we cannot is that in man, and in many, but probably not all, other animals, the power of self-adjustment and self-maintenance declines with the passage of time, and the probability of disease and death increases. The increase in man becomes eventually so steep that while exceptional individuals may outlast a century, there is an effective limit, depending upon our present age, upon the number of years for which any of us can reasonably expect to go on living. The uniformity of this process is one of the earliest unpleasant discoveries which every individual has to make, and although we have many psychological expedients to blunt its impact, the fact of this effective fixity of life-span, and of the decline in activity and health which often determine it, is always in the background of the human mind.

This process of change is senescence, and senescence enters human experience through the fact that man exhibits it himself. This close involvement with human fears and aspirations may account for the very extensive metaphysical literature of ageing. It certainly accounts for the profound concern with which humanity has tended to regard the subject. To a great extent human history and psychology must always have been determined and moulded by the awareness that the life-span of any individual is determinate, and that the expectation of life tends to decrease with increasing age. The Oriental could say 'O King, live for ever!' in the knowledge that every personal tyranny has its term. Every child since the emergence of language has probably asked 'Why did that man die?' and has been told 'He died because he was old.'

1

Introduction

Interesting psychological and historical speculation could be made on the part which this awareness has played in human affairs. From the biologist's standpoint, its main importance has been the bias which it has injected into the study of senescence. The child who asks the question, and receives the answer, is familiar with 'old' clothes and 'old' toys. He has always known that he, his pets, his cattle and his neighbours will become increasingly prone to breakdown and ultimate death the older they get. He has observed from the nursery that inanimate and mechanical systems also deteriorate with the passage of time. He appears at a later age to derive some degree of comfort from the contemplation of the supposed generality, universality and fundamental inherence of ageing—or alternatively from drawing a contrast between Divine or cosmic permanence and his own transience. However inspiring this type of thinking may have been—and it features largely in the past artistic and philosophical productions of all cultures—its influence and its incorporation as second nature into the thought of biologists throughout history has seriously handicapped the attempt to understand what exactly takes place in senescence, which organisms exhibit it, and how far it is really analogous to processes of mechanical wear.

Our object in studying the biology of ageing is to find out why it occurs, and whether and how it can be controlled. This is not a new ambition. The fact that in past generations there was a much higher death-rate at all ages did not make our ancestors any less inclined to rebel against the knowledge that they must decline with age: the protest took the form of legends in which fortunate mortals became actually or effectively immortal—sometimes with effects which punished their presumption: Aurora obtained the gift of immortality for Tithonus, but omitted to obtain perpetual youth. Cadmus and his wife, given the same opportunity, chose the rather wiser course of becoming animals of reputedly indeterminate, or at least very long, life-span, and were metamorphosed to

> 'two bright and aged snakes
> that once were Cadmus and Harmonia'.

Legends of enormous longevity from natural causes, because

they are cheering reservations on the normal life-span, have always been popular, and still exist to mislead research workers. Those for whom legends were not enough adopted another common expedient by making the unpleasant uplifting; and senescence is the subject of a vast body of edifying matter, literary, philosophical and religious. One product of this attitude, the belief that it is impious, and must lead to some form of retributive disaster, to tamper with fate or the process of ageing, is with us today.

There have, however, always been ingenious men who were not prepared to accept these biological limitations in a contemplative spirit. Magic was first of all applied to ward off both disease and old age. With the rise of medicine, physicians came to distinguish between the two. Disease very often did respond to treatment, and it generally tended, in the young, to self-repair: age changes did not. The physicians tended more and more to devote their attention to acute processes of illness and injury, and to share the pious and fatalistic assessment of ageing. Attempts to alter the life-span fell again into the semi-magical province of sages, alchemists and quacks. The Chinese sages had claimed substantial success in prolonging their own life-span, and that of their disciples, sometimes by a studied detachment from the world and its dangers, but also, with greater physiological likelihood, by systems of general and sexual gymnastics of a rather involved kind (Needham, 1957). One of the most successful was reputedly the sage Wei Po-Yang (second century A.D.), who was also, perhaps, the originator of the concept of the philosophers' stone, a substance capable both of producing gold from lead, and of averting the changes of age. This idea played a significant part in scientific history, for the European alchemists of a later period divided their time between the transmutation of the elements and the elixir of life, which was to give them time to enjoy the gold they intended to make. By the end of the last century both these projects had come, with the growth of natural sciences, to be regarded as fundamental impossibilities, which were suitable fields for charlatans and paranoiacs, and should be left alone by responsible scientists. Of the two 'fundamental impossibilities', the transmutation of the elements has beaten the control of ageing by a very long head. Travel to the Moon, another uproariously unlikely project entertained by early alchemists, seems as if it too will do so. Serious research into the control of age processes stands today at about the point where physical chemistry stood when Bécquerel first observed the spontaneous transmutation of a radioactive element—it has moved out of the field of eccentricity and is becoming the subject of more and more coordinated research by the standard methods of experimental biology. It now seems evident that while any large measure of control over human ageing might eventually prove impracticable, it is certainly not a fundamental impossibility of the circle-squaring variety, and we have the assignment of finding out by planned experiment how much can be done in this direction.

Technological research has, of course, the immense advantage over biological that in most cases the problem is one of fulfilling known requirements—the mechanical requirements of space travel have been known, in outline at least, for a century or more. In attempting to alter the rate at which vitality declines with age, the requirements are not known, and the initial problem is to ascertain them.

One result of the involvement of senescence with philosophy and the 'things that matter' has been the prevalence of attempts to demonstrate general theories of senile change, including all metazoa and even inanimate objects, and having an edifying and a metaphysical cast. Prominent among these have been attempts to equate ageing with development, with the 'price' of multicellular existence, with hypothetical mechano-chemical changes in colloid systems, with the exhaustion induced by reproductive processes, and with various concepts tending to the philosophical contemplation of decline and death.

It is not unreasonable to point out that these theories have for the most part deeper psychological and anthropological than experimental and observational roots. Some of them have a few facts on their side. 'Reproductive exhaustion' does appear to induce senescence in fish and in mollusca, and flowering is a proximate cause of death in monocarpic plants, but the general concept, especially when it is made a universal, owes a large debt to the widespread belief in human cultures that sexuality

4

'has its price'. Extensions of mechanical analogies from the wearing out of tools to the wearing out of animal bodies are justifiable in a limited number of cases where structures such as teeth undergo demonstrable wear with use, and where this process limits the life of the organism; but they have also shown a tendency to become generalized in the hands of biologists who are devoted for philosophical, political or religious reasons, to mechanism in the interpretation of human behaviour. Statements that 'senescence is no more than the later stage of embryology' resemble Benjamin Rush's great discovery, that all disease is disordered function. They belong to the category of word-rearrangement games, which have long been played in those fields of study where there is as yet no 'hard news'.

Although the religious, poetic, metaphysical and philosophical literatures of senescence will not be examined here, the detection and examination of analogies based upon them, which have had a great, and generally adverse, influence on the growth of our knowledge of age processes, must clearly play a large part in any critical examination of the subject. The comments of Francis Bacon, who was both a philosophical originator of the scientific method, and the first systematic English gerontologist,[1] provide one of the best critiques of the influence of such analogies and thought-patterns, and they will be quoted without scruple here.

The practical importance of work upon the biology of senescence, beyond the fundamental information which such work might give about the mechanisms of cell differentiation and renewal, can best be seen from the diagrams at Figs. 1–3 and 7. The advance of public health has produced a conspicuous shift in the shape of the survival curve in man so far as the privileged countries are concerned, from the oblique to the rectangular form. This has been due almost entirely to a reduction in the mortality of the younger age groups—the human 'specific age' and the maximum life-span have not been appreciably altered. The medical importance of work on the nature of ageing lies at

---

[1] I dislike this word, but it is probably too well grown for eradication. It should mean 'a student of old men' ($\gamma\acute{\epsilon}\varrho\omega\nu$) and gerontology the study of old men. For the study of age itself, the subject of this book, we require geratology ($\gamma\tilde{\eta}\varrho\alpha\varsigma$), upon which it would be fruitless to insist.

present less in the immediate prospect of spectacular interference with the process of senescence than in the fact that unless we understand old age we cannot treat its diseases or palliate its unpleasantness. At present age-linked diseases are coming to account for well over half the major clinical material in any Western medical practice. We are producing Tithonuses. The physician is constantly referring to the biologist for a scientific basis for geriatrics, and finding that it is not there. The amount of material on which such a foundation could be built has increased, though not very rapidly, during the present century. Its quantity is still inversely proportional to the humane importance of the subject.

There are now several reviews of the modern biological literature. The most recent are those of Lansing (1951, 1952), Birren (1959), Strehler (1962) and Korenschevsky (1961). Some of the more celebrated 'general theories' have received spirited treatment in a review by Medawar (1945). The literature of animal population statistics has been reviewed by Deevey (1947) and that of invertebrate senescence by Szabó (1935) and by Harms (1949). It is a pleasure to acknowledge my indebtedness to these reviews and to the bibliographies of Shock (1951) and of Nikitin (1958: Russian pre- and post-Revolutionary age studies). A great deal of clinico-pathological material upon the age-incidence of various human diseases and the weights of organs throughout life has been collected by Bürger (1954). In a depressingly large number of fields, there has been little new information in the last twenty years. Other reviews of specific topics will be cited in their place. The senescence of plants is not discussed here: it has been well reviewed elsewhere (Crocker, 1939; Heath, 1957; Leopold, 1961).

Senescence is probably best regarded as a general title for the group of effects which, in various phyla, lead to a decreasing expectation of life with increasing age. It is not, in this sense, a 'fundamental', 'inherent', or otherwise generalizable process, and attempts to find one underlying cellular property which explains all instances of such a change are probably misplaced. It is important and desirable to recognize the origins of many such general theories, which owe much to folk-lore on one hand and to the emotional make-up of their authors on the other. The demoralizing effect of the subject of senescence, even upon biologists of the highest competence and critical intelligence, is well illustrated by the following passage from Pearl (1928), the father of animal actuarial studies:

'(Somatic death in metazoa) is simply the price they pay for the privilege of enjoying those higher specializations of structure and function which have been added on as a sideline to the main business of living things, which is to pass on in unbroken continuity the never-dimmed fire of life itself.'

Warthin (1929), whose insistence upon the fundamental impossibility of modifying the tempo of human ageing, now or at any time in the future, has an orgiastic tone quite out of keeping with the rashness of such a prediction, writes:

'We live but to create a new machine of a little later model than our own, a new life-machine that in some ineffable way can help along the great process of evolution of the species somehow more efficiently than we could do were we immortal. The Universe, by its very nature, demands mortality for the individual if the life of the species is to attain immortality through the ability to cope with the changing environment of successive ages. . . . It is evident that *involution* is a biologic entity equally important with *evolution* in the broad scheme of the immortal process of life. Its processes are as *physiologic* as those of growth. It is therefore inherent in the cell itself, an intrinsic, inherited quality of the germ plasm and no slur or stigma of *pathologic* should be cast upon this process. What its exact chemicophysical mechanism is will be known only when we know the nature of the *energy-charge* and the *energy-release* of the cell. We may say, therefore, that age, the major involution, is due primarily to the gradually weakening *energy-charge* set in action by the moment of fertilization, and is dependent upon the potential fulfilment of function by the organism. The immortality of the germ plasm rests upon the renewal of this energy charge from generation to generation.'

This passage is highly typical of the subfossil and recent literature of old age. There can be few branches of biology in which

7

uplifting generalization of this kind has so long been treated as a respectable currency for scientific thought.

In general, the more elaborate the attempts to depict senescence in overall mathematical terms, the more intellectually disastrous they have proved. One of the most celebrated incursions of metaphysics into biology, that which postulates a separate 'biological time', is best expounded in the words of its sponsor, Lecomte du Noüy (1936):

'When we refer to sidereal time as being the canvas on which the pattern of our existence is spread, we notice that the time needed to effectuate a certain unit of physiological work of repair is about four times greater at fifty than at ten years of age. Everything, therefore, occurs as if sidereal time flowed four times faster for a man of fifty than for a child of ten. It is evident, on the other hand, that from a psychological point of view many more things happen to a child in a year than to an old man. The year therefore seems much longer to the child. . . . Thus we find that when we take physiological time as a unit of comparison, physical time no longer flows uniformly. This affirmation revolts one if the words are taken in a literal sense. But . . . the expression "flow of time" . . . is entirely false and does not correspond to a reality. When . . . we say that physical time measured by means of a unit borrowed from our physiological time no longer flows uniformly, it simply means that it does not *seem* to flow uniformly. . . . Must one consider this fact as the indication of a difference of magnitude between our short individual period and the immense periods of the universe? Must we see a proof of the existence of such periods? Who knows? All that we can say at present is that our crude language, lacking appropriate words, translates this knowledge into improper, inadequate expressions such as "There are two species of time" or "Physiological time does not flow uniformly like physical time" . . . We must not let ourselves be duped by these words, etc. . . .'

It is startling how many distinguished biologists have subsequently quoted the notion of a distinct 'biological' time with apparent sanction. Even now, nonsense of almost Teilhardian proportions has lately been written on the same matter by

Reichenbach and Mathers (1959). The alcoholic who draws on his bottle irregularly will find that its progress towards emptiness follows an irregular scale, 'alcoholic time', so that judged by the rate of emptying of the bottle, 'sidereal' time appears to progress unevenly. But variation in rate is hardly an occult, or even an unfamiliar, phenomenon. Like others before him, du Noüy has gone down clutching a platitude and come up embracing a metaphysical system.

In almost any other important biological field than that of senescence, it is possible to present the main theories historically, and to show a steady progression from a large number of speculative, to one or two highly probable, main hypotheses. In the case of senescence this cannot profitably be done. The general theories of its nature and cause which have been put forward from the time of Aristotle to the present day have fallen into a number of overall groups, and have been divided almost equally between fundamentalist theories which explain all senescence, or treat it as an inherent property of living matter or of metazoan cells, and epiphenomenalist theories which relate it to particular physiological systems or conditions. They are also fairly evenly divided between the various categories of Baconian idola. It is a striking feature of these theories that they show little or no historical development; they can much more readily be summarized as a catalogue than as a process of developing scientific awareness. To the fundamentalist group belong, in the first place, all theories which assume the existence of cellular 'wear and tear' (*Abnutzungstheorie*) without further particularization (Weismann, 1882; Pearl, 1928; Warthin, 1929); the mechanochemical deterioration of cell colloids (Bauer, Bergauer, 1924; Růžícká, 1924, 1929; Dhar, 1932; Lepeschkin, 1931; Szabó, 1931; Marinesco, 1934; Kopaczewski, 1938; Georgiana, 1949); and pathological or histological elaborations of these, which attribute senescence to inherent changes in specified tissues, nervous (Muhlmann, 1900, 1910, 1914, 1927; Ribbert, 1908; Vogt and Vogt, 1946; Bab, 1948), endocrine (Lorand, 1904; Gley, 1922; Dunn, 1946; Findley, 1949; Parhon, 1955; to cite only a few from an enormous literature in which the endocrine nature of mammalian senescence is discussed, stated or assumed), vascular (Demange, 1886), or

9

even connective (Bogomolets, 1947). To the epiphenomenalist group belong toxic theories based on products of intestinal bacteria (Metchnikoff, 1904, 1907; Lorand, 1929; Metalnikov, 1937), accumulation of 'metaplasm' or of metabolites (Kassowitz, 1899; Jickeli, 1902; Montgomery, 1906; Muhlmann, 1910; Molisch, 1938; Heilbrunn, 1943; Lansing 1942, etc.), the action of gravity (Darányi, 1930), the accumulation of heavy water (Hakh and Westling, 1934) and the deleterious effect of cosmic rays (Kunze, 1933). There are also general developmental theories which stress the continuity of senescence with morphogenesis (Baer, 1864; Cholodkowsky, 1882; Roux, 1881; Delage, 1903; Warthin, 1929) or the operation of an Aristotelean entelechy (Driesch, 1941; Bürger, 1954), metabolic theories introducing the concept of a fixed-quantity reaction or of a rate/quantity relationship in determining longevity (Rubner, 1908; Loeb, 1908; Pearl, 1928; Robertson, 1923), attainment of a critical volume-surface relationship (Muhlmann, 1910, etc.), depletive theories relating senescence to reproduction (Orton, 1929) and finally an important group of theories which relate senescence to the cessation of somatic growth (Minot, 1908; Carrel and Ebeling, 1921; Brody, 1924; Bidder, 1932; Lansing, 1947, 1951). Most of the older theories have been reviewed, against a background of Drieschian neovitalism in the textbook of Bürger (1954), and historically by Grmek (1958). An extremely sensible undated book by Ernest (n.d.) seems to have had little notice taken of it when it first appeared.

The distribution of dates in this catalogue sufficiently indicates the state of the subject. When Francis Bacon examined the relationship between animal specific longevity, growth-rate, size and gestation period, he concluded that the available facts were unfortunately insufficient to support a general theory. That conclusion remains valid in practically all the instances quoted, but Bacon's self-denial failed to set a precedent for his successors. Almost all these theories, judging from the literature, continue at some point to influence biological thinking: some can be partially, or even largely, justified by the suitable selection of instances. Others did not bear critical inspection at the time they were first formulated, bearing in mind the known behaviour of cells, and the known discrepancies in longevity and in rate of ageing between animals of similar size, histological complexity, and physiological organization. Relatively few are supported by any body of fundamental experiment. The devising of general theories of senescence has employed able men, chiefly in their spare time from laboratory research, for many years. It seems reasonable to assume that almost all the mechanisms which might theoretically be involved have been considered, and if we are to understand what does in fact occur in a given ageing organism, we now need a combination of general observation with planned causal analysis in experimental animals.

The main theories of ageing will be discussed in the text. They were admirably reviewed by Lipschutz in 1915, and have changed remarkably little since. There are, however, a few which should be outlined in greater detail here—either because they are still of importance, or because, though untenable, they have a considerable surviving influence.

The most influential nineteenth-century contribution to this second category was probably that of Weismann, whose theory sprang directly from his distinction between germ plasm and soma. Weismann regarded senescence as an inherent property of metazoa, though not of living matter, since he failed to find it in protozoans and other unicellular organisms. Its evolution had gone hand in hand with the evolution of the soma as a distinct entity, and it was the product of natural selection, arising like other mutants by chance, but perpetuated as a positively beneficial adaptation, because 'unlimited duration of life of the individual would be a senseless luxury'. 'Death', according to this view, 'takes place because a worn-out tissue cannot forever renew itself. . . . Worn-out individuals are not only valueless to the species, but they are even harmful, for they take the place of those which are sound' (1882). This argument both assumes what it sets out to explain, that the survival of an individual decreases with increasing age, and denies its own premise, by suggesting that worn-out individuals threaten the existence of the young. It had the advantage, however, of being an evolutionary theory, and we shall see later that this is the only type of theory which today seems likely to offer a general approach to the emergence of senescence in all the groups which exhibit it. The idea that all somatic cells must necessarily undergo irreversible senescence was challenged early in the century by the studies of Child (1915) upon planarians, and of Carrel (1912) upon tissue culture. The assumption that all higher metazoa must *ex hypothesi* exhibit senescence, however, dies hard, and the fallacious argument based on selection has been repeated as recently as 1937 (Metalnikov, 1936, 1937).

A considerable number of *metabolic theories* were based on the fact that an inverse relationship exists between length of life and 'rate of living'. On the basis of calorimetric experiments, Rubner (1908, 1909) calculated that the amount of energy required for the doubling of weight by body growth was approximately equal in a number of mammals. The energy requirement for the maintenance of metabolism, per unit adult body weight, was also approximately equal between species. Rubner inferred that senescence might, from these energy relationships, represent the completion of one particular system of chemical reactions, depending on a fixed total energy expenditure. He was obliged to erect a special category for man, whose energy requirement was found to be far higher than in laboratory or domestic animals. Loeb (1902, 1908) attempted to find out whether the temperature coefficient of this hypothetical reaction was identical with that of general rate of development. Working with echinoderm eggs at various temperatures, and using a hatchability criterion to determine 'senescence', if the word can be used in such a highly-specialized instance, he concluded that the two coefficients were distinct. The importance of this work has been that its presuppositions have recurred in later studies, where some authors have based very similar inferences about the relationship of growth and senescence to a 'monomolecular, autocatalytic reaction' on the shape and supposed mathematical proportions of the growth curve. As D'Arcy Thompson pointed out, this might equally prove the 'autocatalytic' character of growth in a human population. In fact, with suitable adjustment, curves based on biological material can be made to provide support for almost any hypothesis of this kind.

Little need be said of the various *toxic or pathological* theories of mammalian senescence. There has been endless unfruitful discussion as to how far *senectus ipsa morbus* and how far pathological and physiological ageing can be separated: the most sensible recent exponent of a sharp distinction was Korenchevsky (1961) whose constant propaganda for more research on age processes makes him the obstetrician if not the father of modern gerontology. In his theory the distinction is chiefly a practical matter, since he believed that pathology was likely to yield to treatment, while 'essential' ageing was not: his study makes little contribution to the understanding of the underlying vigour loss, and concentrates rather on endocrinal supplements. We are really left with five historically important theories, or groups of observations: the suggestion of Weismann that senescence is evolved, not intrinsic in all cellular matter; the work of Pearl (1928) which leads to the conception of a 'rate of living', such that factors which retard development or reduce metabolism tend in many organisms to prevent or postpone senescence; the work of Minot (1913, 1908), of which the most important surviving parts are his relation of senescence to the decline of growth, and his insistence upon its continuous and gradual character and its continuity with morphogenesis; the experimental studies of Child (1915), which showed that cellular differentiation and 'senescence' in planarians is reversible, and of Carrel (1912), who demonstrated that some tissue cells derived from adult animals could be propagated indefinitely *in vitro*, and finally the theories of Bidder (1932).

Minot considered that senescence was the direct outcome of cell differentiation, that differentiated cells, by reason of the changes undergone, chiefly by their cytoplasm, in the course of morphogenesis, had become largely incapable of growth or repair. He believed that the negative acceleration of specific growth, found in a very wide variety of organisms, and ultimate senescence, were products of this process, and that the first was a measure of the second. It followed from this that the rate of senescence, so defined, must actually be highest in embryonic life and in infancy, when the rate of differentiation is highest. Many of Minot's concepts, such as the rigid irreversibility of cell differentiation, echoed later by Warthin (1929), the incapacity of differentiated cells for growth, and the necessarily increasing liability to senescence of successive cell-generations, are now disproved or at least impugned. His work, however, leaves with us the two important concepts of a gradual process of senescence linked to morphogenesis, and of a relation between it and the decline of growth-potential. By using negative growth acceleration and rate of differentiation as a direct measure of senescence, Minot arrived at the conclusion that the rate of senescence is highest in foetal, and least in adult, life. This concept has been widely adopted. Its validity depends upon the acceptance of Minot's definition; if senescence be regarded, as we shall regard it, in terms of deteriorative change in the organism's power of resistance, the idea requires qualification.

A far more important question, which had been latent in the literature since Ray Lankester (1870) pointed to the apparent non-senescence of fish, was raised by Bidder (1932). With the exception of Metchnikoff (1904, 1907) who was attempting to relate longevity to the form of the digestive tract, very nearly all biological theorists had assumed that senescence occurs in all vertebrates. This is probably so, but if it is not, then manifestly the general theories of senescence based on degree of tissue differentiation, irreplaceability of neurones, and other such systems fall to the ground. Bidder pointed out that there were several lower vertebrates in which there was no ground for suspecting that the mortality ever increased with increasing age, beyond the inevitable increment from accumulation of evident injuries. He suggested that vertebrate *senescence is a correlate of the evolution of determinate growth and of a final absolute size*. Bidder regarded determinate size as a property which had evolved as a result of the migration of vertebrates to dry land. He pointed to a number of instances in fish where constant expectation of life, capacity for growth, and general vigour appeared to persist indefinitely (Bidder, 1925). Bidder's argument is of importance, and is worth quoting in full.

'Giant trees, cultures of chick cells and of *Paramecium*, measurements of plaice and of sponges, all indicate that indefinite growth is natural. Galileo proved it fatal to swiftly moving land animals, therefore swiftly moving mammals and birds were impossible until their ancestors had evolved a mechanism for maintaining specific size within an error not impairing adequate efficiency. Even without evidence of evergrowing organisms, we could not suppose that the close correspondence to specific size, which we see in all swiftly moving creatures of earth or air, results from mere "senescent" fading-out of the zygotic impulse to cell division and cell increase. Specific size is probably most important to birds, with their aeroplane mechanics strictly enjoining conformity of scale to plan; but to men it is most noticeable in man. Only familiarity prevents marvel at the rarity of meeting a man more than 20 per cent taller or shorter than 5½ ft., or of discovering his remains in any place, or any race, or any epoch. Probably our erect posture enforces accurate propositions of length to weight, for running.

'Adequate efficiency could only be obtained by the evolution of some mechanism to stop natural growth so soon as specific size is reached. This mechanism may be called the regulator, avoiding the word "inhibitor" so as not to connote a physiological assumption. However ignorant we are of its nature, its action is traced in anthropometric statistics; a steady diminution in growth rate from a maximum at puberty to a vanishing-point in the twenties. That the regulator works through change in the constitution of the blood is shown by the perpetual division of Carrell's chick cells in embryonic plasma, whereas cell division is ended in the heart of a hen.

'I have suggested that senescence is the result of the continued action of the regulator after growth is stopped. The regulator does efficiently all that concerns the welfare of the species. Man is within 2 cm. of the same height between 18 and 60, he gently rises 2 cm. between 20 and 27, and still more gently loses 1 cm. by 40 or thereabouts. If primitive man at 18 begat a son, the species had no more need of him by 37, when his son could hunt for food for the grandchildren. Therefore the dwindling of cartilage, muscle and nerve cell, which we call senescence, did not affect the survival of the species, the checking of growth had secured that by ensuring a perfect physique between 20 and 40. Effects of continued negative growth after 37 were of indifference to the race; probably no man ever reached 60 years old until language attained such importance in the equipment of the species that long experience became valuable in man who could neither fight nor hunt. This negative growth is not the manifestation of a weakness inherent in protoplasm or characteristic of nucleated cells; it is the unimportant by-product of a regulating mechanism necessary to the survival of swiftly moving land animals, a mechanism evolved by selection and survival as have been evolved the jointing of mammalian limbs, and with similar perfection' (Bidder, 1932).

Bidder's theory, besides raising the question of senescence as as effect lying outside the 'programme' imposed by natural selection, posed the highly important suggestion that there may be two categories of vertebrates—those whose life-span is fixed as in mammals, and those whose life-span is not fixed. From the theoretical point of view the establishment of the truth or falsity of this might have been the key problem in the elucidation of mammalian ageing, since the disproof of almost all the major existing theories of senescence would follow from the demonstration that it is not universally present in vertebrates. This might appear a simple issue of fact, but for reasons which will appear later a clear demonstration one way or the other has been remarkably difficult to achieve.

Bidder's theory marks the last major attempt to produce a hypothesis of vertebrate senescence before the current irruption of physicists into the field of ageing studies which followed the discovery of the apparent age-accelerating effects of radiation. These stochastic theories will be dealt with later: apart from them, no new picture of the general biology of ageing has been suggested since Bidder's, although its evolutionary basis has been discussed (Haldane, 1941; Medawar, 1952; Strehler, 1962). The decline in abstract speculation about old age is probably in itself a very good augury for research. Much of the previous published matter abundantly justified the view of Bacon that 'the method of discovery and proof whereby the most general principles are first established, and then intermediate axioms are tried and proved by them, is the parent of error and the curse of all science'.

0·2 *The Problem Today*

The concern of scientists—as against mystics, quacks, and therapeutic optimists—with the control of human age processes, if we date it to Metchnikoff and Claude Bernard, is less than a hundred years old; the engagement of science in studying it as an immediately realizable project is less than ten. Gerontology in its modern sense dates from about 1950.

In these ten years its advocates have generated a large body of printed matter, set up many institutes, and held many conferences, from which, so far as the fundamental understanding and control of age processes are concerned, virtually nothing hard emerges which could be put honestly to a lay committee as evidence of 'definite progress'. The view of some sources of research money that gerontology has now deservedly talked itself out of work is therefore comprehensible: but this ignores the time which is required, in any pioneer project, to be spent in cutting brushwood and reclaiming ground before a crop of fundamental experiments can be sown, let alone harvested. Though some of the time and effort spent so far has been wasted, a certain amount has been achieved in defining the problem, clearing old errors, raising a generation which knows the possibilities of age research, and discharging various ill-judged or superficial ideas which would have had to be voided at some point. Accordingly, although it has borne no fruit yet in medicine, the work done may later prove more important than it now appears to be.

The root questions which determine the form of the age problem remain much as they were in 1950. In man and other warm-blooded vertebrates, vigour declines and disease-susceptibility multiplies with increasing age. The rate of this increase under the best conditions has a characteristic value in each species, and is exponential, so that there is a maximum practicable life-span which further betterment does not lengthen.

Mammals are made up of three biological components: cells multiplying clonally throughout life (white corpuscles, epithelial cells), cells incapable of division and renewal (neurones), and non-cellular material which may have much or little turnover (collagen, intercellular substance). There are, accordingly, three grand classical hypotheses of the mechanism of senescence (not necessarily mutually exclusive), which must at some stage be dealt with—that vigour declines through change (epigenetic, mutational, infective, immunological) in the properties of multiplying cells; that it declines through loss of, or injury to, non-multiplying cells; and that it declines through primary changes in the 'inert' materials of the body. All these are old hypotheses dating from Francis Bacon; none has yet been investigated by convincing experiment. At present, interest in mutation and in matters such as somatic aneuploidy has focused attention on the first hypothesis—that new cells in old animals are not so good as new cells in young animals. Szilard's recent speculations (1959a, b) fit better to the second hypothesis —that irreplaceable cells are lost with time. The third hypothesis has generated extensive and important work on collagen and related substances.

One preliminary of any choice between these possibilities has been the need to observe the ageing and age-mortality relationship of animals other than men and rodents (which until recently were the only mammals for which we had life tables), and the study of factors which appear to hasten or delay the decline of vigour. This has been begun, though slowly. Another requirement is the detailed study of cell populations and numbers at different points in the life-cycle; a third is the comparison of the new cells of old animals with those of young animals. None of these has yet been adequately attacked. The decline of brain-cell population at various ages in man, guinea pig, rat, and even the honey bee and termite has been very variously estimated, whereas histochemical studies of old and young animals still frequently fail to distinguish between young cells in an old organism and cells which are themselves old—or between animals such as rotifers, nematodes, and insect imagos, in which there is no cell division, or little, and mammals in which fixed and endlessly dividing cells exist together.

Throughout its history the study of ageing, as we have seen, has been ruinously obscured by theory, and particularly theory of a type which begets no experimental hypotheses. The discussion of methods which has taken place, and which has been quantitatively the main activity of gerontology so far, has been worth while in laying some of these philosophical ghosts, and though it is depressing to see them being raised again from time to time by the darkeners of scientific counsel, the most important recent contributions to theory, such as Szilard's stochastic and Burnet's immunological speculations, all carry direct experimental consequences. It is noticeable that most of these theories have come from experimenters of international stature who are themselves working in other fields; serious progress in experimentation on age processes is really now waiting for some experimenter of equal calibre to devote his whole time to it.

It will be necessary here to discuss a number of theories, most of which have been contributed in this way—leaving aside, on one hand, mere speculation, and on the other the contribution of information theory, which at present records only established actuarial concepts, though in a form which may prove instructive, or even decisive, in the end. We cannot as yet decide upon which particular information store ageing makes its inroads, the answer depending upon the choice between our three overriding hypotheses—cell loss (predominantly of neurones, in this case) faulty copying, and mechanochemical failure. Thus, though the difference in life-span between species can be treated as a difference in initial information content, we are no nearer translating this into material terms. Even though none of the most recent suggestions seems likely in itself to 'explain' ageing, they merit close attention as evidence of the way in which ageing research and control have come to present themselves in practical terms to scientists of high ability, and it is this fact, rather than the theories themselves, which makes it possible that fundamental progress in the understanding of the loss of vigour with ageing may be closer than the standard of experimental papers might lead us to think. Understanding and control are of course very different things. The medical relevance of understanding the age process will depend upon what we understand it to be.

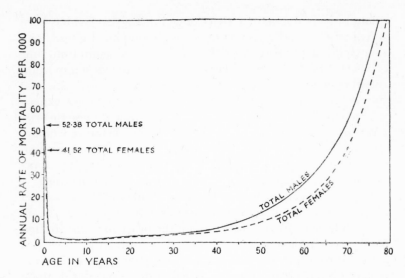

Fig. 1.—Annual rate of mortality per 1000 by sex: United States, 1939–41.

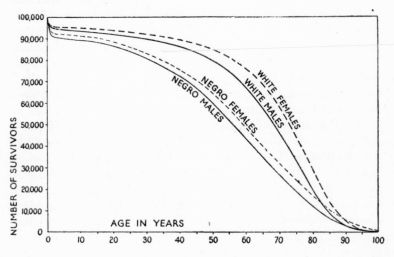

Fig. 2.—Number of survivors out of 100,000 born alive, for each race by sex: United States, 1939–41.

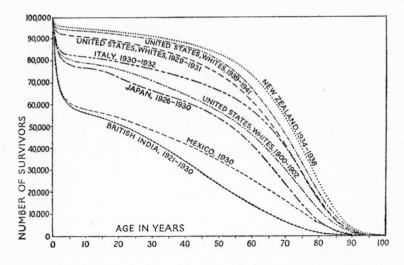

FIG. 3.—Number of survivors out of 100,000 male live births, from recent life-tables for selected countries.

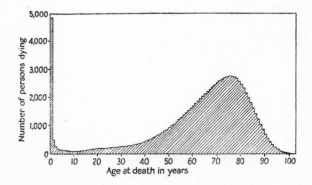

FIG. 4.—Frequency distribution of ages at death in a cohort starting with 100,000 live births, based on the mortality of white males: United States, 1939–41.

1

THE NATURE AND CRITERIA OF SENESCENCE

1·1 *The Measurement of Senescence*

SENESCENCE is a deteriorative process. What is being measured, when we measure it, is a decrease in viability and an increase in vulnerability. Other definitions are possible, but they tend to ignore the *raison d'être* of human and scientific concern with age processes. Senescence shows itself as an increasing probability of death with increasing chronological age: the study of senescence is the study of the group of processes, different in different organisms, which lead to this increase in vulnerability.

The probability that an individual organism which has survived to time x will die before time $x + 1$ depends on the *rate of mortality* (q) per 1000, meaning the number, out of 1000 individuals living at time x, who have died by time $x + 1$. The *force of mortality* (μ) is given at any age x by

$$\mu_x = - n^{-1}\frac{dn}{dx} = \frac{-d}{dx}\ln . n$$

where n is the number of individuals which have survived to age x.

In most organisms, the likelihood of dying within a given period undergoes fluctuations, often large, throughout the life-cycle. Senescence appears as a progressive increase throughout life, or after a given stadium, in the likelihood that a given individual will die, during the next succeeding unit of time, from randomly-distributed causes; the pressure of the environment, which it has successfully withstood in the past, it now ceases to be able to withstand, even though that pressure is not

22

increased. It is rare that we can determine the vulnerability of an individual. Our estimate of it is determined statistically, upon a population. The demonstration of such an increase in vulnerability is a necessary condition for demonstrating senescence: it is, obviously, only a sufficient condition if selective mortality from age-distributed external causes is ruled out. Real populations are subject to mortality both from random and from age-distributed causes—the variation of exposure rate throughout life is familiar in man; grown men are subject to risks which do not affect children, and so on. Differences in 'risk' throughout life have been studied in some other animals, such as the locusts whose causes of death were analysed by Bodenheimer (1938) or the gall-fly *Urophora* (Varley, 1947). Pearson (1895), in his mathematical analysis of the curve of human survivorship into five components, attempted to limit the meaning of 'senile mortality' to one such component, reaching its maximum incidence between 70 and 75 years of age. This would be an ideal solution if it were practicable, but Pearson's analysis is artificial in the extreme, and his 'five separate Deaths' directing their fire at different age groups are not biologically identifiable. In general, however, a progressively increasing *force of mortality* and decreasing expectation of life in a population, if significant variation in exposure rate can be excluded, is evidence of the senescence of its individual members. The preliminary test for senescence in an animal species depends, therefore, on the life-table of an adequate population sample, studied with suitable precautions against selective causes of death.

The expected differences in behaviour, and form of life-table, between populations which age and which do not age are shown in Figs. 5a, b. In a population not subject to senescence and exposed only to random overall mortality, the decline of numbers is logarithmic, and animals die, *ex hypothesi*, from causes which would have killed them at any age. In a population exposed only to death from reduced resistance, due to senescence, the curve approaches a rectangular form: after a certain age, animals die from causes which would not have killed them in youth. In one case the force of mortality is constant, in the second it rises steadily with age. Thus in rats the force of mortality rises after the ninth month of life in a geometrical progression (Wiesner and Sheard, 1934). Real survival graphs are commonly intermediate in form between the two ideal contours. Pearl and Miner (1935) distinguished three main types of observed death-curve, varying in skewness from the nearly rectangular in organisms with a low standing death-rate throughout life, but showing a tendency to die almost simultaneously in old age, to the logarithmic decline characteristic of populations which show no senescence, or which die out before it can become evident (Fig. 6). A fourth theoretical type, in which the curve is rectangular but inverse to that

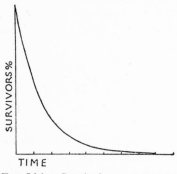

Fig. 5(*a*).—Survival curve at a constant rate of mortality (50 per cent per unit time).

Fig. 5(*b*).—Survival curve of a population which exhibits senescence.

found in the ideal senescent population, was recognized by Pearl (1940) as a theoretical possibility; it seems to be realized in nature among organisms which have a high infant mortality, but whose expectation of life increases over a long period with increasing age. This pattern of survival is characteristic of some trees (Szabó, 1931) but probably also occurs in animals. 'There may be animals in which the expectation of life increases continuously with age. This may be so for many fish under natural conditions. It certainly goes on increasing for a considerable time. Thus in a species where the expectation of life was equal to the age, or better, to the age plus one week, no members would live for ever, but a small fraction would live for a very long time. A centenarian aware of the facts would pity a child,

24

with an expectation of life of only a few years, but would envy a bicentenarian' (Haldane, 1953).

The simplest and oldest attempt to depict the age-decline in terms of actuarial mathematics is that of Gompertz (1825), expressed in the function

$$R_m = -\frac{1}{n} \times \frac{dn}{dt} = R_0 e^{\alpha t}$$

where n = number of survivors at time t, and α (the slope constant) and R_0 (the hypothetical mortality at time = 0) are constants.

Makeham's approximation simply adds to this a standing element of mortality independent of age, represented by the constant A

$$R_m = R_0 e^{\alpha t} + A$$

while Teissier's approximation describes those survival curves, common in laboratory practice, where, owing to small samples, mortality is zero for the first few intervals, giving a 'plateau of adult vigour' (Teissier, 1934)—

$$\mu_x = e^{a(x-b)}, \qquad x > b.$$

μ_x being the force of mortality at an age x, beginning to rise after the plateau of duration b has elapsed.

A number of more subtle theoretical models have been devised both by actuaries, who use them predictively, and by biometricians attempting to formulate a hypothesis of ageing. Most of these depend on a combination of declining vigour, random environmental attack, and random oscillation of one or more physiological quantities about a fixed or a moving point of homoeostasis. They have been well reviewed by Strehler (Mildvan and Strehler, 1960; Strehler, 1962).

The accumulation of vulnerability with age is an all-round and non-specific process. We can translate this into more concrete terms. The age distribution of pedestrian deaths in road accidents is similar in contour, excluding early infancy, to the general distribution of human deaths from all causes (Fig. 7). This index is highly correlated with vigour, in its biological sense, for it represents a combination of sensory acuity, speed of avoidance, and power of recovery when hit.

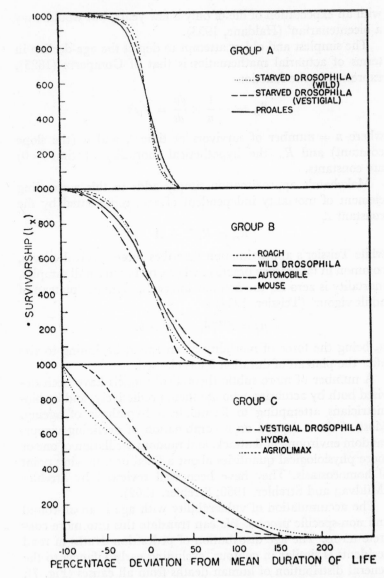

Fig. 6.—Types of survival curve (from Pearl, after Allee *et al.*, 1949).

The Nature and Criteria of Senescence

No single parameter is sufficient to describe an observed survival curve. If the life-span of a species is to be given as a single figure, e.g. in comparing man and horse, the last decile is probably the most useful measurement, as the approximate proportions of the 'physiological' curve can sometimes be

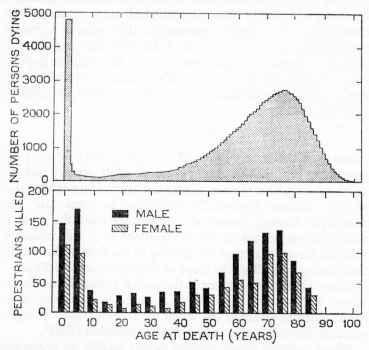

FIG. 7.—Distribution by age of all deaths in a privileged community (above) and of pedestrians in road accidents (De Silva, 1938; Lauer, 1952).

guessed from it. The true index of the rate of ageing is presumably the differential of the force of mortality, and it would seem logical at first to express all curves where ageing is in question in terms of mortality or its derivates. But in real survival experiments all measures derived from q_x, the observed mortality, have a very large scatter, unless vast numbers are used, and standard smoothing techniques all introduce assumptions of regularity. Both the curve of survival (L_x/t) and the mean duration of life are largely affected by a few early deaths. Comparison of crude mean longevities, in particular, is quite meaningless in terms of the pattern of ageing, unless the causes and distribution of deaths are also compared.

Under good conditions the survival curves of mammals, and of many other organisms, tend to the form originally described by Gompertz (1825). This 'physiological' curve represents the distribution of a vitality parameter. The smooth curve of survivorship drawn by actuaries is intended for prediction of average behaviour. Unsmoothed curves for smallish populations, though consistent, are often better represented by straight-line approximations, or conform roughly to Teissier's equation (1934),

$$\mu_x = e^{a(x-b)}$$

where μ_x is the force of mortality at age x, and $b < x$: in this case there is a well-marked period of adult vigour, and the curve begins with a plateau of zero mortality. If we assume that vitality declines continually according to some law (not necessarily linear), factors that uniformly raise the level of environmental attack or lower resistance to it will reduce b, whereas factors that alter the spacing of the lives in the vitality distribution will affect the slope of the subsequent decline.

Neary (1960) has christened the period before the decline in vigour has brought any individual to the point at which the environmental attack is too much for it 'induction'—it represents the plateau constant in Teissier's equation (1934).

When multiple life-shortening factors modify an arithmetic survival curve they commonly flatten it, first into a straight line, and, when still more severe, towards a logarithmic decay, the mortality being then independent of age. There is a tendency for the ends of the curve to remain pegged, however, the last half-decile succumbing only to very severe conditions.

The resulting family of hysteresis-like curves makes up the 'parallelogram of survival', typical of animals having a definite life-span, and from which that life-span can be inferred (see Fig. 3). The pronounced 'tail' is probably the result of heterogeneity; it might well not be found in experiments on F_1 hybrids between inbred lines. Curves of this kind are usually taken to represent an increment in general mortality rather than a change in the rate of ageing—there is no way of estimating from them how far age changes in survivors at a given time have been accelerated by previous hardship.

Some real animal populations decline in an approximately logarithmic manner. The 'potential immortality' of individuals in a population following such a path of decline, an entirely meaningless phrase which has caused much philosophical agitation in the past, is not more significant as a practical issue than

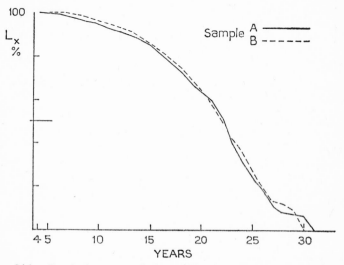

Fig. 8(*a*).—Survival curves of thoroughbred mares foaled in 1875–80 (Sample A) and 1860–4 (Sample B).

the 'potential' meeting of any pair of railway metals at infinity. No population of organisms which is subject to a constant overall death-rate contains 'potentially' immortal individuals. The only advantage which a non-senescent organism possesses over senescent forms is that the odds in favour of its death within a fixed period remain constant instead of shortening with the passage of time.

The survival curve of some 3000 thoroughbred mares, from figures in the General Stud Book, is closely similar in form to that of civilized man (Comfort, 1958a, b; Figs. 8*a*, *b*, *c*).

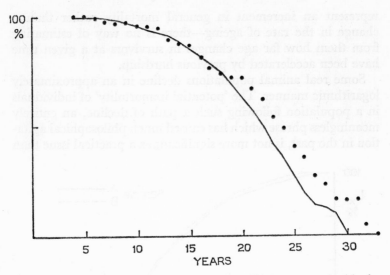

Fig. 8(*b*).—Survival curve of Arabian mares (dots) compared with the curve for English thoroughbreds (solid line).

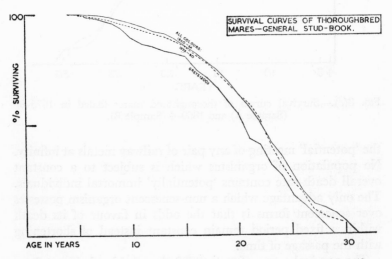

Fig. 8(*c*).—Survival curves of thoroughbred mares by coat colour (from Comfort, 1958a, b; 1961a).

This human survival curve, in societies possessing developed medical services and a high standard of living, is intermediate between the rectangular and log-linear contours, but approaches the rectangular, with an initial decline due to infant mortality.

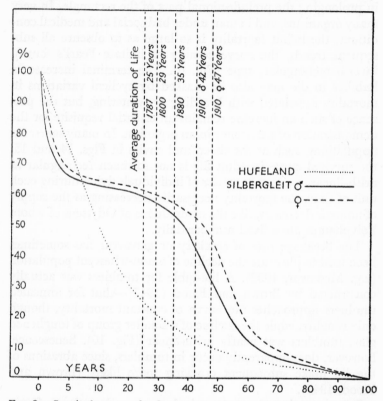

FIG. 9.—Survival curves of a German population. Hufeland's table (1798) is based on 'experience' and estimates. Silbergleit's data are based on official statistics as given in the *Deutschen Statistischen Jahrbuch* for 1915. Both sets of data relate to N. Germany (from Vischer, 1947).

Figs. 1–3 and 9 show, first, the comparative curves of mortality for populations in the present century living under different conditions of economic and climatic advantage, and second, the change in form of the life-table for North German populations between 1787 and 1800. Many life-tables for populations before the advent of scientific medicine are given by Dublin (1949).

The significance of technical and economic privilege is nowhere more evident than in the study of life-tables. The effects of public health upon the life-table are expressed rather in making it approach more closely to the rectangular shape than in prolonging the preinflectional part of the rectangle. In very many organisms, and in man under bad social and medical conditions, the infant mortality is so large as to obscure all subsequent trends, the curve coming to imitate Pearl's fourth, inverse rectangular, type (Fig. 6). The terminal increase in liability to die may also be masked by cyclical variations in mortality associated with breeding or wintering, but the presence of such an increase remains an essential requisite for the demonstration of senescence in an organism. In many senescent populations, such as the sheep and cavies in Figs. 14 and 15, the survival curve in adult life is not so much rectangular as arith-linear, a constant *number* of individuals dying during each unit of time, the mortality necessarily decreasing as the supply of animals decreases, like the companions of Odysseus of whom Polyphemus ate a fixed number daily.

The breakage rate of crockery or glasswear has sometimes been used to illustrate the decline of a non-senescent population (e.g. Medawar, 1952). A life-table for tumblers was actually constructed by Brown and Flood (1947)—that for annealed tumblers approaches the curve of constant mortality, though only roughly, while the decline of a smaller group of toughened glass tumblers was nearly arith-linear (Fig. 10). Senescence, however, does apparently occur in tumblers, since abrasions of the lip make subsequent cracking more likely (Brown and Flood, 1947).

It is convenient to treat survival curves such as those of man or *Drosophila* as combinations of the log-linear 'environmental' curve, found where the standing death-rate is high, with a terminal rectangular decline due to senescence, since it is evident that not all those individuals who die in middle life owe any part of their misfortune to the senile increase in vulnerability, however early in life this is taken to begin.

Bodenheimer (1938) draws a useful distinction between the 'physiological' longevity of a species—that attained under optimal conditions in a genetically homogeneous population and approaching the longest recorded life-span within the species; and the 'ecological' longevity, which is the mean longevity observed empirically under given conditions. The ideal rectangular

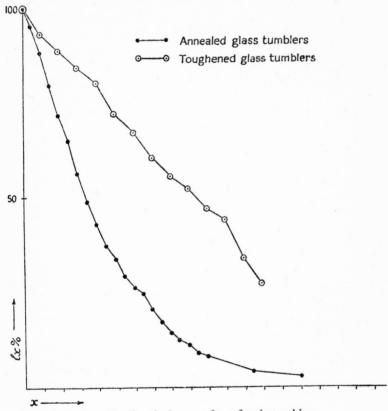

Fig. 10.—Survival curves for cafeteria tumblers.
A = 549 annealed glass tumbers ● — ●
B = 241 toughened glass tumblers ⊙ — ⊙
Time: 1 scale division = 2 weeks for Curve A, 5 weeks for curve B.
(Drawn from the data of Brown and Flood, 1947)

'physiological' curve postulated by Bodenheimer is a convenient abstraction, at most, since the genetic and environmental conditions laid down for it cannot in practice be obtained in any real population. But in some forms the observed life-table in laboratory culture or domestication approximates to the ideal rectangular form, and this approximation is closest of all in some human societies. It is, however, pointless in terms of the actuarial definition of senescence to pursue a 'physiological' as opposed to a 'pathological' senescence in most laboratory animals. If senescence is measured as increased *general* vulnerability, Bodenheimer's 'physiological' longevity represents only the approximate region in which the rise in the curve of vulnerability to all assaults of the environment becomes so steep that even major protection against such assaults is insufficient to prolong life very greatly. The pattern can be modified and the apparent physiological longevity increased by removing specific causes of death—e.g. enteritis and ear disease in old rats (Korenchevsky, 1949) but the postponement of death obtainable in this way is itself limited, and argument about 'natural' death, apart from pathological processes, in mammals is quite otiose.

It is manifestly impossible to demonstrate senescence from life-tables unless the mortality in early and adult life is sufficiently low, and the number of animals reaching old age is therefore sufficiently high, for an endogenous increase in susceptibility to death-producing factors of random incidence to be evident. Thus wild mice die at a rate which precludes their reaching old age, but mice kept under laboratory conditions have a life-table similar to that of Western European human populations in the year 1900 (Leslie and Ranson, 1940, Fig. 52, p. 153; Haldane, 1953): not even the most cherished laboratory population can receive as detailed medical attention as civilized man, but if such were possible, the life-table of mice might then approach that for Western European man in 1953.

Organisms which undergo senescence, as judged by the life-table, also exhibit *specific age*, meaning an age at death which is characteristic of the species when living under conditions approaching Bodenheimer's 'physiological' conditions.

Some of the limitations of the statistical definition of senescence have recently been re-stated by Medawar (1952). It is obvious that any survival curve can be simulated by judicious, or injudicious, choice of material. Tables based only on age at death, a single arbitrary event, are open to serious criticism if

34

they are used as indices of a *continuous* process of declining vitality. The shape of such a curve is a measure of many things, including the genetic homogeneity of the sample. The incidence of various risks itself varies between age groups: the statistical appearance of senescence would, for example, be found in the life-table of any population of fish which was subject to frequent fishing with a net of fixed mesh size. Selective predation certainly produces effects of this kind of nature. The increased force of mortality among men of military age during a war is not a manifestation of senescence. On the other hand, some causes of mortality, such as cancer (Rutgers, 1953), have a curve of incidence which parallels the total curve of mortality. In employing the force of mortality as an index of senescence it is essential, as we have seen, to exclude so far as possible external factors which are not of random incidence in relation to age, yet this cannot be done with strict logical consistency. In the case of human life-tables, large secular changes in cause and incidence of death may occur within an individual life-span, while constitutional differences in rate of senescence between individuals ensure that the genetical composition of the survivors at, say, age 60, is not representative of the whole cohort under study. These sources of error are, in fact, capable of avoidance or correction for most practical purposes, but they must always be recognized in inferring senescence from any life-table.

Since there is no direct way of measuring the liability of an individual to die without actually killing it, the statistical definition of senescence, although it reflects a real process in individuals, can only be tested upon a *population*. For this purpose the biologist uses tools originally made and sharpened by the actuary.

The differences between actuarial and biological approaches to mortality-measurements are in the main the differences between the prospective and retrospective use of statistics. The most practically important of these differences, for the kind of problems we have in hand, is the value we attach to smoothness. For almost all prospective purposes it is convenient in the first instance to assume some degree of uniformity, to recognize as few and as gross modalities as possible, and to deal with minor modalities by smoothing. For most retrospective purposes, the main consideration is to extract as much reliable, or even suggestive, information from scanty data as the limits of significance will allow. This will require the use of methods which will exaggerate fine structure where it is present. The biologist's main requirement in using standard actuarial techniques of research on age is that he shall be able to distinguish clearly between regularities which probably exist in the material, and

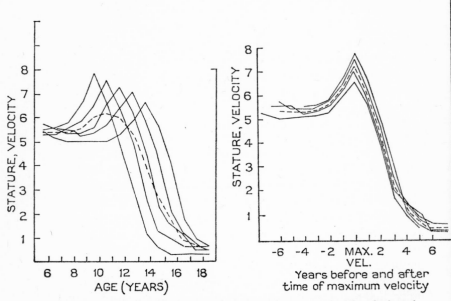

Fig. 11.—Relation between individual and mean velocities during the adolescent spurt. Left, the height curves are plotted against chronological age; Right, they are plotted according to their time of maximum velocity. ———, Individual curves; – – –, mean curve (from Tanner, 1955).

any regularities which may result from the methods themselves. Most animal populations are heterogeneous for life-table purposes. Curves based on such material are averages, which are serviceable for prediction of limits, but often misleading as indications of the pattern of a biological process. Fig. 11 illustrates such an effect in human growth curves, from the study by Tanner (1955); it compares the longitudinal plots of growth velocity against age in five individual children, the smoothed average which would be obtained by combining the measurements, as they would be combined in a cross-sectional study, and the same measurements as percentage deviates. The true age-velocity curves are typically peaked. Many instances quoted to demonstrate that 'Nature does not progress by leaps' are a direct result of this type of treatment. Where, as in this case, longitudinal as well as cross-sectional studies are made the error is evident: in the case of age-wise vigour loss we have still no means of doing this.

It is evident that in applied biology, and especially in medicine, it is desirable to be able to infer not only the existence of senescence in a species but the degree of senile change in a given individual. This estimate must be based on secondary criteria, and can be made with accuracy only in forms whose life-cycle, like that of man or of *Drosophila*, has been subject to intensive study. The importance of the statistical definition of senescence is that it means we have to resort to adequate population studies. An over-common practice has been to keep a single specimen, a bird or a bullfrog, for ten or twenty years, and, when it is found dead, having been so for hours or possibly days, to describe histological appearances in its tissues in a note entitled 'Senile change in the nervous system of *Passer* (or *Bufo*)'. While senescence cannot be inferred from every life-table in which the force of mortality rises, neither can descriptions of 'senile' changes be properly based on single observations upon supposedly ageing organisms belonging to groups whose life-cycle, in relation to senescence, is not fully known.

In practice, other criteria than the life-table can be applied or organisms whose life-cycle is familiar, as secondary indices of senescence; these are distinct from mere measures of chronological age, based upon the morphology or scales, teeth or otoliths. Certain factors which are, in effect, direct measures of vigour or of vulnerability, such as the mortality from burns (Ball and Squire, 1949), or even the annual absenteeism from sickness (Schlomka and Kersten, 1952) follow the general force of mortality in man. The supposed decline in the rate of wound healing proposed as a measure of senescence by du Noüy (1932) was based on grossly inadequate clinical material and is not supported by later work (Bourlière, 1950, Gillman, 1962), though the rate of contracture in full-thickness wounds is related to age (Billingham and Russell, 1956). Less general criteria such as skin elasticity in man (Evans, Cowdry and Nielson, 1943; Kirk and Kvorning, 1949), organ weight and relative organ hypoplasia in rats (Korenchevsky, 1942; 1949), heart rate in Cladocerans (Ingle, Wood and Banta, 1937; Fritsch and Meijering, 1958; Fritsch, 1959; Meijering, 1958, 1960), milk

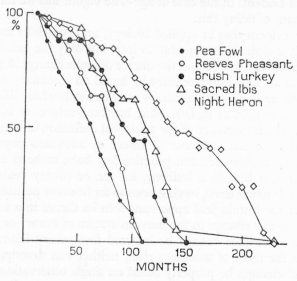

Fig. 12.—Survival curves of birds in the London Zoo, corrected for accidental deaths and losses (Comfort, 1962).

yields in cattle (Brody, Ragsdale and Turner, 1923), egg production in fowls (Clark, 1940, Fig. 19, p. 92), histological appearances of many kinds, and estimations of general or special metabolism are of value within sharply-defined limits, but all are subject to considerable variation apart from the general senile process. In retarded Cladocera, for example, where mean life-span is artificially prolonged by postponing growth, the heart rate fails to decline before death to the low levels normally found in old age (Ingle, Wood and Banta, 1937). Minot (1908), Hertwig and others considered that a steady decrease in the nucleocytoplasmic ratio was a general

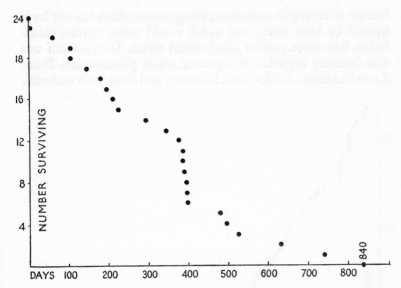

FIG. 13.—Orkney Vole (*Microtus orcadensis*). Survival of 24 individuals—sexes combined (London Zoo).

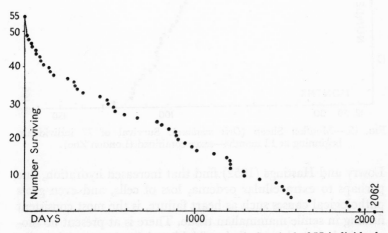

FIG. 14.—Patagonian Cavy (*Dolichotis patagona*). Survival of 55 individuals—sexes combined (London Zoo).

feature of ageing in organisms, a suggestion which has not been upheld by later work, and which would today require translation into more precise biochemical terms. Dehydration was also formerly regarded as a general senile phenomenon. From a recalculation of older data, however, and from fresh material,

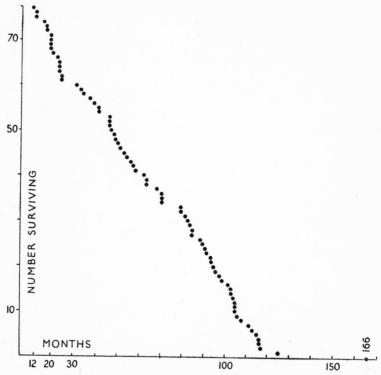

FIG. 15.—Mouflon Sheep (*Ovis musimon*). Survival of 77 individuals, beginning at 12 months—sexes combined (London Zoo).

Lowry and Hastings (1952) find that increased hydration, due perhaps to extracellular oedema, loss of cells, and even gross pathological causes such as heart failure, is the most consistent finding in senile mammalian tissue. There is at present no biochemical sign characteristic of 'oldness' in tissues or in cells, and the search for one may well reflect a fundamental misconception. It is in assessing the relevance of all such criteria to the main phenomenon of senescence, the decline in resistance to random stresses, that the statistical approach is essential. All assertions about senescence based upon pathological anatomy, or upon general theories which treat it as a single process, are open to question.

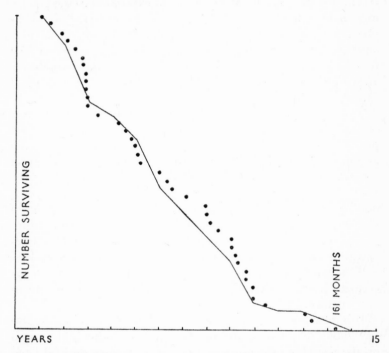

FIG. 16.—Irish Wolf hounds. Survival of 67 individuals from 12 months of age—sexes combined. Line—whole sample, annual totals. Points—38 individuals whose exact date of death was known, to scale (data from Miss D. Gardner).

The *decline of growth rate* throughout life in some or all tissues appears to be a near-universal feature of metazoa.

'The specific growth rate always falls: living tissue progressively loses the power to reproduce itself at the rate at which it was formed. Minot arrived at this generalization, which should rightly be known as "Minot's Law", from the collation of his percentage growth-rate curves; and it was he who first recognized that the point of inflection of the integral curve of growth, and the division it makes between a period of positive and negative acceleration, is not of critical importance. The progressive dissipation of "growth energy" which this first law affirms was thought by Minot to be an expression of the phenomenon of senescence—"ageing" with its everyday implications. Senescence is not, in this view, a process which sets in after a preliminary period of maturation has run its course: senescence *is* development, looked at from the other end of life' (Medawar, 1945b).

The use of this criterion, which is a readily measurable one, and can be applied to smallish groups of animals with suitable precautions, as well as to single tissues or organs, implies the acceptance of Minot's definition of senescence. The definition is defensible. On the other hand, the decline in specific growth rate is not a measure of senescence in its actuarial sense, since it does not run parallel with the force of mortality, and it would not be even an obligatory precursor of senescence if mortality only increased with age in those animals whose capacity for renewal or growth in some or all tissues has fallen to zero. It is with actuarial, deteriorative senescence that we are here concerned—if senility implied *only* the decline of growth rate in man, it would cause little public concern.

It is possible that future work will produce a workable and justifiable 'direct measure' of senescence in individuals, based on the time-lag in cell-division of tissue explants derived from old animals (Cohn and Murray, 1925; Suzuki, 1926; Medawar, 1940). No practical test of this kind has yet been developed, however—meanwhile the critical observations on the distribution of senescence in vertebrates have almost all to be made upon organisms (large fish, crocodiles, tortoises) where life-table studies are out of the question. In these forms it is relatively easy to observe histologically or by a mating test, the degree of reproductive power persisting in individuals of known age. Inferences based on 'reproductive' senescence are therefore easy to draw, compared with the insuperable difficulties involved in measuring the force of mortality in such cases.

Reproductive decline is a very general feature of those vertebrates which undergo senescence as judged by the increasing force of mortality: its evidences in various forms include gonadal changes, loss of secondary sexual characters, cessation of ovarian cycles, and a fall in sperm production, fertilizing power, hatchability, litter size and viability. These changes follow a time scale which is different from that of the increase in force of mortality, however, and which bears no constant relation to that increase in different species. The gonad often appears to behave as an 'organism' having its own determinate life-span, but this is equally true of other structures, such as the thymus. The limited life of the gonad is in a special category only because, in terms of evolutionary teleology, the gonad is the significant part of the organism. Ageing of the whole organism after a prolonged post-reproductive period is a process which is realized only by human interference, at least so far as most species are concerned, and not 'envisaged' by evolutionary teleology. It could be argued that once gonadal senescence has become established in a species, eventual somatic senescence is as a rule inevitable from the withdrawal in post-reproductive life of the selection-pressure towards homoeostasis. A clear physiological link between the activity of the gonad and the growth and survival of the animal has been demonstrated in a few forms (e.g. *Daphnia*, Edlén, 1937, 1938), although even in *Daphnia*, oogenesis continues until death (Schulze-Röbbecke, 1951). In many vertebrates, however, even total castration has little or no adverse effect on longevity, and may increase it. Although senescence of the gonad is, in an evolutionary sense, the most important form of ageing, it is not self-evident that in the artificially-protected animal it must always be followed by generalized somatic senescence, unless the two processes are causally related. Such an identification reflects, once more, a human preoccupation. Reproductive function, because of its ease of measurement, remains at most a justifiable test of continuing vitality in old animals—fertility indicating the absence of irreversible organ changes in one important system.

Metabolic decline, either measured directly by calorimetry and manometry, or inferred from reduction in spontaneous activity, has also been regarded as an index of senescence—often on theoretical grounds, as representing the accumulation of in-active 'metaplasm' at the expense of active protoplasm (Kasso-witz, 1899, etc.) or the completion of a 'monomolecular auto-catalytic reaction' such as that postulated by Robertson (1923) or Bertalanffy (1941). The decline of heart rate in Cladocerans (Ingle, Wood and Banta, 1937) has already been mentioned. The mean resting heart rate in man also tends to decline throughout foetal and postnatal life. Child measured the age of hydromedusae by the decline in their rate of pulsation (Child, 1918). In some invertebrates (planarians, Child, 1915; hydro-medusae, Child, 1918; molluscan adductor muscle, Hopkins, 1924, 1930) and in some isolated vertebrate tissues (articular cartilages, Rosenthal, Bowie and Wagoner, 1940, 1941, 1942; rat blood vessels, Lazovskaya, 1942, 1943; avian muscle, Glezina, 1939; rabbit muscle, Cheymol and Pelou, 1944; rat brain homogenate, Reiner, 1947; liver, kidney and heart homo-genates, Pearce, 1936; mouse lymphoid tissue, Victor and Potter, 1935) O_2 uptake has been reported to decline with age.

In house-fly muscle Rockstein and Gutfreund (1961) found a decline in adenosine monophosphate and a piling-up of tri-phosphate, which appears to be due to a loss of phosphatase activity. Calorimetric experiments on the whole mammal indi-cate a general decline in heat production with increasing age (Sondén and Tigerstedt, 1895; Benedict and Root, 1934; Magnus-Levy and Falk, 1899; Shock, 1942, 1948; Benedict, 1935; Boothby *et al.*, 1936; Kise and Ochi, 1934). This decline, however, like that of growth-energy, is greatest in early life, and relatively slight in man after the age of 50 (Shock, 1953). It does not parallel the senescent increase in mortality. There is also gross individual variation. Kunde and Norlund found (1927) no significant decrease in the basal metabolism of dogs up to 12 years of age. In rats, Benedict and Sherman (1937) found a slight decrease in heat production with increasing age, measured in the same individuals, but with the onset of senescence the body weight itself declined, so that the metabolism per unit body weight appeared to increase. In man O_2 uptake per litre intra-cellular fluid shows no decrease with age (Shock, Watkin and Yiengst, 1954). A fuller bibliography is given by Shock (1951,

1953). It is not so far possible, in most organisms, to base intelligible estimates of individual senescence upon changes in metabolic rate.

1·2 *Forms of Senescence*

Increase in death-rate and decrease in resistance after a certain age might be expected in a number of model systems. The curve of failure rate for mechanical devices such as lamp bulbs, telephone switchboards (Kurtz and Winfrey, 1931), or radar units bears a superficial resemblance to the mortality curve of a senescent population, both in cases where all-or-none failure results from wear or from the passage of time (lamp filament failure, crystallization of metals, changes in condenser dielectrics) or where wear is cumulative and inefficiency increases to the point of failure (frictional wear, decline of cathode emission). The resemblance to biological senescence is closest in cases where several coincident processes ultimately become self-reinforcing. The 'death-rate' of motor-cars, plotted by Griffin (1928) and Pearl and Miner (1935) is closely similar to that of wild-type *Drosophila* (Fig. 6).

1·2·1 MECHANICAL SENESCENCE

A few precise analogies to the failure of a non-replaceable part in a mechanical system are known to occur in organisms. Deterioration of the waxy epicuticle in insect imagines and of the teeth in the African elephant (Perry, 1953), the mongoose (Pearson and Baldwin, 1953), the shrew (Pearson, 1945; Pruitt, 1954) and some large carnivores are examples of strictly mechanical senescence. Such changes would ultimately kill the animal. Similar, though less obvious, mechanical changes may contribute to senescence in other forms. It is probable that the gradual loss of nephra in the mammalian kidney is an example of the incidental loss of essential structures, but one which rarely reaches the point of causing death *per se*. On the other hand, the differences between an old cart and an old horse are sufficiently striking to make the extensive acceptance of 'wear' as an explanation of senescence, and the resort to mechanical analogies based on the 'spontaneous slow decomposition' of explosives

(Lepeschkin, 1931) or the behaviour of inanimate colloids (Růžícká, 1924; Dhar, 1932) difficult to accept. 'The old organism does not contain old colloids, it contains newly-formed colloids of an old character' (Lansing): this is not, however, universally true, and important molecules may in fact not be undergoing renewal (Gross, 1962). The mean half-life of human protein is 80 days, of liver and serum proteins 10 days, and that of the carcase proteins 158 days (Bender, 1953). High protein turnover in adult life has been found in some isotope studies (Shemin and Rittenberg, 1944); the turnover of other materials, such as collagen, decreases almost to zero with increasing age (Perrone and Slack, 1952; Neuberger and Slack, 1953). This possible distinction had been pointed out even before the discovery of colloids: 'Quoniam vero duplex est duratio corporum: altera in identitate simplici, altera per reparationem: quarum prima in inanimatis tantum obtinet, secunda in vegetabilibus et animalibus; et perficitur per alimentationem' (*Hist. Vitae et Mortis*).[1]

But as Gross (1962) points out in reviewing work since 1954, it now looks as if the turnover of many body constituents, and not only of scleroproteins, has been considerably over-rated in criticizing the theory of colloid ageing (Comfort, 1956)—'the point of view of the colloid ageing school might be summarized by asking the question: is it possible that at least one phase of the ageing process is a steady increase in crystalline order on the level of macromolecular aggregation, which requires little energy transfer, does not involve "dynamic" processes, but does cause steady attrition by removing important molecular elements from the cellular machinery?' (Gross, 1962). It is certainly not *im*possible, in the light of the evidence which Gross summarizes. Electronic delocalization—'tautomeric shift and erroneous coupling'—has also been invoked as a subtler type of molecule spoilage leading to ageing (Pullman and Pullman, 1962).

A chemical extension of the idea of 'mechanical' senescence

---

[1] Since there are in fact two ways in which bodies maintain their identity, the first, which applies only to inanimate objects, is simply by remaining the same. The second, which applies to plants and animals, is by renewing themselves; and they do this by means of nourishment.

could be based more plausibly on the existence of expendable enzyme systems renewable only by cell division, to explain the ultimate death of some fixed postmitotic cells (Cowdry, 1952); this concept will be discussed later on. In all organisms except those which are capable of total regeneration, mechanical injury of a more general kind must accumulate with time, but this process will vary greatly in rate under different environmental conditions. The constancy of the specific age in forms which senesce is a strong argument against the primacy of 'mechanical' ageing: whether it negatives chemo-mechanical ageing is more doubtful. The stability of the rate of age change in collagen suggests it does not.

1·2·2 'ACCUMULATION' AND 'DEPLETION'

In addition to a limited number of cases in which mechanical wear normally, or potentially, terminates an animal life-cycle, most of the other postulated 'causes' of senescence such as the accumulation of metabolites (Metchnikoff, 1915; Jickeli, 1902) and the exhaustion of stored irreplenishable reserves, do very probably contribute to senescence in specific instances. The very large literature of calcium and pigment accumulation in the cells of higher animals (reviewed by Lansing, 1951) deals with changes which are probably reversible consequences, rather than primary causes, of an underlying senile process. Lansing (1942) found, however, that reduction in the calcium content of the medium greatly increased the life-span of rotifers. A similar increase was produced by a single immersion in weak citrate solution. Accumulation of calcium with age was demonstrated in the same organisms by microincineration. Similar processes are described in plants (Molisch, 1938; Ahrens, 1938; Lansing, 1942). The 'life' of spermatozoa, though by no means analogous, has been shown to be prolonged by chelating agents which bind Cu^{++} and Zn^{++} (Tyler, 1953). In the case of the rotifer, at least, the evidence for an accumulative element in senescence is fairly strong.

Depletion certainly terminates the life-cycle of some non-feeding insect imagines, especially among Lepidoptera (Norris, 1934; Waloff, Noriss and Broadhead, 1947), and possibly other types of imago (Krumbiegel, 1929a, b). Many animals die or become more vulnerable, as a result of the depletion or physiological derangement caused by spawning (Orton, 1929). The life of female ticks which normally die 4–5 days after oviposition can be increased to 30 days by injecting sucrose into the body cavity (Achan, 1961). The incidence of parental mortality in molluscs is reviewed by Pelseneer (1935). Attempts to explain the human menopause in terms of exhaustion of the supply of ova will be discussed later. There is no evidence of a 'depletive' senescence in mammals, unless the decline of growth rate be taken as evidence of the exhaustion of some hypothetical substance.

1·2·3 MORPHOGENETIC SENESCENCE

The accumulation of injuries presents no biological problem—it can easily be seen in structures such as skin, and the only serious difficulty lies in assessing how much it adds to ageing in particular structures or animal species.

But beside the processes of mechanical or metabolic senescence, and sometimes affecting the same organisms if they are protected from these, we also need a further, morphogenetic senescence to explain the sequence of events we see in many organisms. This senescence has been considered to arise directly from effects of the processes of cell development which give the species its typical shape, size and organ structure; either through changes in cell behaviour, or through the effects of differential growth. It expresses itself as a decline in the capacity to regenerate or maintain structures or conditions which, during growth and for a variable period after growth stops, are normally regenerated and maintained. Morphogenetic senescence is a cumulative failure of homoeostasis, affecting the body as a whole, to which coincident or dependent mechanical failure or accumulative processes may contribute, but which appears to be part of the processes which control cell-differentiation and regulation. More accurately, it appears to represent the withdrawal of co-ordination between these processes, so that physiological homoeostasis 'falls apart'. The characteristic pathological change of ageing is an increase in the number of pathological changes. It is this form of senescence which characterizes higher vertebrates and is particularly well seen in man. The chief evidence that this, morphogenetic, senescence is more than the 'sum of environmental insult' which was formerly invoked to explain it, is the existence in many organisms of specific age, analogous to specific size and possibly related to it, which displays little environmental, but marked inter-race and inter-specific, variation.

Much information about the behaviour of self-restoring and self-regulating systems, and a number of important general concepts, can be had from the study of mechanical models. These analogies can, strictly, only make clearer single components in the process of maintaining physiological stability; the most important feature of 'cybernetics' and homoeostasis in the organism has no precise mechanical analogy. This is the fact that the homoeostatic process, the state of quantitative invariance, or self-restoration, in various physiological systems, goes with qualitative and quantitative change in the nature of the systems themselves, their specificity, relative proportions, and function —in other words, it changes with developmental change. It looks very much as if senescence occurs when these long-term changes, which are probably controlled or initiated largely by the same humoral mediators which function in day-to-day homoeostasis, pass out of control, or reach a point beyond which homoeostasis is no longer possible.

This argument ultimately stands or falls by the result of our study of the phylogeny of senescence. Mammalian senescence seems to result from morphogenetic processes which ultimately escape from the homoeostatic mechanisms that operate during adult vigour. If, on the other hand, some other vertebrates were able to reach a state of growing, or self-replacing, equilibrium, even over limited periods, such an equilibrium would be most likely to be found in those forms where differential growth is least evident. The evidence on this point will be examined later.

1·3 *Senescence in Evolution*

Senescence has often been regarded as an evolved adaptation, rather than as an inherent result of having a body. This view, which is reasonably well in accord with the existing, and very incomplete, evidence of its distribution in phylogeny, was held by Weismann in spite of his insistence on the constrast between germinal immortality and somatic mortality. Weismann, however, regarded senile change, and the limitation of the individual life-span, as a positively beneficial adaptation, and his argument is, as we have seen, at least potentially circular.

It is hard but not impossible to devise a system in which *short* life is selected as a character of fitness. (Ribbands, 1953, found an apparent example in worker bees, where the summer brood could increase its working life by consuming pollen, but uses it instead to rear additional larvae.) In any circumstances where a high number of generations in unit time has an adaptive value, the Weismannian argument against individual longevity might hold. Leopold (1961) has argued a case for the adaptive value of parental death and of transience of organs in plants, and much of what he says could apply equally to seasonal animals. The most obvious modifications of life-span in phylogeny seem, however, to be chiefly in the other direction. The development of social insects probably depended upon the evolution of long-lived sexual forms, and it is very likely that something of the kind occurred in human phylogeny, in connection with the development of social behaviour and the family unit. Neurones having a long potential life had to be evolved as a condition for the development of elaborate learned behaviour and long parental dependence; and with the development of rational power and social organization, the advantages of possessing the experience of even a few long-lived members was probably very high in any early hominid community. The social animals, especially man, provide one of the best examples where longevity depending on factors outside the reproductive period can theoretically be subject to positive selection in terms of fitness. Blest (1960) found a marked difference in the length of post-reproductive life between species of butterflies with protective and with warning coloration—it is clearly advantageous to a species with warning colours that post-fertile adults should be about for predators to experiment with, so as to educate them at the least cost to the fertile.

The chief objection to Weismann's idea of senescence as an

adaptive effect is the rarity of its demonstrable occurrence in nature. In all but the few forms discussed on pp. 151-7 senescence is a *potentiality,* not a benefit or a handicap; it is realized only when we interfere artificially with the animal or its environment, and it is arguable whether evolution can select for such potentialities. Bidder, it will be recalled, considered that senescence in mammals was an evolutionarily unimportant 'by-product' of an important positive adaptation, the limitation of size. It would indeed be possible to attribute senile change to the effects of such by-products 'coming home to roost' after the end of the reproductive period. More recently it has been suggested that senescence is to be regarded not as the positively beneficial character which Weismann believed it to be, but as a potentiality lying outside the part of the life-cycle which is relevant to evolution. It has certainly been 'evolved', in that the living system which senesces has evolved, but it has not evolved as a physiological mechanism. The line of argument which appears most plausible is that suggested by Medawar (1945, 1952). It seems probable, for a number of reasons, that except in certain social animals there can be little effective selection pressure against senescence as such. In any wild communities of animals, even if they did not age, there will always be more young reproducing than old reproducing individuals; the difference is enough to offset the advantage in number of progeny which arises from a longer reproductive life. Death from senescence is itself in many species so rare in the wild state that failure to senesce early, or at all, has little value from the point of view of survival. In many forms the cessation or reduction of breeding capacity happens well before senescence proper—with certain exceptions in social animals. What happens later, in the post-reproductive period, is theoretically outside the reach of selection, and irrelevant to it. Indeed, Medawar's view is really an evolutionary correction of one of Samuel Butler's bright ideas—that cells age for lack of a 'racial memory' to instruct them how to go on living to ages of which their immediate ancestors had no experience, and that they die because they become puzzled how to continue. A consequence even more important than the mere failure of evolutionary processes to operate in favour of the postponement of senescence follows from the same facts. In view of the constant reproductive preponderance of young individuals, the postponement of the action of a harmful genetic effect until late in the reproductive life is almost as good, in selective value, as its complete elimination: the longer the postponement, the closer the equivalence. The evolutionary 'demon' is concerned only to clear the part of the life-span in which he works, not the parts which might be reached if the environment were artificially made more favourable. This mechanism, by acting to move all adverse genetic effects which are capable of postponement and all the consequences of divergent but temporarily beneficial systems into the late reproductive or post-reproductive life, may itself provide a partial explanation of the evolution of senescence, as Haldane (1941) has already suggested. In this case we would expect the balance in man to be such that the force of mortality is lowest when reproductive activity is potentially highest, though the observed lowest level falls rather earlier than this (10–12 years in males, Greville, 1946).

The selectionist argument which regards senescence as the decline of evolved survival-power through successive age groups is most convincing when we apply it to mammals and birds: among invertebrates, reservations require to be made. In those which are predominantly seasonal, with a total life-span less than one year, and which winter as fertilized adults, it is by no means true that at all times of the year young individuals must outnumber old in a free-running population. The autumn contingent of overwintering animals will consist of 'old' individuals. In such forms, the selective advantage of different genotypes will vary from season to season, and there will be an ultimate requirement that the adult be capable of living long enough to overwinter. Forms producing two broods annually will tend to select fertility in the spring brood and longevity in the autumn, but with a time-lag of one generation between selection and potential expression. The mechanism of selection in such a system must be very complicated.

In mammals some selective advantage would also presumably attach to longevity where older males are polygamous and younger males compete for the remaining females (deer, baboons). The solipsist model of selection operating on 'the individual' can obviously be upset by any selection pressures introduced into the system by interaction between individuals, and by community-patterns of ecological behaviour in the species; the idea of an 'individual' animal unsupported by the rest of the ecological community in which it lives is in fact un-biological, and large unpredictable selection pressures affecting the life-span may well arise from such hidden social relationships.

In spite of this criticism, the theory of senescence as a measure of declining selection-pressure is important. The declining evolutionary importance of the individual with age may be expressed in another way in the 'morphogenetic' senescence seen in mammals. At the point where a system of differential growth ceased to be regulated by forces which arose from natural selection, it would cease to be under effectively direc-tional morphogenetic control, and would resemble an auto-matic control device which has run out of 'programme'. In any such system the equilibrium must be increasingly unstable. These two views of senescence, as accumulation of delayed lethal or sublethal genetic effects, and as a withdrawal of the evolutionary pressure towards homoeostasis with increasing age, are complementary, though probably only partial, pictures of its evolutionary significance. The concept of senescence as exhaustion of programme also restores a far greater unity to our definition of ageing, which includes a great many effects having little in common beyond their destructive effect on homoeostasis. All such effects fall within the idea of deteriora-tion lying outside the 'terms of reference' of each species, as laid down by natural selection. The 'flying bomb' which failed to dive on its objective would ultimately 'die' either of fuel exhaustion, or through wear in its expendable engine. If its design had been produced by evolution, and its evolutionary relevance ceased at the moment of passing its objective, or decreased as a function of the distance flown, both these events would be outside the programme laid down by the selective equilibrium, as they were outside the calculation of the design-ing engineers. Death in such an expendable system may result from one of many factors, and even, as Bidder recognized, from the consequence of processes which contribute to fitness during earlier life, such as systems of differential growth. We shall find a good deal of gerontology *is* primarily the study of a living system's behaviour after its biological programme is exhausted. The various evolutionary explanations of ageing already combine to offer us some idea of the reasons why this may be so.

ᥫ 2 ᥫ

THE DISTRIBUTION OF SENESCENCE

2·1 *Character of the Evidence*

To find out which animals exhibit an increasing mortality with increasing age, we should ideally keep large numbers of each species, or of representative species, from birth to death, under optimal conditions of captivity. In point of fact, apart from the impracticability of keeping any significant number of species in this way, the results would be both artificial and potentially misleading. It is possible to invent about animal senescence a paradox rather analogous to the principle of physical uncertainty: it is 'virtually unknowable' or, in other words, meaningless to ask, whether certain organisms are 'susceptible to senescence', because the organism is biologically dependent on its environment: in the wild state these forms never normally live long enough to reach senescence, while domestication or protective interference with the environment brings about changes in physiology and behaviour which produce effectively a different organism. The object of the paradox is to point out the fruitlessness of argument over 'potential' behaviour which is practically unrealizable. Almost all our detailed knowledge of senescence comes either from the observation of man, or of domestication-artefacts such as the laboratory mouse or the laboratory strains of *Drosophila*. In the wild state it is most unlikely that any species of *Mus* or of *Drosophila* reaches old age with sufficient regularity to be subject to study. In most cases we are creating for study a state which has no part in the life-cycle as it has been shaped by evolution, but is at most a potentiality. This must be taken into account on every occasion when theories of the evolution of senescence are being based on the appearance of senescence in domestic animals.

Life-tables for mammals other than man and the mouse are still few, though some data have been collected for horses (Comfort 1958a, 1959), dogs (Comfort 1956, 1960a), and various zoo animals (Comfort: see Figs. 8, 12–17).

2·1·1 ANIMAL LIFE-TABLES

If we had a comprehensive account of the relation between growth, development, mortality and chronological age in a sufficient range of representative species, the truth of most of the general theories which have been put forward to explain senescence could probably be tested by inspection. The actuarial studies which we already have, combined with maximum age records, suggest that in invertebrates there is an inverse relationship between degree of cell replacement and liability to senile change. It is now of great importance to obtain accurate data for the relation of age to mortality in the main types of vertebrates, and in as many different species as possible. Ageing and general metabolic activity in rats are dissociable, at least prior to maturity, as growth and development are dissociable in the tadpole; it is therefore quite one of the most important problems of age studies to find out, if possible, which components of the developmental 'programme' in mammals determine the timing of senescence. Given a sufficient range of comparative information, we might expect to answer this question either directly, from observed correlations, or by a relatively small number of fundamental experiments.

There are no wholly consistent correlates of life-span. 'Neither do those things which may seem concomitants give any furtherance to this Information (the greatness of their Bodies, the time of their bearing in the Womb, the number of their young ones, the time of their growth, and the rest) in regard that these things are intermixed—sometimes they concur, sometimes they sever' (Bacon). The metabolism of small birds measured by their oxygen consumption is higher than that of rodents, and apparently it does not decline with age like that of many mammals (Benedict and Talbot, 1921). This suggests that in phylogeny other causes than the increase in metabolic rates have operated to shorten the maximum life-span. The growth of birds, as Bacon (1645) pointed out, ceases relatively earlier than

56

that of mammals, and much more definitively; the epiphyses of rats never join, and they may continue in growth, or be made to grow in response to somatotrophin, at any age, while no further growth occurs in birds after the attainment of adult size.

There are also important discrepancies between the maximum ages reported in closely related mammals. The most extensive figures are for rodents: thus *Mus bactrianus* has been reported to live and remain fertile longer than any strain of *Mus musculus* (Green, 1932), while species of *Peromyscus* and *Perognathus* live almost twice as long [*Peromyscus maniculatus gambelli* 5 years 8 months (Sumner, 1922); *Peromyscus maniculatus gracilis* 5 years 10 months (Dice, 1933; Rabb, 1960); *Perognathus longimembris* > $7\frac{1}{2}$ years (Orr, 1939)]. These differences are not closely related to size—*Micromys minutus* reaches nearly 4 years in similar circumstances (Pitt, 1955). Leslie and Ranson (1940) and Leslie and co-workers (1955) found a difference in specific longevity between colonies of *Microtus arvensis* and *Microtus orcadensis*, though this might reflect the results of domestication and better culture. Such differences are clearly of great importance to our understanding of age processes, but so far none of the attempts to correlate them with quantities such as the duration of pregnancy or the relative length of pre-adult development is satisfactory—chiefly because the figures assumed for the specific ages of the different species are arbitrarily drawn from the maximum age records, some of them quite inaccurate. Most of the valid correlations which can be made out have been reviewed by Bourlière (1946).

The closest correlate of life-span in mammals is the 'index of cephalization' or relative excess of brain weight over the predicted value derived from a universal brain-body weight equation (Friedenthal, 1910; Sacher, 1957). Friedenthal's conclusion was that 'der Klügste am längsten lebt'.

In view of questions like these, one of the most important requisites for the understanding of mammalian age processes and the factors which time them is a full range of vertebrate vital statistics, based on animals living under conditions of captivity sufficiently good for a fair proportion of them to reach old age. These figures are almost wholly lacking. So far as can be ascertained, up to 1960 no life-table had been published for a captive population of any fish, reptile or amphibian. One incomplete life-table exists for domestic poultry, and it is based on an assumed equation to cover losses from culling (Gardner and Hurst, 1933); there is no other table for birds in captivity. Apart from these, we have had satisfactory actuarial data only for man, laboratory rats and mice, and a few other small rodents, with partial figures for culled populations of agriculturally important animals [e.g. Merino ewes (Kelley, 1939)]. There are thus no data for any vertebrates other than mammals; the figures which might throw light on the evolution of mammalian senescence, those for poikilotherms, birds and marsupials, have never been sought.

One consequence of this lack of information is that we have no experimental mammal intermediate in size between man and the small rodents whose rate of ageing is actuarially known. There are no published actuarial data for rabbits: their modal specific age for all strains is probably about 8 years, but large hybrids may reach ages as great as 15 years (Comfort, 1956). Data for guinea pigs have been collected and briefly reported (Rogers, 1950) but we have no comparison of strains. Accordingly, many physiological and other differences described in the literature between young and 'old' animals are in fact differences between infant and young adult animals, and even where this is not so it is impossible to establish correlations between such changes and the rate of ageing from maximum age records alone.

2·1·2 METHODS OF OBTAINING VERTEBRATE DATA

It is difficult, but not impossible, to obtain actuarial statistics for vertebrates, and as they are virtually essential to any biologically directed attack on age problems, we should devote our attention to getting them, as a matter of urgency. They represent an expendable problem, moreover, since time once spent will not require to be re-spent later.

Age-mortality data can be obtained in three ways: (1) from populations of animals specially kept under close observation throughout life, (2) from analysis of existing records, (3) by cross-sectional studies which indicate the simultaneous mortality in each age group over one period of time, instead of the successive mortalities of the survivors of a cohort followed throughout life. The results of (3) will differ numerically from those obtained from the same animals by the first two methods if there is a secular change in mortality during the lives of the longest-lived individuals. With this method we should include cross-sectional studies of animals which can be aged by inspection, particularly the analyses of fish populations by means of catch curves (Ricker, 1948). The number of instances in which wild populations can be used for ageing studies is, however, so far small; although even in small birds whose mortality is substantially constant, ringing studies show that more individuals reach old age than the early death-rates would lead us to expect (Haldane, 1953).

It is evident that we can expect to obtain figures for most of the long-lived animals only from existing records. These include kennel and stud books, notes kept by laboratories or by amateurs, and the record files of zoological gardens. The material varies greatly in quality, and the statistical treatment which it requires is different from that which serves for laboratory or human actuarial work, since the data consist of multiple small samples, and in most cases there are substantial losses from the record by sale, culling, or deliberate killing in the course of experiments.

TABLE I

BRAIN WEIGHT, BODY WEIGHT AND ASSUMED LIFE-SPAN IN DOGS

Breed	Body Wt. (Kg) y	Brain Wt. (gm) z	log x_1	log x_2	log $x°$	$x°$ (years)
Pekinese	5·6	58·7	1·40	1·28	1·30	20
Dachshund	8·2	70·9	1·33	1·20	1·28	19
Fox terrier	7·8	67·9	1·31	1·18	1·20	(≮16)
Mastiff	42·2	116·5	1·30	1·17	1·15	14
Leonberger	47·6	113·0	1·29	1·28	1·15	14
St. Bernard	47·0	113·7	1·34	1·20	1·15	14

log x_1 = 0·636 log z — 0·225 log y + 1·035 (Sacher's equation).
log x_2 = 0·6 log z — 0·23 log y + 0·99.
$x°$ = observed or assumed life-span.
Body and brain weights from Stephan (1954). Life-spans from Comfort (1960a).

The Distribution of Senescence

Within a single species, the difference in observed longevity of the various breeds of dog follow the direction predicted by Sacher (1957) from the distribution of life-span with brain and body weight in different groups of mammalian species. Table I gives some of Stephan's data (1954), together with the expected values of log x from Sacher's equation:

$$\log x = 0.636 \quad \log z - 0.222 \quad \log y + 1.035$$

where x = life-span in years, y = body weight, and z = brain

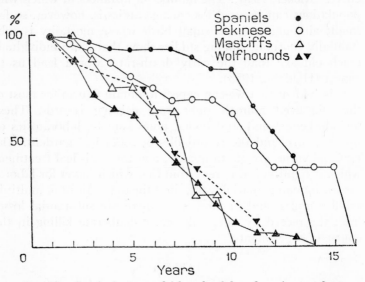

Fig. 17.—Survival curves of 4 breeds of dogs from 1 year of age (Comfort, 1960a).

weight, both in grams. Comparing these with observed or assumed values of x ($x°$), on the assumption that most of Sacher's figures for mammalian life-spans are derived from maximum records and that the longevity of other big breeds which are known to be short-lived (such as the St. Bernard) resembles that of mastiffs, we find that most, although not all, of Stephan's data yield values for x which fit reasonably well to a similar equation with changed constants:

$$\log x = 0.6 \quad \log z - 0.23 \quad \log y + 0.99$$

The rest could no doubt be fitted by further manipulation,

but more complex comparisons are pointless until the real life-span of more breeds is known. The figures so far are at least consistent, however, with the idea that the rule regarding index of cephalization applies empirically to interbreed as well as interspecific differences.

TABLE II

LONGEVITY AND SURVIVAL BY COAT-COLOUR OF THOROUGHBRED MARES

Group	n	$e_{x=4}$	V_e	Median
All colours:				
Foaled 1875	285	17·26	0·34	22·43
1876	245	17·65	0·21	22·43
1877	233	17·44	0·21	22·49
1878	248	17·49	0·30	22·15
1879	261	16·13	0·16	20·81
1880	221	16·01	0·18	21·81
1875–80	1,492	17·04	0·046	22·18
1860–64	1,250	17·31	0·044	22·07
Bays (1875–79)	568	16·68	0·08	22·03
Blacks (1854–1900)	358	16·53	0·15	21·95
Chestnuts (1875–79)	262	17·23	0·20	22·50
Greys (1845–1920)	200	15·57	0·28	20·43

(Comfort, 1958)

Domestic goats, 15 and probably up to 20 years (20 years 9 months—female wild goat, London Zoo).

Carnivora: *cats* are the longest lived of the small domestic mammals. Mellen (1940) from questionnaires sent out in Canada and the U.S.A. obtained these records: gelt males, 21, 21, 22, 23, 24, 24, 25, 28, 31 years; entire males, 23, 24, 26; females, 21, 21, 22, 31. These were owners' estimates, but at least one 31-year record was well supported. 33 years has been claimed (Mellen, 1940). Figures for cats in England in recent years included at least ten apparently authentic cases over 20, and one gelt male alive at 28 (Comfort, 1956c).

Dogs very seldom exceed 18 years, and only exceptionally reach 20. There are remarkably few claims of greater longevity in the literature (34 years, Lankester, 1870). In many breeds the limit is far lower, large breeds being shorter-lived than small (see Table III, Comfort, 1956b, 1960a). Size differences in dogs are predominantly differences in parenchymatous cell number, not cell size (Rensch, 1954)—the same applies to neurones, judging from posterior root fibre counts in Terriers and Great Danes (Häggqvist, 1948). Crude comparisons of man–dog ages are of doubtful value in any breed (Cairey, 1954; Lebeau, 1953).

TABLE III

SURVIVAL OF FOUR BREEDS OF DOGS FROM KENNEL RECORDS

	Pekinese Kennels D, K, Y ♂♀	Cocker spaniels Kennel M ♀	English mastiffs ♂♀	Irish wolfhounds C	Kennel R ♂♀
N *	91	38†	23	9	91
Age (years)					
1	1·0000	1·0000	1·0000	1·0000	1·0000
2	·9663	1·0000	1·0000	·88	·8876
3	·9301	·9701	·8857		·7019
4	·8741	·9383	·7440	·88	·6419
5	·8062		·7440	·77	·6049
6	·7482		·6377	·77	·4814
7	·6880	·9383	·6377	·44	·3827
8		·8935	·2125	·33	·2716
9	·6880	·8394	·2125		·1728
10	·6281	·8394	0·0		·0864
11	·4711	·6595			·0370
12	·3664	·5396			·0370
13		·4197		0·0	·0246
14		0·0			0·0
15	·3664				
16	0·0				

* N = number from total sample alive at 1 year.

† Males omitted from computations because there was reason to suspect selection. Mean for 7 males 114 months, range 96–168.

(From Comfort, 1960a.)

In a lifetime study of beagles (Anderson, 1961) about one-third had died by ten years of age, but signs of 'true senility' were said to be present from five years on, as judged by pathological findings.

2·1·3 AGE DETERMINATION IN ANIMALS

This usually depends on the presence of some structure which grows annually in a consistent pattern, making it possible, once the pattern is known and has been shown to be consistent, to age the animal as one ages a tree by the rings in its stump. Examples of such ring-producing structures include pelecypod (but not gastropod) shells, discussed later: otoliths, bones, teeth, horns and fish scales. In mammals, the chief structures which can be used like this are the teeth of seals (by counting the incremental cementum layers: Laws, 1953; Scheffer, 1950; Hewer, 1960), the horns of sheep and goats (Murie, 1944; Ferrara, 1951), the wax earplugs of whales (Laws and Purves, 1956) and the antler-pedicels of caribou (Banfield, 1960)—the last not being strictly ring-forming structures, though they undergo annual increment. Apart from progressive plumage changes like that in the lyrebird, there seem to be no incremental ageing methods for birds. Many reptiles can now be aged by growth zones in the bones—in particular, the ectopterygoids and squamosals of snakes (Bryuzgin, 1939; Petter-Rousseaux, 1953); Peabody (1958) found evidence of a drought some years previously in the zones laid down by a bullsnake (*Pituophis*), and readable zonation in the bones of lizards, crocodiles, and fossil Australian lizards (Peabody, 1961): these papers review the literature. There is a large literature of scale-reading in fish (see, for example, Frost and Kipling, 1949; pike, scales and opercular bones: Jhingran, 1957; Indian carp: Hartley, 1958; salmon, etc.). Other annulus-forming structures are the otoliths (Irie, 1957; *Gasterosteus*, 1950; Jones and Hynes, etc.), vertebrae (tuna, Galtsoff, 1952; *Raia*, Ishiyama, 1951; Daiber, 1960; shark—Haskell, 1948–9), opercular bone (e.g. carp, Bardach, 1955), dermal spines and fin rays (*Squalus*, Holden and Meadows, 1962; Boyko 1946: Channel catfish, Marzolf, 1955, etc.). Section of sturgeon fin rays has revealed ages up to 82 years (Chugunov, 1925; Milne and Milne, 1958). These references represent only a minute part of a vast literature of direct age determination by ring-counting in fish. Of amphibia, only *Necturus* appears so far to have been aged by similar means (Senning, 1940).

Other methods of ageing animals, particularly mammals, are chiefly of use for population studies, and are not suitable for maximum age determination, since they distinguish only 'old' from 'adult' or 'young' without specific reference to years. They can sometimes give more precise information, however, if combined with year-group analysis of a population—here again, only representative papers can be quoted in this list. Such methods include the examination of teeth in horses; of the baculum; of tail pelage in squirrels (Sharp, 1958); moult pattern in *Microtus* (Ecke and Kinney, 1956); epiphyseal fusion in rabbits (Taylor, 1959)—a criterion which is much used in man, but is highly unreliable, owing to the large scatter in rates of development (Tanner, 1955)—ovum counts in primates (Laws, 1952) and tooth impressions in deer (Flyger, 1958). Age determination in game and furbearers is reviewed by Habermehl (1961).

Maximum longevity records of animal species have a definite, but limited, use in giving a comparative picture of the possible longevity in different forms. They can give no direct evidence of the distribution of senescence, but they can provide an important test of a number of general theories—those based, for example, on the exhaustion of neurones (Vogt and Vogt, 1946; Bab, 1948) are difficult to reconcile with the variation in specific age and potential longevity between closely-related forms. A large scatter of maximum recorded ages is in itself suggestive, but not of course demonstrative, evidence of an indeterminate life-span, except in cases where it is evidence only of improving cultural methods and better understanding of the requirements of the animal under laboratory or domestic conditions. For a very large range of species we can readily infer a 'potential' age which is never attained, either in the wild, because of accident and predation, or in captivity, because the animals cannot be kept alive in captivity—the 'potential' longevity of snakes, chamaeleons (Flower, 1925, 1937) or mammals of little known habits (pangolins—Flower, 1931) are cases in point. 'Concerning the length and brevity of life in beasts, the knowledge which may be had is slender, the observation negligent, and tradition fabulous; in household beasts the idle life corrupts; in wild, the violence of the climate cuts them

64

off' (*Historia Vitae et Mortis*). With most birds, fully domestic mammals, hardy reptiles such as tortoises, and man, however, maximum records can be taken to represent in some real degree the extreme length of time for which the species, or its hardier genotypes, can remain self-maintaining if protected from gross disease or accident. Theories of senescence must fit these data, or at least not contradict them, to be available as working hypotheses.

2·2 *Maximum Longevities in Animals*

Apart from the observations collected by Bacon, which were remarkably critical and accurate compared with the wildness of later estimates, the accurate study of animal life-spans virtually begins with the enormously painstaking studies of Chalmers Mitchell (1911) and Flower (1925, 1931, 1935, 1936, 1937, 1938[1]) in purging a vast body of legendary and anecdotal material which encumbered the subject. Much of this legendary material unfortunately persists in other books and papers (*Tabulae Biologicae*—Heilbrunn, 1943; Nagornyi, 1948; Hammond and Marshall, 1952; Schmidt, 1952; Wurmbach, 1951; Birren, 1959) deriving their data from Korschelt (1922). The scepticism of Flower's papers was very valuable, in view of the exorbitant claims made for parrots, elephants and so on, but it seems probable that birds, in particular, are in fact capable of living considerably longer than Flower's maximum figures suggest. Better data may, in time, become available, though the value of such records is still not sufficiently widely appreciated and many opportunities must have been lost through failure to keep track of individual specimens. No recent writer has dealt equally painstakingly with the longevity of invertebrates.

The data on vertebrate senescence which follow are those of Flower, except where otherwise stated. Some more recent records have been added, including a number derived from the

---

[1] Those references marked 'Flower MS.' refer to the card-index of data and letters from biological workers which Flower was preparing against a revision of his first mammalian list, and which was uncompleted at his death. This index is in the library of the Zoological Society of London, and includes also bird and reptilian records and the skeleton of a list of invertebrate longevities.

series of longevity studies published by the Penrose Laboratory
of the Philadelphia Zoo in the years prior to 1942 (Duetz, 1938,
1939, 1940, 1942).

2·2·1 MAMMALS

The longest-lived species is man. *Elephas indicus* is known to
reach 60 years: a few individuals may reach or exceed 70 in captivity (77?—Mohr, 1951). The only other mammals which are
known to approach or exceed 50 years are the horse, hippopota-
mus (49 years 6 months: 1953—*Ann. Rep. N.T. zool. Soc.*, *53*, 12),
Rhinoceros unicornis (49 years—Flower, 1931) and probably the
ass (47 years?—Flower MS.). Many larger mammals, including
baboons and other large primates, cats, bears, African elephant,
equines, tapirs, can approach or exceed 30 years (chimpanzee,
39—Tomilin, 1936; baboon, *Papio papio*, 27—Duetz, 1938;
P. anubis, 30+ —Krohn, in press; gibbon, *Hylobates lar*, 32+
—Duetz, 1938; (*Tarsius*? about 20, Ulmer 1960); domestic cat,
31—Mellen, 1939, 1940; 27, Comfort, 1955: Chapman's zebra,
40—Weber, 1942). A large group, including almost all rumi-
nants, many medium-sized herbivores and carnivores, large
bats and the larger rodents (beaver, capybara, the domestic
rabbit) have recorded maximum ages between 12 and 20 years
(golden agouti, 15—Duetz, 1938). The maximum ages of very
many rodents and small carnivores are not accurately established, since few specimens have been kept, but it is likely that a
very large group among these forms has a potential life-span
approaching 10 years. (*Lutra canadensis*, ♂ 14½—Schaffer, 1958;
fox, 15—Sheldon, 1949; ♂ fox, 14—Wheelwright, 1941;
♂ bobcat, 25—Carter, 1955; *Platypus*, 14—Manville, 1958.)
The small Chiroptera certainly have a much longer life than
most mammals of comparable size—ringed horseshoe bats have
been recovered after at least 7 years (Bourlière, 1947), and
have lived at least 16 years (Cockrum, 1956; Dorst, 1954; Van
Heerdt and Sluiter, 1955). This agrees with their slow rate of
reproduction.

The shortest-lived mammalian group (<5 years) includes
rats, mice, voles and other small rodents, and the small insecti-
vores. [Rat—4 years 8 months in a white rat probably already
1 year old—Donaldson, 1924; Simms, 1958; laboratory mouse,

3 years 3 months—Kobozieff, 1931; *Apodemus sylvaticus*, 6 years (Neuhaus, 1957); *Micromys minutus*, nearly 4 years—Pitt, 1945; golden hamster (*Cricetus auratus*), usually 2–3 years maximum —Bruce and Hindle, 1934; Deansley, 1938; one specimen in London Zoo, 3 years 11 months—Flower MS.; guinea pig, 7 years 7 months—Rogers, 1950; *Blarina*, 18 months—Pearson, 1945; *Sorex fumeus*, 13–14 months—Hamilton, 1940; *Crocidina leucodon*, about 4 years (Frank, 1956).] The real life-span of whales has never been established, but it is almost certainly not more than 30–50 years at the most (Ohsumi *et al.*, 1958), and probably less. The age of maturity of whales has been placed as low as 2 years (John, 1937). Ruud *et al.* (1950) found that blue whales reach sexual maturity in about 5 years—no individual in their very large sample was apparently older than 12 years, judged by the baleen pattern. The life-span of dolphins in the wild appears to be of the same order (15 years—Sleptzov, 1940; 30+, one specimen—Parker, 1933). A female humpback whale is recorded with 95 striations in its wax earplug: reckoning 2 striations per year of life, this animal should have been about 47 years old. Few exceed 30 (Chittleborough, 1959).

Little is known about longevity in marsupials or monotremes —or if known it has not been put on record (*Echidna* nearly 40 years—Duetz, 1942: *Platypus* certainly 10 and probably 14 years in captivity—Manville, 1958).

Detailed records of many other mammalian species are given by Flower.

Recent data on the longevity of seals were reviewed by Laws (1953), upon the basis of tooth sections. Captive records include *Otaria byronia*, 23 years, *Eumetopias stelleri*, 19 (Flower, 1931); one female, 22 (Fiscus, 1961); *Zalophus californianus*, 23; *Arctocephalus pusillus*, 20 (Bourlière, 1951); *Phoca vitulina*, 19 (Sivertsen, 1941); *Halichoerus grypus*, 41–2 (Matheson, 1950). In the wild, *Callorhinus ursinus* has reached 21+ years (Schaffer, 1950); *Mirounga leonina* ♂ 20; ♀ 18 (Laws, 1953).

The *maximum age records of horses and domestic pets* are of importance because these animals are the only mammals kept throughout life in sufficient numbers to give any estimate of the extreme age for the species. In spite of the likelihood of exaggeration and mistake, records of domestic pets kept singly, throughout life, by intelligent witnesses, provide evidence as good as that from laboratory stocks and sometimes better than that from zoos, since reliable mnemonic evidence is better than unreliable documents.

Horses very probably exceed 40, most higher claims refer to ponies. Smyth (1937) reported a 46-year-old brood mare which foaled for the 34th time at 42—this case appears authentic. (Horse, 62—Flower, 1931—this is the celebrated but quite unauthenticated 'Old Jack'; jennet, reputed 60—Wright, 1936; pony, 54—Rothschild *fide* Flower, 1931; Shetland pony, 58— *The Times*, 3/5/44; roan pony, 52—*The Times*, 12/4/44; all probably legendary. Iceland pony, 47—*The Times*, 7/8/34; many records between 40 and 45.) A zebra has reached 40 in captivity (Weber, 1942). *Asses*—probably exceed 40 (47— Flower MS. from a press report; but an 86-year-old ass in *The Times*, 29/11/37, can hardly be taken seriously). A 48-year-old mule is reported (Galea, 1936).

In an investigation of age records in the General Stud Book, the highest were reached by Arabians, three mares reaching 31 years, and one dying in its 33rd year (born 1911, died 1943; last covered, but barren, 1942). The two oldest thoroughbred mares in the sample were alive at 30 years. The Stud Book has not been searched in detail for higher records—the oldest mare so far encountered (Blue Bell, by Heron out of Jessie) was foaled in 1851 and died in 1885 at the age of 34. The stallion Matchem (1749–81) reached a reputed age of 33: in the obituary lists of the Stud Book one other stallion reached 32, and four reached 31. For all mares reaching 4 years of age, the mean age of death was 21·2 years (Comfort, 1958).

Domestic goat: 15–20 years (20 years 9 months, female wild goat, London Zoo).

Carnivores: *cats* are the longest lived of the small domestic mammals. Mellen (1940) obtained records, from questionnaires sent out in the U.S. and Canada, of up to 31 years in gelt and entire males. 33 years has been claimed. Figures for England in recent years include ten colourable cases over 20, and one gelt male alive at 28 (Comfort, 1955). *Dogs* only exceptionally reach 20 years, chiefly the smaller breeds. See pp. 59–62.

Rodents: the *rabbit* can almost certainly exceed 15 years (10 years 3 months in the laboratory—Tegge, 1936; buck 13 years —Barrett-Hamilton, 1911; buck, chinchilla × Belgian hare, 11 years two cases; English buck, 14 years, both authenticated —Comfort, 1955). American cottontail, 10 years in captivity— Lord, 1961. Flower MS. contains a plausible correspondence with the owner of a rabbit (doe) which was said to have exceeded 18 years and was still alive.

2·2·2 BIRDS

Flower's longest 'incontestable' record in captivity (Flower, 1925, 1938) was 68 years in *Bubo bubo*. This is probably too low. Records exceeding 70 years in parrots, swans, and several large predators given by Gurney (1899), though less fully proven, are probably substantially correct (condor, 65—Sosnovski, 1957; goose, 46—Rankin, 1957, 33—Porter, 1958).

The maximum life-span in birds is not proportional to size (humming birds—two species 8 years in captivity, Conway, 1961). It is materially longer than in mammals of comparable size and activity. Many species can live 30–40 years, including small and active birds such as pigeons (Flower, 1938, Fitzinger, 1853: *Streptopelia risoria*, 40 years, *Columba livia*, 30 years, *Goura cristata*, ♂ 49, ♀ 53 years), while even the smaller passerines have a potential life of 10–15 or more years in captivity (29 years in a chaffinch—Moltoni, 1947) and ages of this order are occasionally reached even in the wild state (Perry, R. 1953). It has been properly remarked that

> *A robin redbreast in a cage*
> *Lives to a tremendous age.*

Extensive aviary records are given by Chalmers Mitchell (1911).

The Distribution of Senescence

TABLE IV

MAXIMUM RECORDED LONGEVITIES IN 45 SPECIES OF BIRD
(Flower, 1938)

	Proven	*Years* *Reported*
Eagle Owl (Bubo bubo)	68	
Greater sulphur-crested Cockatoo (Cacatua galerita)	56	69, 80, 120
Bateleur Eagle (Terathopsius ecaudatus)	55	
Vasa Parrot (Coracopsis vasa)	54	
Condor (Vultur gryphus)	52	
White Pelican (Pelicanus onocrotalus)	51	
Grey Parrot (Psittacus erythacus)	49	73
Golden-naped Parrot (Amazona auropalliata)	49	
Australian Crane (Megalornis rubicunda)	47	
Golden Eagle (Aquila chrysaëtos)	46	80
Adalbert's Eagle (Aquila adalberti)	44	
Blue-and-yellow Macaw (Ara ararauna)	43	
Grey Crane (Megalornis grus)	43	
Leadbeater's Cockatoo (Cacatua leadbeateri)	42	60
Caracara (Polyborus tharus)	42	
Chilean Eagle (Geranoaëtus melanoleucus)	42	
White-tailed Eagle (Haliaetus albicillus)	42	
Sarus Crane (Megalornis antigone)	42	
Rough-billed Pelican (Pelicanus erythrorhynchos)	41	
Manchurian Crane (Megalornis japonensis)	41	
Asiatic White Crane (M. leucogeranus)	41	
Herring Gull (Larus argentatus)	41	44, 49
Banksian Cockatoo (Calyptorrhynchus banksii)	40	
Bare-eyed Cockatoo (Cacatua gymnopis)	40	
Western slender-billed Cockatoo (Licmetis pastinator)	40	
Tawny Eagle (Aquila rapax)	40	
King Vulture (Sarcorhamphus papa)	40	
Ceylon Fish Owl (Ketupa zeylonensis)	39	
Cinereous Vulture (Aegypius monachus)	39	
Red-and-blue Macaw (Ara macao)	38	64
Griffon Vulture (Gyps fulvus)	38	117
American Crane (Megalornis americana)	38	
Californian Condor (Pseudogryphus californianus)	37	
Shoebill (Balaeniceps rex)	36	
Domestic Goose (Anser anser domesticus)	35	80
Slender-billed Cockatoo (Licmetis tenuirostris)	34	85
Canadian Goose (Branta canadensis)	33	47
Orange-winged Parrot (Amazona amazonica)	30	71
Roseate Cockatoo (Cacatua roseicapilla)	30	47
Domestic Pigeon (Columba livia domestica)	30	35
Domestic Dove (Streptopelia risoria)	30	42
Emu (Dromiceius novae-hollandiae)	28	40
Ostrich (Struthio camelus)	27	40
Egyptian Vulture (Neophron percnopterus)	23	101
Crowned Pigeon (Goura cristata)	16	49, 53

The Distribution of Senescence

The longevity of tortoises is one of the few popular beliefs about animal life-span which is correct, though it has been exaggerated. There is no clear evidence that the larger species

TABLE V

MAXIMUM RECORDED LONGEVITIES OF CHELONIANS
(Data from Flower, 1937, except where otherwise stated)

		Years	
Testudo sumeiri	Marion's Tortoise	152+	
elephantopus	Galapagos Tortoise	100+	
graeca	Greek Tortoise	102, 105	
	♀♀ alive	58	Moysey, 1963
daudini	Daudin's Tortoise	100+	
hermanni	Hermann's Tortoise	90+	
radiata	Radiated Tortoise	85+	
gigantea	Giant Tortoise	68–180	
sulcata	Spurred Tortoise	42	
marginata	Margined Tortoise	28	
Terrapene carolina	Carolina Box-tortoise	123+	
		118+	Dittmars, 1934
		129*	Oliver, 1953
		88+*	Deck, 1927
		65*	Edney and Allen, 1951
Emys orbicularis	European Pond-tortoise	70–120	Rollinat, 1934
Macroclemmys temminckii	Snapping Turtle	58+, 47	Conant and Hudson, 1949
Clemmys guttata	Speckled Terrapin	42+	
Pelusios derbianus	Derby's Terrapin	41+	
subniger		29+	Conant and Hudson, 1949
Sternotherus odoratus	Stinkpot Terrapin	52+	Conant and Hudson, 1949
Kinosternon subrubrum	Pennsylvania Terrapin	38+	
Chelodina longicollis	Longnecked Terrapin	37+	
		31+	Conant and Hudson, 1949
Caretta caretta	Loggerhead Turtle	33	
Malaclemmys centrata	Diamond-backed Terrapin	?40	Hildebrand, 1932
Cuora trifasciata	Three-banded Terrapin	26+	
Geoclemmys reevesi		24+	Conant and Hudson, 1949
Geochelone radiata		30+	Eglis, 1960

* Marked individual recovered in the wild.

are potentially very much longer-lived than some small forms. The maximum authenticated records include *Testudo sumeirii*, 152+ (years); *T. elephantopus*, 100+; *T. graeca*, 102, 105; *T. daudini*, 100+; *T. hermanni*, 90+; *Emys orbicularis*, 70–120 (Flower, 1925, 1937; Rollinat, 1934; Korschelt, 1931); *Terrapene carolina*, 118+ (Ditmars, 1934), 88+ (Deck, 1926), 64 (Edney and Allen, 1951), the last two in the wild. The age of the royal tortoise of Tonga, said to have belonged to Capt. Cook, and still living, is unsupported by documents, but may well be authentic.

The longevity of turtles and luths (Parker, 1926, 1929) and of crocodiles has been assumed, upon a basis of recorded sizes, to be very great, though the longest captive record of a crocodile is 56+ years (Flower, 1937). *Alligator sinensis* has been kept 52 years (Lederer, 1941), and *A. mississippiensis* 41 years in the London Zoo (1912–53). The records of snakes are limited by their poor survival in zoos. (*Eunectes murinus*, 29 years (Flower, 1937), 28 (Perkins, 1948); *Epicrates cenchris*, 27 (Perkins, 1948).) Lizards: *Anguis fragilis*, 33 years (Hvass, 1938), 32 (Flower, 1937), 27 (Thummel, 1938); *Sphenodon punctatus*, 28+ (Flower, 1937); *Heloderma suspectum*, 20 (Conant and Hudson, 1949); *Ophisaurus apodus*, 11 years 7 months (Conant and Hudson, 1949), 24 years (Perkins, 1948). The maximum life-span appears to be relatively brief in chamaeleons, but this may simply be due to failure to thrive in captivity.

2·2·4 AMPHIBIANS

'Amphibia, those cold and doubtful beings, can prolong their existence to an extraordinary length' (Hufeland, 1798).

Here again the figures in relation to size and growth give no very clear evidence that the life-span is sharply determined. The maximum records are in *Megalobatrachus* (52+ years— Flower, 1936; 65+ years—Schneider, 1932) but many small species are capable of very long life (*Triton* spp., 35 years— Smith, 1951; *Triturus pyrrhogaster*, 25—Walterstorff, 1928; *Amphiuma punctatum*, 25—Koch, 1952; *Triton marmoratus*, 24, 21— Wendt, 1934; *Pleurodeles waltl*, 20—Noble, 1931). *Siren*, 25 years, *Amphiuma*, 26—Noble, 1931; *Salamandra salamandra*, 24, *Bufo bufo*, 36, *Hyla coerulea*, 16, *Rana catesbiana*, 15, *Xenopus laevis*, 15

The Distribution of Senescence

(Flower, 1925; 1936), *Rana temporaria*, 12 + years (Wilson, 1950), *R. esculenta*, 14+, 16+, *R. temporaria*, 9+ (Sebesta, 1935), *R. catesbiana*, 8–10 years in wild and up to 16 in captivity— (Durham and Bennett, 1963): *Gastrophryne olivacea*, 7–8 years in the wild (Fitch, 1956). *Leptodactylus pentadactylus*, 15 years 9 months (Conant and Hudson, 1949).

2·2·5 FISH

Seriously acceptable records of longevity in the larger fish are very few. The longest accepted by Flower are *Silurus glanis*, 60+ years, *Anguilla anguilla*, 55, *A. chrisypa*, 50 (Flower, 1935). Some of the more celebrated legends of fish longevity (up to 170, 200, 300, or 400 years in carp, and 250 years in pike) are revived by Backmann (1938) and by Wurmbach (1951). 'Wenn auch diese Angaben hier und da übertreiben sein sollten', remarks Wurmbach, 'so kann doch gar kein Zweifel daran herrschen, dass der Karpfen wirklich ausserordentlich alt wird, und das Alter des Menschen weitaus übertrifft'—this is quite possibly true, but a 34 lb. pike taken in 1961 proved on scale examination to be 13 or 14 years old. Many exaggerated estimates have been based upon size, as extrapolations of the normal mean growth rate for the species—upon this basis, a 720 kg. sturgeon should be about 200 years old, and occasional examples weighing 1200 to 1600 kg. would be of fantastic antiquity. In no case, however, are any of these estimates supported by fin ray section studies, and the extrapolation is almost certainly unjustified. A beluga of 424 cm. and just over 1 metric ton in weight was actually found to be about 75 years old.[1] It is a matter of considerable biological importance to get proper age determination upon exceptionally large specimens of this kind. 75-year-old sturgeons have been taken in Russia (Chugunov, 1949) and one of 82 in America (Milne and Milne, 1958). A halibut brought to Grimsby in 1957 was 10 feet long, weighed 36 stone, and was aged at 60+ years by scale examination. It was a female and apparently both fertile and growing.

[1] I am very much indebted to Professor S. S. Turov of Moscow University Museum for a long series of sturgeon records.

The life-span of small fish is certainly limited in captivity (*Aphya pellucida*, 1 year; *Lebistes*, 1–2; *Xiphophorus*, 2–3; *Molliensia latipinna*, 3–4; *Betta pugnax*, 1½–2—Wurmbach, 1951). A few species of *Gobius* and *Latrunculus* must be regarded as annuals, even in captivity (Bourlière, 1946; Meyers, 1952). In this field there is little new information since the seventeenth century. 'The life of fishes is more doubtful than that of land beasts, since, living below the waters, they are less observed. Dolphins are said to live about thirty years; this is obtained by experiment upon some of them, the tail being marked by cutting; they grow for ten years. In Caesar's fishponds were certain *Muraenae* found to have lived to the sixtieth year. Indeed, they were grown with long use so familiar, that Crassus the orator mourned for the death of one. The pike, of freshwater fish, is found to live the longest, sometimes to the fortieth year. But the carp, bream, tench, eel and the like are not held to live above ten years. Salmon grow quickly and live not long, as do also trout; but the perch grows slowly and lives longer. How long the breath governs the vast bulk of whales and orcae, we have no certain knowledge; neither for seals, nor for innumerable other fish' [1] (*Hist. Vitae et Mortis*). Most of these figures are reasonably congruent with Flower's list. Full lists of aquarium records have recently been given by Hinton (1962).

2·2·6 INVERTEBRATES

Previous lists of invertebrate longevities (*Tabulae Biologicae*; Heilbrunn, 1943; Nagornyi, 1948, etc.), apart from the excellent data collected by Weismann (1891), almost all spring directly from the opinions of Korschelt (1922). These are based on data

---

[1] 'Piscium vita magis incerta est, quam terrestrium, quum sub aquis degentes minus observantur. . . . Delphini traduntur vivere annos circa triginta; capta experimento in aliquibus a cauda precisa; grandescunt autem ad annos decem. Deprehensae sunt aliquando in piscinis Caesarianis muraenae vixisse ad annum sexagesimum. Certe redditae sunt longo usu tam familiares, ut Crassus orator unam ex illis defleverit. Lucius, ex piscibus aquae dulcis, longissime vivere reperitur; ad annum quandoque quadragesimum . . . at carpio, abramis, tinca, anguilla et huiusmodi non putantur vivere ultra annos decem. Salmones cito grandescunt, brevi vivunt, quod etiam faciunt trutae; at perca tarde crescit, et vivit diutius. Vasta illa moles balaenarum et orcarum, quamdiu spiritu regatur, nil certi habemus; neque etiam de phocis . . . et aliis piscibus innumeris.'

from the older literature, largely unsupported by exact references, some accurate, but others highly speculative. The type of evidence which has got into such lists is well exemplified by the 15–20-year life-span of the crayfish. This, though probably correct, appears to owe its origin to an aside by T. H. Huxley (1880) to the effect that 'it seems probable that the life of these animals may be prolonged to as much as fifteen or twenty years' (*The Crayfish*, p. 32). The large *Tridacna* may in fact be the longest-lived invertebrate, in view of high records of age in much smaller pelecypods, but the literature contains no information of any description about its life-span, and the relationship between great size and great age is perpetually being disproved in other animals. Of a supposedly 18-year-old *Helix pomatia* Korschelt writes elsewhere: 'Gewiss hat diese Angabe von vornherein wenig Wahrscheinlichkeit für sich, aber als unmöglich wird man dieser Langlebigkeit nach dem, was man von anderen Tieren weiss, nicht bezeichnen dürfen' [1] (1922, p. 36, footnote).

A proper survey of the longevity of invertebrates can hardly yet be undertaken—the information is mostly lacking. It seemed wisest in compiling Table VI, which includes a few of the longest and most interesting invertebrate records, to give not only the record and source, but the type of evidence upon which the record is based. In invertebrates which metamorphose, length of larval life often depends entirely upon environment and food, while in other forms adult life can be punctuated by very long spells of diapause. Figures for these forms should therefore when possible indicate the circumstances of life. Larval life-spans have in general been omitted from Table VI. The most reliable records are in all cases those of animals kept, like Labitte's (1916) beetles or the Edinburgh sea anemones (Ashworth and Annandale, 1904) under close observation in captivity. Evidence from growth rings requires very careful scrutiny. Some purely inferential evidence, as of the age of termite primaries, is probably reliable. There are also some surprisingly high records in the wild, especially for pelecypods,

---

[1] 'No doubt these findings have little probability in themselves, but one cannot dismiss such longevity records as impossible, in view of what is known of other animals.'

where the method of ageing by rings of growth has been well upheld by other evidence. The life-span of common invertebrates certainly remains a wide-open field for those with facilities and an unlimited capacity for taking pains, and one where any reliably-attested information is worth putting on record.

The life-spans and senescence of molluscs may be taken as typical. The subject was last reviewed, and the literature cited with customary thoroughness, by Pelseneer (1935). The existing figures are here summarized in Table VI, which also shows the circumstances of the record (wild population, captive specimen or specimens) and the nature of the evidence from which age has been estimated. I have drawn most of the records prior to 1935 from Pelseneer's bibliography (1935), adding symbols to classify the nature of the evidence, and subsequent records from the literature.

As in so many instances where age and longevity are discussed, many repeatedly-quoted figures for molluscan life-spans (Korschelt, 1922; Heilbrunn, 1943; Spector, 1956; *Tabulae Biologicae*) are based on unsupported guesswork and require revision. Flower, to whom we chiefly owe the critical assessment of animal age records, unfortunately published only one unimportant paper on molluscs (Flower, 1922) and did not live to complete a study of invertebrate life-spans. His notes for this study are in the Library of the Zoological Society, where the Director has kindly allowed me to make use of them. Longevity is an aspect of animal life which is surprisingly often ignored, or treated by inference, in the discussion of life-cycles. Most of the accurate information which we have comes from the work of a few individuals (Hazay, 1881; Lang, 1896, etc.; Künkel, 1908, 1916, 1928; Weymouth, 1923, etc.; Oldham, 1930, 1942, 1942a; van Cleave, 1934, etc.) who have reared or observed mollusca and kept critical records.

We so far have laboratory life-tables only for a few small pulmonates (*Limnaea columella*, Baily, 1931, Winsor and Winsor, 1935; *L. stagnalis appressa*, Crabb, 1929, Noland and Carriker, 1946; *Physa gyrina*, De Witt, 1954; *Bulinus truncatus*, *Planorbis boissyi*, Barlow and Muench, 1951).

Age-mortality studies in wild populations, depending on methods

76

of year-group counting or ageing by growth rings, deal mainly with economically important bivalves, though van Cleave and co-workers (1932, 1934, 1935, 1937) and later authors (Hunter, 1953; Cleland, 1954) have studied some fresh-water gastropods. Weymouth (1923) wrote of age determination in molluscs: 'Of 14 papers by 13 different authors, 1 flatly denies that age can be told from the shell, 2 are unwilling to commit themselves, 5 feel that there is some sort of connection between age and the lines, but that they are of no material use even if their annual recurrence could be established, and 6 go on record as believing that the rings are annual. . . . In only 2 can the case be considered as firmly established on adequate data.'

It now seems agreed that growth rings can be used as a measure of age in pelecypods, and that they give reliable results if estimates are confined to species, and to localities, where annual deposition of a single ring, or a fixed and consistent pattern of rings, can be confirmed experimentally (Fairbridge, 1953; Haskins, 1955). In some forms the sculpture bears no consistent relation to seasonal growth. Other species which can be shown experimentally to lay down well-defined yearly rings at one station may fail to do so at another (Newcombe, 1936; Mead and Barnes, 1904—*Mya*). Rings are produced by any check to growth which causes recession of the mantle edge (Coker, Shira, Clark and Howard, 1919) whether seasonal, climatic, or due to handling and other experimental interference (Coe and Fox, 1942—*Mytilus*). Their relation to the seasons differs from species to species, and where they are annual they may represent the effects of temperature, of storm disturbance, or of growth-suspension during spawning.

Sculptural rings in short-lived species are occasionally, but not consistently, useful for the separation of broods. *Sphaerium solidulum* forms no annual ring (Foster, 1932), but adults of the normally annual or biennial *Ancylus fluviatilis* show a sufficiently definite growth check to enable over-wintered animals to be identified (Hunter, 1953); a few may show as many as four rings (Berg, 1948). Ageing by annuli works best in pelecypods with a long life and growth-period and a large final size, and much work upon the life-spans of freshwater mussels depends upon ring determination. In *Quadrula* Isely (1931) confirmed the one-for-one correspondence between annuli and years of life by recovering marked specimens alive after a 15-year interval. By ring measurements these mussels must have been at least 20 years old when marked. Crozier (1918) successfully aged *Chiton tuberculatus* by counting the annual striae on the valves; opercular markings have also been used (Hubendick, 1948; Kubo and Kondo, 1953), but there is no generally-available method of ageing gastropod shells or their opercula by inspection of sculpture. There is also an obvious objection to the use of ages based on annuli if conclusions are then to be drawn about the relation of senescence to continued growth, since arrests of growth lasting for years would leave no record in this system of notation, and the narrowness of the rings at high ages may make them uncountable. Ring-counting is clearly inapplicable to forms in which growth at right angles to the mantle edge is determinate, ending with the formation of a definite lip, after which the only gain is in shell thickness (Foster, 1936—*Polygyra*). The alternative method of ageing from statolith sections, suggested by Pelseneer (1932), may be feasible, though the wild ages he quotes appear too high, but it has not been used in practice. For the study of large field samples it might conceivably be possible to recover the statoliths by some means other than individual dissection.

It may perhaps also be possible, over the next decade, to identify the growth rings in shells which have been deposited since large-scale radioactive pollution of sea and air began, at least in areas near the test-sites, if not generally. If present estimates of Sr^{90} and Ca^{45} fallout are correct, the rise at each new atmospheric pollution may be detectable in the shells of European molluscs, especially those, like *Margaritana*, which concentrate calcium from acid and upland surface drainage water.

Diapause presents a special problem in estimating molluscan life-spans. Its duration cannot be determined by examining the shell, and periods spent in it almost certainly count little, if at all, towards the physiological age of the animal. Diapause in land forms and in the drought-resisting freshwater species can certainly last for a substantial fraction of the 'life-span' as ordinarily reckoned, and may well exceed it. According to Fischer (1931) normal hibernation in land molluscs may last annually for 5–6 months. *Cepaea nemoralis* in the Paris region hibernates intermittently from October to April (Lamotte, 1951). It has been claimed that *Oxystyla capax* has survived 23 years in aestivation (Baker, 1934)—the evidence in support of this is equivocal, but there is no reason to doubt circumstantial accounts of prolonged diapause in some of the older literature (*Helix aperta*, 3 years—Darbishire, 1889; *Buliminus pallidior*, 6 years—Stearns, 1877). Even *Planorbis corneus* and *Limnaea peregra* are said to have remained alive for 3 years 7 months under dry conditions (Wilkins, 1948), and a freshwater bivalve (*Aspatharia*) survived a year in somebody's pocket (Dance, 1958). Some small species have an active life-cycle of considerably less than a year, which they expand by overwintering in the immature state at a much-reduced growth rate (*Omalogyra*, Fretter, 1947). In pluriennial forms, diapause represents a large and incalculable extension of the potential life which needs to be considered in assessing marking records, and in making genetical or parasitological assumptions based on the usual length of generations.

In species with a wide climatic range, individuals from colder stations are longer-lived and slower-growing than those from warm (Weymouth and McMillin, 1931) but in general closely-related species from temperate and tropical countries seem to have similar life-spans at the temperatures to which they are adapted. The life-spans of pluriennials with a wide altitude-range (e.g. *Arianta arbustorum*) may not differ very greatly at high and low altitudes if, as is possible, much the same fraction of the year in each case is spent in diapause.

In the laboratory, littermate *Planorbis* of an unidentified species (probably derived from *P. corneus*) placed individually in jars at 100 days of age, had median further life-spans of 125 days at a constant temperature of 23° C., and of 280 days at the room temperature of an unheated laboratory (range 7 to 20° C.) (Comfort, 1957).

79

The Distribution of Senescence

TABLE VI

MAXIMUM RECORDED LONGEVITIES OF VARIOUS INVERTEBRATES

Notes.—Ages are in years unless otherwise stated. The figures given represent the greatest age observed or inferred in the reference quoted, and include both extreme records and partial records, e.g. the statement that a species 'is not sexually mature before 5 years of age' is scored as >5, and the statement 'rarely survives into a fourth year' as <5.

Symbols in the third column indicate the nature of the evidence cited, and are as follows:

w = under wild conditions
c = individual(s) in captivity
g = estimate of age based on growth (annuli, yearly grouping, etc.)
L = full or partial actuarial data, life-table, survival curve.

Porifera

Suberites carnosus	15	c	Arndt, 1941
Adocia alba	9	c	Arndt, 1941

Coelenterata

Actinia mesembryanthemum	65–70		Dalyell, 1848
		c	Korschelt, 1922
Cereus pedunculatus	85–90	c	Ashworth and Annandale, 1904
			Stephenson, 1935
			Warwick, 1954
			(personal commun.)

Platyhelminths

Schistosoma haematobium	25	h	Kirkland, 1928
	28	h	Christopherson, 1924
Clonorchis sinensis	25	h	Moore, 1924
Gastrodiscus aegyptiacus	9	h	Christopherson, 1924
Taeniorrhynchus saginatus	>35	h	Penfold, Penfold and Philips, 1936
Diphyllobothrium latum	29	h	Riley, 1919
'Echinococcus cysts'	56	h	Lawson, 1939*
Dugesia tigrina (= Planaria maculata)	6–7	c	Goldsmith, 1942
Dendrocoelum lacteum	5	?	Bresslau, 1928–33

Nematoda

Loa loa	15	h	Coutelen, 1935
Wuchereria bancrofti	17	h	Knabe, 1932
Necator americanus	12	h	Sandground, 1936

Rotifera—see Table IV

Annelida

Eisenia foetida	3–4½	c	Rabes, 1901
Lumbricus terrestris	5–6	c	Korschelt, 1914
Allolobophora longa	5–10	c	
Sabella pavonina	>10	c	Wilson D. P., 1949

Arthropoda
(Arachnida)

'Tarantula' (aviculariid)♀	11–20	c	Baerg, 1945
Avicularia avicularia ♀	>7	c	Didlake, 1937
Tegenaria derhami ♀	7	c	Savory, 1927

* See also Coutelen *et al.*, 1950; Davaine, 1877; Wardle and McLeod, 1952, pp. 116–17.

The Distribution of Senescence

Arthropoda
Filistata insidiatrix ♀	10, 11	c	Bonnet, 1935
Physocyclus simoni	4	c	Bonnet, 1935
Teutana grossa ♀	6	c	Bacelar and Frade, 1933
Psalmopoeus cambridgii	5½	c	London Zoo, Flower MS.
Lasiodera curtior	4½	c	London Zoo, Flower MS.

(Crustacea)
Astacus	15–25		inference Friedel, 1880
Homarus	50		inference Herrick,1898, 1911
Leander serratus ♀	5–6		inference Solland, 1916
Oniscus asellus	4½	c	
Philoscia muscorum	4	c	
Porcellio scaber	3¾	c	Collinge, 1944
dilatatus	3½	c	
Platyarthrus hoffmanseggi	5+	c	
Armadillium vulgare	4+	c	
Balanus balanoides	>5	w	Moore, 1934

(Insecta)
Thysanura
Ctenolepisma longicaudata	total 7	w	Lindsay, 1940

Ephemeroptera
Cloëon dipterum	imago 4 wks	c	Vane, 1946

Isoptera
Neotermes castaneus ♀ ♂	imago >25 yrs	w	Snyder fide Howard, 1939
Nasutitermes-physogastric♀	20–40	w	v. Hagen, 1938
'Termite primaries'	60–?	w	Richards, 1953

Lepidoptera
Nymphalis antiopa	imago 12 wks	c	
Calliophrys rubi	imago 6 wks	c	Frohawk, 1935
Maniola jurtina	imago 44 days	c	

Coleoptera*
Blaps gigas	imago >10 yrs	c	
Timarcha sp.	imago >5	c	Labitte, 1916
Carabus auratus	imago 3–1	c	
Dytiscus marginalis	imago <3	c	Blunck, 1924
Prionotheca coronata	imago 6, 7+	c	London Zoo, Flower
Akis bacarozzo	imago >4	c	MS.
Cybister laterimarginalis	imago 5½	c	Sharp, 1883

Hymenoptera
Apis mellifica ♀	imago >5	c	Pflugfelder, 1948
Lasius niger ♀	imago >19	c	Goetsch, 1940
Stenamma westwoodi ♀	imago 16–18	c	Donisthorpe, 1936
Formica fusca ♀	imago 10+	c	Janet, 1904
♀	imago 15+	c	Lubbock fide Weismann, 1882
sanguinea ♀	imago 5+	c	Lubbock fide Weismann, 1882
Lasius niger ☿	imago ⎫ >7	c	Lubbock fide Weismann, 1882
Formica fusca ☿	imago ⎭		

---

* For a discussion of the longevity of beetle larvae, see Howard, 1939; also Latter, 1935 (*Cossus*); Linsley, 1938 (*Stromatium*).

Echinodermata

Echinus esculentus	>8	w	Moore, 1935
Psammechinus miliaris	>6	c	Bull, 1938
Asterias rubens			
(reaches sexual maturity)	5–6	c	Bull, 1934
Marthasterias glacialis	>7	c	Wilson, 1954 (personal comm.)
Ophiothrix fragilis	>5	c	*Zool. Gart.*, 1930

Gastropoda

Amphineura

Katharina tunicata	3	w	Heath, 1905
Ischnochiton magdalenensis	3–4	w	Heath, 1905
Chiton tuberculatus	12	w	Crozier, 1918
Cryptochiton stelleri	?4	w	Heath, 1905
Chaetopleura apiculata	4	w	Grave, 1933

Prosobranchia

Haliotis rufescens	>13	w g	Bonnot, 1940
Trochus niloticus	>12	w	Rao, 1937; Pannikar, 1938
Gibbula umbilicalis	5	w	Pelseneer, 1934
Nerita japonica	2–3	w	Suzuki, 1935
Neritina fluviatilis	5	w	Geyer, 1909
Patella vulgata	15	w g	Fischer-Piette, 1939
Patina pellucida	1–2	w	Graham and Fretter, 1944
Acmaea dorsuosa	15	w g	Abe, 1932
Patelloida grata	>15	w g	Hamai, 1937
Valvata piscinalis	annual	w g	Cleland, 1954
Calyptraea chinensis	5	w g	Wyatt, 1961
Littorina littorea	2–3?	w	Moore, 1937
	10	c	*fide* Marshall, 1898
	20	c	*fide* Pelseneer, 1894
scabra	♂ 4 ♀ 5	w	Sewell, 1924
obesa	3–4	w	Sewell, 1924
Rissoella diaphana opalina			
Skeneopsis planorbis	annuals	w	Fretter, 1947
Omalogyra atomus			
Hydrobia ulvae	5	c	Quick, 1924
	>3	w	Rothschild and Rothschild, 1939
Lioplax sp.	♂ 1 ♀ 2	w	van Cleave and Chambers, 1935
Paludina contectoides	<3	w	van Cleave and Lederer, 1932
	9	c	Geyer, 1909
contecta	♂ 4¹¹⁄₁₂ ♀ 5		
	♂ 3½ ♀ 4½	c	Oldham, 1931
bengalensis	♂ 1 ♀ 3	w c	Annandale and Sewell, 1921
malleata	♂ 4 ♀ 7	w	Niwa, 1950
Campeloma rufum	>2	w	van Cleave and Altringer, 1937
	>4	w	Medcoff, 1940
Bithynia tentaculata	>2	w	Schäfer, 1953
Pila sp.	5	c	Flower, 1922

Prosobranchia
Melanoides lineatus	2–3	c g	Sewell, 1924
Acrostoma variabile	2	c w	Sewell, 1924
Nassa obsoleta	3	w	Dimon, 1905
Nucella lapillus	>5	w	Moore, 1938
Trichotropis cancellatum	<3	w	Yonge, 1962

Opisthobranchia
Haminea hydatis	4	w	Berrill, 1931
Philine aperta	3–4	w	Brown, 1934
Aplysia punctata	annual	w	Eales, 1921; Miller, 1960
Limapontia capitata	annual 2	w} c}	McMillan, 1947; Miller, 1962
Limapontia depressa var. pellucida	annual	w c	Kevan, 1934, 1939, 1941
Chromodoris zebra nodosus	annual annual	w} w}	Garstang, 1890
Melibe leonina	annual	w	Guberlet, 1928
Eolis amoena	sub-annual: 2 mos.	w	Risbec, 1928
Elysia viridis	some >1	c w}	
Actaeonia senestra	subannual	c w}	
Archidoris pseudoargus	>2	w}	
Polycera quadrilineata	>1	w}	
Acanthodoris pilosa	2	w}	
Onchidoris fusca	2	w}	Miller, 1962
muricata	annual	w}	
pusila	annual; some 2	w}	
Goniodoris nodosa	annual; some 2	w}	
Doto coronata	1	w}	
Hero formosa	>2?	w}	

Pteropoda
Limacina retroversa	>1	w	Redfield, 1939

Pulmonata
Carychium tridentatum	biennial	w c	Morton, 1954
Limnaea luteola	3	w	Seshiya, 1927
columella	max. 139 days	c L	Bailey, 1931
	max. 225 mean 128·8}	c L	Winsor and Winsor, 1935
palustris	max. 8–10 mos.	c L	Forbes and Crampton, 1942
bulimoides	6 mos. 25 mos.	w} c}	Olsen, 1944
stagnalis appressa	max. 14 mos.	c	Noland and Carriker, 1946
Myxas glutinosa	annual	w	Cooper, 1931
Bulinus truncatus	max. 13 mos.	c L	Forbes and Crampton, 1942
Planorbis corneus	2–3	w	Boycott, 1936
	6	c	Oldham, 1930
boissyi	1½	c L	Barlow and Muench, 1951
magnificus	2	w	Dale, 1907
Indoplanorbis exustus	2	c	Sewell, 1924
Ancylus fluviatilis	annual	w g	Hunter, 1935
	>3	w g	Berg, 1948

83

Pulmonata

Physa gyrina	annual 3	w c }	De Witt, 1954
Abida secale	3	c	*fide* Flower MS.
Achatina zebra	$6\frac{1}{2}$	2	Longstaff, 1921
Rumina decollata	12	c	Vignal, 1919
Testacella spp.	5–6	?	*fide* Taylor, 1907
scutulum	>580 days }	w, marked	Barnes and Stokes, 1951;
haliotidea	>570 days }		Stokes, 1958
Vitrina brevis	17 mos.	c	Künkel, 1920
pellucida	12 15 mos.	w	Taylor, 1907
Polita villae	$5\frac{1}{2}$	c	van der Horst, 1929
Arion empiricorum	16–18 mos.	c }	
simrothi	16 18 ,,	c	
subfuscus	12 13 ,,	c }	Künkel, 1916
hortensis	11–12 ,,	c	
bourguignati	12–13 ,,	c }	
Limax flavus	3	c	Szabó and Szabó, 1929, 1936
cineroniger	5	c	Oldham, 1942a
arborum	$2\frac{1}{2}$–3	c	Künkel, 1916
	17 mos.	c	Szabó and Szabó, 1929, 1936
	—	L	Pearl, 1935
Geomalacus maculosus	$6\frac{1}{2}$	c	Oldham, 1942b
Eulota fruticum	5–$6\frac{1}{2}$	w c	Künkel, 1928
Theba cantiana	2	w	Taylor, 1917
Helix pomatia	6–7	c	Künkel, 1916
	3	w	Lang, 1896
aspersa	5–6	c	Welch, 1901
	$5\frac{1}{2}$	c	Gain, 1889
	8–10	c	Welch *fide* Taylor, 1907
(Cepaea) nemoralis	5–6	?	Lamotte, 1951
	7	c	Brockmeier, 1888, 1896
hortensis	9	c	Lang, 1904
Helix (Levantina)			
spiriplana	15	c	Vignal, 1923
(Arianta)			
arbustorum	5	c	Künkel, 1916
(Campyloea)			
cingulata	4–5	c	Künkel, 1916
Euparypha pisana	>3	w	Taylor, 1907
Cochlicella acuta	>1	w	De Leersnyder and Hoestlandt, 1958

Bivalvia

Nucula turgida	max. 10–11	w g	Allen, 1952
nucleus	>12	w g }	Allen, 1960
sulcata	>17	w g }	
Mytilus edulis	8–10	w g	Williamson, 1908
californiensis	>3	w g	Coe and Fox, 1942
variabilis	5	g	Sewell, 1924
Ostrea edulis	>12	w g	Orton and Amirthalingam, 1930
	12	L	Walne, 1961
virginiaca	4–6	w	Grave, 1933
Meleagrina vulgaris	7		Herdman, 1904
Pecten jessoensis	>8	w g	Bazykalova, 1934
irradians	2 (fished)	w	Gutsell, 1930
maximus	22	w g	Tang, 1941

Bivalvia

Notovola meridionalis	>16	w g	Fairbridge, 1953
Megalonaias gigantea	54, 36	w g	Chamberlain, 1933
	53	w g	Haas, 1941
Lampsilis anodontoides	>8	w g	Chamberlain, 1931
siliquoidea	>12	w g	Chamberlain, 1931
	>19⎫		
recta	>18⎪		
ovata	>19⎪		
Fusconaia flava	12⎬	w g	Grier, 1922
Amblema plicata	16⎪		
Pleurobema coccineum	12⎪		
Elliptio dilatatus	12⎭		
Elliptio complanatus	12	w g	Matteson, 1948
Anodontoides			
subcylindraceus	9	w g	Grier, 1922
Tritogonia verrucosa	>11	w g	Chamberlain, 1931
Quadrula sp.	20–50	w g	Lefèvre and Curtis, 1912
	>30	marked	Isely, 1931
Margaritana	70–80	w g	Rubbel, 1913
margaritifera	>60	inference	Geyer, 1909
	100	inference	Israel, 1913
Unio crassus	15	w g	Brander, 1956
tumidus	15	w g	Brander, 1956
	>8	w g	Saldau, 1939
pictorum	13–15	w g	Brander, 1956
	>8	w g	Saldau, 1939
Pseudanodonta complanata	>14–15	w g	Brander, 1956
Anodonta piscinalis	10–15	w g	Brander, 1956
Sphaerium solidulum	<2	w	Foster, 1932
occidentale	>1	w	Herrington, 1948
Cumingia tellinoides	4	w	Grave, 1933
Tellina tenuis	5	w g	Stephen, 1931
Cardium corbis	>16	w g	Weymouth and Thompson, 1930
	7	w g	Fraser, 1931
edule	5	w g	Stephen, 1931
	14	w g	Cole, 1956
Tivela stultorum	20	w g	Weymouth, 1923
	>12	w g	Coe, 1947
Dosinia exoleta	>7	w g	Kristensen, 1957
Venus mercenaria	25–40	w g	Hopkins, 1930
	17	w g	Belden, 1912
striatula	>10	w g	Ansell, 1961
Donax cuneatus	>3	w	Nayar, 1955
Venerupis pullastra	>8	w g	Quayle, 1952
Scrobicularia plana	18	w g	Green, 1957
Cochlodesma praetenue	4–5	w	Allen, 1958
Amphidesma ventricosum	>9	w g L	Rapson, 1952
Siliqua patula	19–25	w g	Weymouth and McMillin 1931
Ensis siliqua	11–12	w g	Kristensen, 1957
Mya arenaria	>8	w g	Newcombe, 1935, 1936
Teredo navalis	2	w	Grave, 1928

Cephalopoda

Loligo pealii	3–4	w	Williams, 1909
subulata	1½	c	Flower, 1922
Spirula spirula	annual	w g	Bruun, 1943

85

TABLE VII

MAXIMUM RECORDED LONGEVITIES OF ROTIFERS
(Bibliography from Hyman, 1951)

Asplanchna sieboldii	2–3 weeks	c	Tannreuther, 1919
Proales decipiens	12 days	c	Liebers, 1937
sordida	22 days	c	Jennings and Lynch, 1928
			Lynch and Smith, 1931
Cupelopagis vorax	40 days	c	Cori, 1925
Euchlanis triquetra	21 days	c	Lehmensick, 1926
Epiphanes senta	8 days	c	Ferris, 1932
Brachionus pala	12–19 days	c	Chu, 1934
Euchlanis dilatata	23 days	c	Leibers, 1937
Keratella aculeata	29 days	c	Kolisko, 1938
Epiphanes brachionus	17 days	c	Kolisko, 1938
Floscularia conifera	18 days	c	Edmondson, 1945
Lecane inermis	14 days	c	Miller, 1931
Philodina roseola	10 days		
citrina	21 days		
megalotrocha	17 days	c	Spemann, 1924
Rotaria macrura	58 days		
rotatoria	20–50 days		
Callidina sp.	5 months	c	Zelinka, 1891
Adineta vaga	15–22 days		
barbata	21 days		
Habrotrocha constricta	34 days	c	Dobers, 1915
Macrotrachela			
quadricornifera	2 months		
Mniobia russeola	30 days		

2·3   *Maximum Life-Span in Man*

Human longevity records are even more notorious than those of animals. They depend largely on unsupported memory and tradition in a field where the emotional premiums of exaggeration are high. 'Furthermore, even though this satisfaction and vanity, of which we have spoken, were absent, yet such is the peculiar and perpetual wandering of the human Intellect, that it is more moved and roused by affirmatives than by negatives, whereas properly it ought to be just to both, nay even, in the forming of any axiom, the force of the negative instance is the greater' (*Novum Organum*). King (1911) found in the 1911 census a discrepancy between the size of the 85–90-year-old age group and that of the next higher group, which was almost certainly due to exaggeration. William Thoms (1873), founder of *Notes and Queries*, and Young (1899) devoted much time to exposing the pretensions of past supercentenarians. In some of the 'documented' cases, the life-span of father, son, and grandson of the same names were apparently conjoined in one record. Young's greatest authenticated record was a few weeks short of 111 years.

The actuarial probability of an individual's exceeding the age of 150 years, on the life-data of 1939, has been estimated at $(\frac{1}{2}^{50})$ (Greenwood and Irwin, 1939). Pütter (1921) calculated on a basis of German vital statistics for the years 1871–91 that ages over 105 were effectively impossible, and that for every million persons reaching 20 years, the number reaching 109 would be $4\cdot8 \times 10^{-10}$: 'danach wäre es nunmehr wohl an der Zeit, die Berichte über 120, 130, 140, 150 usw.-jährige dahin zu verweisen, wohin sie gehören: ins Reich der Fabel'. This scepticism has proved excessive, especially as regards the population-frequency of centenarians (see Freudenberg, 1951). The existence of supercentenarians cannot be disproved by statistical means unless the distribution of ages is really continuous, since ordinary life-tables have no defence against, say, a rare genotype with double the normal potential life-span. The number of persons reaching 100 years is in any event too small for statistically significant estimates of the rate of increase in the force of mortality after about 90 years of age. Pütter's estimate was based on the assumption that this increase continued at the same rate as in earlier life. The relation between observation and calculation in this part of the life-table is fully discussed by Greenwood and Irwin (1939).

In a good many mammalian curves the 'limit' is about twice the modal age of adult death—this would give a 'limit' in man of 150, if the analogy were sound. In all probability it is not.

Subsequent writers have been content to rely on direct observation, provided that only records supported by proper documentary evidence are taken seriously (Forster, 1945; Tomilin, 1938). The minimum requirements are these laid down by Thoms (1873)—documentary evidence of *birth* (or baptism), of *death or present age*, and of *identity*. The third of these, as Pearl (1928) points out, is commonly the key to false records of extreme age. The best of such evidence, from compulsory birth certification, has been available in England since

87

1837, and would now be available for records up to 118 years (1955). By critical standards of comparable severity the greatest human age to be authenticated with reasonable certainty has been said to be 120 years (Fisher, 1923). A considerable number of cases between 110 and 115 years have also stood up to examination (e.g. Bowerman, 1939; Backman, 1945; Korenchevsky, 1947; Ernest (n.d.)). The greatest age to be authenticated in England and Wales by actual birth certificate, however, is 109 years, while in one case the absence of a birth certificate indicated an age in excess of 111 years.

Ernest (n.d.) accepts four records over 110 years, all colourably supported; these were Mrs. Ann Pouder of Baltimore, born 1807 in London, died 1917; Mrs. Ann Neve of Guernsey, born 1792, died 1903, 44 days before her 111th birthday; The Hon. Katherine Plunket, of Kilsaran, Ireland, born 1820, died 1932, aged 111 years 327 days (this lady's birth is recorded in a church register for 1820, but at one time she gave her own date of birth as 1834); and Pierre Joubert, of Quebec, born 1701, died 1814—his records were investigated in 1870 by the Official Statistician of Canada. This, if correct, makes him the present world titleholder for fully authenticated longevity, at 113 years 100 days.

Claims of extreme longevity in particular districts abound. Metchnikoff investigated statements of this kind in Bulgaria and the Caucasus. Bazilievitch (1938a, b) led an expedition to investigate the celebrated longevity of Abkhasians, and examined several claimants in detail. Two of these were reputed to be over 130 years old. The evidence (identity papers and memory of events in the Caucasus during the early nineteenth century) is given by Bazilievitch in careful detail; much of it is extremely entertaining, but far from conclusive, although the subjects were certainly very old men (Bazilievitch, 1938b).[1] In recent years very large numbers of claims to extreme longevity have been made in Russia (e.g. Rokhlina, 1951; Nagornyi,

[1] Professor G. Z. Pitshelaouri, of Tbilisi University, who very kindly showed me his unpublished data on the longevity of Abkhasians, has found several subjects whose reputed age exceeds 130 years and is colourably supported by baptismal registers—one man still living took part in, and accurately describes, the Crimean war of 1854–6. I have failed to obtain a paper by Mishaikov (1929) giving statistics for centenarians in Bulgaria.

1948; Lukyanov, 1952; Nikitin, 1954). Dealing with the figures in the 1926 census of the U.S.S.R., which showed proportions of 3·5 and 3·8 centenarians *per thousand* gross population in Daghestan and Abkhasia respectively, as to 1·8 per million among Volga Germans, Tomilin (1938) says 'We must doubt the factual truth of these figures, since no documentary evidence of the age of persons who had passed the century mark was produced.' The analysed distribution of age groups in the Abkhasian census shows exactly the same deficiency in the 85–89 and 95–99 year groups, compared with the 90–94 and 100 + groups, which was observed by King (1911) in England. 'Without special documentary evidence of the accuracy of these age-data, we cannot conclude definitely that the relative number of persons reaching the age of 100 and over in the general mass of the population of Abkhasia is really higher than in the population of Russia' (Tomilin, 1938). More recent figures for the Siberian provinces give proportions of centenarians ranging from 32 per 100,000 inhabitants in Yakutsk, 20 in Altai and 12–13 in a number of regions to 1–0·5 in Sakhalin and Kamchatka. Among these centenarians villagers greatly outnumber townspeople (Berdishev and Starikov, 1960). The figure for the whole U.S.S.R. has been given as 21,708, or 10 per 100,000

TABLE VIII

NUMBER AND MAXIMUM AGES OF CENTENARIANS DYING
IN ENGLAND AND WALES

(Registrar-General's statistics)

Year	Number and probable maximum age	
	Men	Women
1940	20 (105)	102 (108)
1941	18 (112)	91 (108)
1942	12 (107)	79 (108)
1943	21 (108)	92 (106)*
1944	21 (109)	85 (105)*
1945	19 (105)*	71 (106)*
1946	22 (105)*	94 (108)*
1947	19 (106)*	97 (108)*
1948	19 (103)*	107 (115)
1949	27 (104)*	133 (106)*
1950	22 (102)*	131 (107)*
1951	33 (104)*	142 (109)*
1952	24 (105)*	147 (107)*

* = verifiable by birth certificate.

89

(*Daily Telegraph*, 5/4/61). The number of old people per unit of population is, of course, a very bad measure of longevity, for it can be sharply reduced by an increase in babies or a decrease in migration of young people to other areas, but it gives some idea of absolute numbers. It can also be lowered by more accurate census returns. The fall in the estimated number of centenarians in Yugoslavia per 100,000 inhabitants from 30 in 1921 to 10 in 1948 is probably due to this cause (Grmek, 1958). In America, Nascher's investigation of John Shell, reputed to be 131, showed him to be in fact about 100 years old (Nascher, 1920). In England and Wales, the oldest persons dying between 1930 and 1945 appear to have reached ages of 112 and 109 years (Korenchevsky, 1947). A woman who died at St. Asaph, Flintshire, in 1948 may have reached 115 years, and had certainly reached 111.

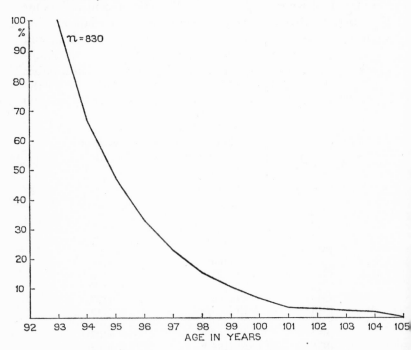

Fig. 18.—Form of the tail of the human survival curve above 92 years (from the data of Greenwood and Irwin, 1939).

The Distribution of Senescence

Sporadic records of supercentenarians such as Old Parr, whose tomb in Westminster Abbey credits him with an age of 152 years, whose body was examined by Harvey, and whose complete lack of documentation was exposed by Thoms (1873), occur in almost all cultures: a long series of similar anecdotes is given by Gould and Pyle (1898). The best recent summary of these often-paraded examples is that of R. T. Gould (1945). Parr was beyond reasonable doubt an impostor (Ernest, n.d.). Walter Williams, the 'Old Rebel', who died in 1959 in Texas, claimed to be 117 years old and the last survivor of the Confederate Army. He could not be traced in any army list, but received a military funeral, and was doubtless an old soldier in one sense or other (see *Illustrated London News*, 2/1/60). Though in most cases the stories conform closely to the childhood fantasy of 'going on living for almost always', they may also indicate that authenticated records do not yet represent the extreme of human longevity under all conditions. There is some ground, apart from the absence of critical record in backward countries, to associate extreme *individual* longevity with a low rather than a very high standard of living throughout life (Gumbel, 1938), an argument which fortunately has not so far been advanced to justify starvation as a social policy. Extreme records in man, occurring in excess of statistical probability, are chiefly of interest in suggesting that after a certain age the rate of increase in the force of mortality is not maintained, either by reason of selection or from other causes.

2·4 *Distribution of Senescence in Vertebrates*

Actuarial senescence is known, or reasonably assumed, to occur in all mammals, provided they live long enough. It is less easily recognized, but apparently equally universal, in birds. There are so far no satisfactory life-table studies of birds under domestic conditions apart from a single paper on fowls already cited (Gardner and Hurst, 1933), but individuals kept as pets certainly become increasingly enfeebled after an age which is fairly constant for the species, and the reproductive senescence of poultry, marked by a steep decline in egg production, is well known to farmers (Clark, 1940; Brody, 1945; Fig. 19). This decline can be reduced by mild hypothyroidism (Turner and Kempster, 1948). The pair of crowned pigeons which lived, according to Fitzinger (1853), for over 40 years, mated and laid throughout life, but hatched no offspring after the age of 18 or 20 years (Flower, 1938). Spermatogenesis likewise appears to decline (Payne, 1952). The life-span of birds is longer in proportion to size and metabolic rate than that of mammals, and

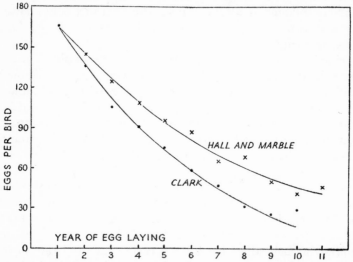

Fig. 19.—The decline in egg production in successive years of laying—domestic fowls. (Drawn from the data of Clark and of Hall and Marble.)

the scatter of age in senescence as shown by aviary records appears, superficially at least, to be rather greater within a species.

We are familiar with the ageing of warm-blooded animals because we keep them. It is among the 'cold-blooded' vertebrates that the real uncertainty begins. We keep fish, but only the smaller forms—we do not, apart from zoological gardens and occasional pet tortoises, keep reptiles; as for amphibia, Hilaire Belloc wrote incontrovertibly concerning lonely people who keep frogs that

by the way
They are extremely rare.

92

The Distribution of Senescence

The general assumption that all vertebrates must necessarily undergo a senescence at least superficially similar to that of mammals has prejudiced even those biologists who have kept frogs for long periods, with the result that very little real information unbiassed by this assumption has been published. The assumption will probably prove to be correct, but it cannot be lightly made. It is evident that some senile change, in the form of an accumulation of injuries, must occur in all vertebrates with the passage of time, and be reflected in the force of mortality. But this effect is certainly small and inconstant compared with the 'morphogenetic' senescence which determines the life-span of mammals. It is this morphogenetic component which we are concerned to detect and estimate in lower vertebrates. Unfortunately for such a study, the life of many of these creatures, whether it ends in senescence or not, is, as we have seen, long enough to make ordinary short-term laboratory observation useless.

Bidder's opinions on the relation between perpetual youth and continuing growth have already been quoted (p. 14). Three types of growth-pattern are theoretically possible in vertebrates—growth to a maximum size, ceasing when this is reached: growth *toward* a limiting size which is approached asymptotically: and growth *without* a limiting size. In the third of these cases, the specific growth-acceleration can be negative —i.e. the growth-rate continually declines—but it could theoretically do so in such a way that, given a sufficiently long life, *any* final size could be reached. These last two modes of growth correspond to convergent and divergent series. Thus in the series

$$(1)\ 1 + \tfrac{1}{2} + \tfrac{1}{4} + \tfrac{1}{8} \ldots \lim 2,$$

and the series

$$(2)\ 1 + \tfrac{1}{2} + \tfrac{1}{3} + \tfrac{1}{4} + \tfrac{1}{5} \ldots,$$

the increment at each term decreases (the specific growth rate falls), but whereas in (1) the series tends to a limiting size (specific size), in (2) it does not, and can be indefinitely continued so that any sum is ultimately attained. The terms 'indeterminate growth' and 'indeterminate size' have been differently used by different writers. D'Arcy Thompson wrote, 'It is the rule in fishes and other cold-blooded vertebrates that growth is asymptotic and size indeterminate' (1942). If the growth of an animal is in fact asymptotic, its size is limited by the sum of the asymptotic series. 'Indeterminate' growth without limit, but with a decline in the specific growth-rate, strictly follows the pattern of the divergent series. For this reason it would be desirable, but it is not empirically possible, given real biological material, to distinguish between 'asymptotic' and 'indeterminate' growth. In both cases the rate of growth declines with advancing age; but in the second case the potential size is unlimited.

Distinctions of this kind, however, are based upon the fitting of equations to points derived by averaging observations upon populations of animals, and in spite of the real value of such biometric applications, in the study of growth curves they very often tended to lose contact with the real behaviour of real animals. It is possible in practice to distinguish only between species, or particular populations of a given species, which continue throughout life to get tangibly bigger, given suitable conditions, and forms where the maximum size is reached relatively early in life, is fixed for the species, and does not increase further with increasing age even under the most favourable conditions. The chief obstacle to wide generalization about the determinacy or indeterminacy of growth in lower vertebrates, and in other forms such as pelecypods, lies in the fact that arrest of growth at an *apparent* specific size can be brought about by environmental conditions. In some cases growth can be resumed after stopping like this—in others, apparently, it cannot. There are also large differences within each of the main groups of poikilothermic vertebrates. In many reptiles and small fish, continued growth after a relatively early age is no more evident than in the male rat. In amphibia, 'many species, particularly some tropical forms, seem to have an absolute size, which the males soon attain, but this does not hold for many salamanders, nor for some Northern frogs' (Noble, 1931). In many cases the male has an absolute size and the female has not. If enough data were available, the variety of growth-patterns is more than sufficient to test Bidder's hypothesis—unfortunately, corresponding data upon age/mortality relations are almost entirely lacking.

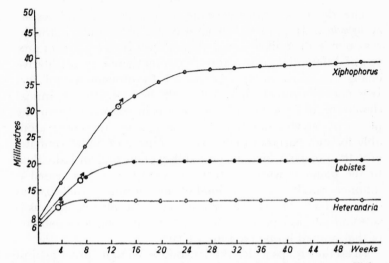

Fɪɢ. 20(*a*).—Growth in length (mm.) of male fish of the genera *Xipho-phorus*, *Lebistes* and *Heterandria* during the first year of life. Sexual maturity is indicated by ♂ (from Wellensieck, 1953).

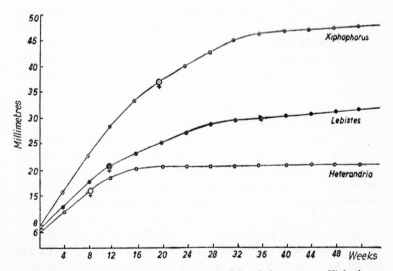

Fɪɢ. 20(*b*).—Growth in length of female fish of the genera *Xiphophorus*, *Lebistes* and *Heterandria* during the first year of life. Sexual maturity is indicated by ♀ (Wellensieck, 1953).

The idea of a 'self-maintaining' vertebrate is not impossible *ex hypothesi*. It is in fact what we should expect if growth-cessation is an equilibrium process, if there is no important process of differential growth at work, and if there is no qualitative change in the regenerative power of cells throughout adult life. It is not self-evident, though it might be true, that an animal should be obliged to increase in size in order to retain the power of carrying out running replacements. It seems reasonable for our purposes to regard an animal of 'indeterminate' growth as one in which the probability of nursing an individual to the point at which increase in somatic size has ceased is infinitely small, and an animal of 'indeterminate' life-span as one in which the survival rate under favourable conditions is substantially independent of age, however long a population of that animal is observed from birth.

In all the groups which Bidder considered to be proof against senescence, there is wide variation in life-cycle and growth-pattern, which is very probably reflected in differences of their capacity for age changes. Some aquarium species of fish certainly 'age' as judged by their declining reproductive powers: in the larger sea fish this has not been clearly demonstrated. Contradictory views of fish senescence were given to Flower (1935) by two acknowledged authorities, one on aquarium and the other on marine ichthyology, and based on small and large teleosts respectively, but more recent work suggests that the distinction is artificial (see p. 111). In other forms there is an obvious sex difference in growth-maintenance, in longevity, or in both. The specific age might also be indefinite in mammals which nevertheless became more liable to die, as individuals, with increasing age. It was implied by Ricker (1945) that fish might senesce individually, i.e. undergo a waning of vitality and resistance with age, but that there is no sharp *specific* age—the life-span of each individual would be limited by senescence, but the senile process would reach its critical point at a much more variable age than in mammals: as if the menopause in human beings were to occur with approximately equal probability in any year after the menarche. Such senescence would be real, but could not readily be detected actuarially.

Very nearly all these problems require abundant new data

to settle them finally though a fair amount of progress has been made. The general evidence of the distribution of vertebrate senescence which will be given here is both fragmentary and equivocal. It does, however, contain some facts which suggest that Bidder's hypothesis is too simple and that the *manner* of growth-cessation, rather than the fact of it, is the main determinant of the mammalian pattern of senescence.

2·4·1 FISH

The 'indeterminate' growth of fish, on which Bidder based his hypothesis, has often been discussed (Hecht, 1916; Keys, 1928; Huxley, 1932; Vaznetzov, 1934; Thompson, 1942; Wellensieck, 1953). Many large species of teleosts can continue to grow throughout life, and the rate of decline of their growth-rate is considerably slower than, e.g., in most reptiles. The *locus classicus* of continued growth without evidence of senescence, actuarial or reproductive, is the female plaice. Here the evidence supports Bidder in that growth in the male plaice ceases relatively early, and there is evidence that it has a shorter life-span than the female (Wimpenny, 1953). On the other hand, in many small teleosts reproductive senescence is known to occur, and both the sexes appear to exhibit specific age, in spite of the fact that growth in the female may continue throughout life. The reproductive failure of many teleosts with increasing age is familiar to aquarists. So is the tendency of particular species to have a limiting age, although there have previously been no published life-tables for any teleost in captivity by which this impression could be confirmed. The growth of some small teleosts has been studied (Felin, 1951; Wellensieck, 1953).

There is a good deal of evidence from wild populations that small teleosts, and perhaps teleost species generally, undergo both reproductive and actuarial senescence comparable to that of mammals (Gerking, 1957, 1959). The most dogmatic assertions on this score are those of pathological anatomists. On the basis of concretions occurring in the testis of a single teleost species (*Astyanax americanus*), Rasquin and Hafter (1951) hold that the 'appearance of senility changes shows that the teleosts conform to the common vertebrate pattern of ageing despite a widespread misconception to the contrary'. The decline of fertility in some aquarium species provides more solid evidence in support of this view. Many species of fish are in any case exposed to a specialized series of fluctuations in mortality associated with reproduction—the difficulties of treating these fluctuations as a form of senescence in those species which always die after breeding, such as the male of *Callionymus* (Chang, 1951) and the lamprey, are indicated by observations upon other fish in which there are a limited number of survivors from each breeding season, and these thereafter acquire a new lease of life. It is doubtful if any cyclical or potentially cyclical change in mortality can properly be called senile. In *Callionymus lyra* in the wild, the male appears to live 5 and the female up to 7 years. The males disappear, probably through death, but possibly by migration to deeper water, after breeding once. Females may first breed in their third, fourth, or fifth year of life, depending on their rate of growth, and probably breed more than once (Chang, 1951). In such a case, the late-developing females would very probably have a longer total life-cycle.

Studies of wild populations are almost always conducted under conditions where the standing force of mortality throughout life is very high, and they therefore give little information about mortality trends in the latter part of the life-cycle of the longer-lived forms. Excluding the very high larval mortality, populations of many species of fish, studied in the wild, show an age structure and a pattern of death similar to that found in birds, i.e. a high constant mortality unrelated to age and a virtually constant expectation of life (Frost and Smyly, 1952 (Fig. 21); Deevey, 1947). Substantial differences in life-span may be dictated by availability of food organisms of a size suited to adult feeding, and by competition between the fry of the observed species and adults of other species. Some populations of minnows show apparent specific age which is exceeded in other populations of a closely-related species by a very large factor (Frost, 1943; Tack, 1940). In *Pimephales promelas*, Markus (1934) observed apparent specific size and specific age in all but a few exceptionally large individuals. This was apparently due to the fact that there was an overall mortality of 80 per cent following spawning; the survivors, and individuals which took no part in breeding during their first year of maturity, continued growth until the next breeding season. If reproduction is avoided, life may be prolonged—Bidder (1932) points out that eels, which, it is believed, normally die after spawning, live

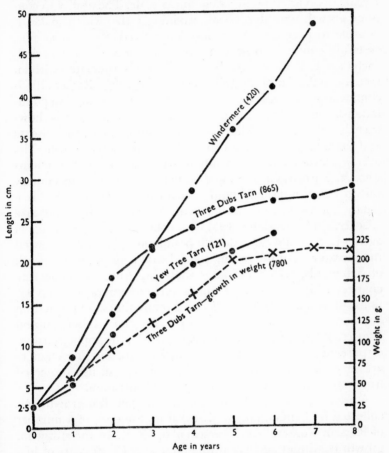

FIG. 21.—Growth of trout in Windermere and the small tarns (Frost and Smyly, 1952).

many years in captivity (Flower, 1925). Frost and Smyly (1952) found considerable differences in growth-rates and in the form of the growth curve between brown trout inhabiting tarns and those inhabiting Windermere (Fig. 21). The age structure of the tarn population agreed well with a steady annual survival rate of 35 per cent between the second and eighth year of life. In these fish growth had become very slow, whereas in the Windermere population individual fish were still growing at 7 years upon an approximately linear scale. The ability to continue growth may depend on attaining a size which makes it possible to prey on smaller fish. Long-lived fish such as pike certainly continue to grow measurably for very long periods (Schloemer, 1936) but the increase in size is associated with an increase in the size of the prey taken (Frost, 1954). Ricker (1945) comments that 'senile death is an everyday occurrence' in population-studies of the Indiana sun fish. This conclusion is, however, based upon the failure of known sources of death (disease and predation) to account for the disappearance of fish. The overall mortality rates actually found in marking experiments were 56 per cent for small and 58 per cent for older specimens. But in many unfished populations of other species there is a steady increase in mortality with increasing age and size (Ricker, 1948). Gerking (1957) has collected strong evidence of ageing in a number of wild fish populations, and has reviewed the literature. An interesting special case is the parental death of Salmonids, which die after spawning from the endocrine changes which accompany migration: non-migratory populations survive, and individuals breed many times. This question has been studied and reviewed by Robertson (Robertson and Wexler, 1959, 1962; Robertson *et al.*, 1961), the apparent cause of parental death is hypercorticoadrenalism, but the changes are very like those which occur with old age in fish protected from parental-migratory death by early castration.

A great deal of important information upon fish growth was collected by Schmalhausen (1928) from the data of a number of Russian workers (e.g. Tereschenko, 1917). In the sturgeon, growth continues actively throughout at least 30 years of life, with little decline in rate at sexual maturity (about 15 years). In the bream, on the other hand, the growth-constant shows a more regular and progressive decline. These fish were found to mature at about 3 years, and degenerative changes in the gonad were usually evident from the sixth year on—two definite stadia could be observed in the growth curve, one following puberty, and the other following this gonadal senescence, the growth-coefficient settling down to a steady value thereafter without further decline up to 13 years of age (Figs. 22, 23 and 24). This rather closely resembles the pattern reported in the goldfish.

In *Xiphophorus* and *Lebistes* the male exhibits sharp specific size, but the female may continue to grow measurably throughout life, the pattern of growth differing little from that of the plaice (Wellensieck, 1953). Yet in these forms previous experience suggests that there is no striking difference between the

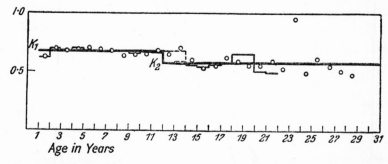

Fig. 22.—Growth-constant for growth in length of the sturgeon, *Acipenser stellatus*, at various ages. Broken line—females: single points—males: thick line, mean value for males; dashes, mean value for females. $K_1 = 0.67$, $K_2 = 0.58$ (from Schmalhausen, 1928).

survivals of the two sexes in captivity (Bellamy, 1934). In *Heterandria* both sexes reach a virtual limiting size (Wellensieck, 1953), Fig. 20*a*, *b*. In the goldfish, according to exhibition breeders, fertility reaches a maximum under aquarium conditions in the third year of life, declining thereafter, and almost all fish are sterile by the seventh year. Breeding at 10 years is recorded (Hervey and Hems, 1948). When the reproductive life is over, however, the fish may improve greatly in condition, and appear much less sensitive to environmental damage than before. In exhibition fish the life-span appears to be about 17 years, though much older examples are known. The extreme record of longevity appears to be between 30 and 40 years. Rate of growth is extremely variable. One specimen, kept in a six-gallon tank, reached a length of only 4 inches in 25 years (Hervey and Hems, 1948).

In none of these cases is it clear how large a part of the potential life-cycle is actually covered by the observed growth

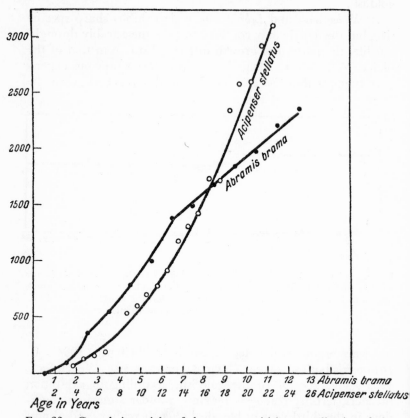

Fig. 23.—Growth in weight of the sturgeon (*Acipenser stellatus*) and the bream (*Abramis brama*). Scale for *A. stellatus* 1 Russian lb = 100. Scale for *A. brama* 1 g. = 1 (after Schmalhausen, 1928).

curve. In most fish the rate of growth does in fact decline with age, though in many the effective reproductive life appears to have ceased long before this decline has produced an almost stationary body-size. The reproductive decline, moreover, does not appear to involve any decrease in vigour, and may actually imply the reverse, in view of the hazards which reproduction involves for many fish.

In the small teleosts, it ought to be possible to answer most of these questions by direct experiment. For this purpose the guppy (*Lebistes*) is proving a particularly suitable experimental animal, both because of the ease with which it can be reared and handled for purposes of measurement, and because of the

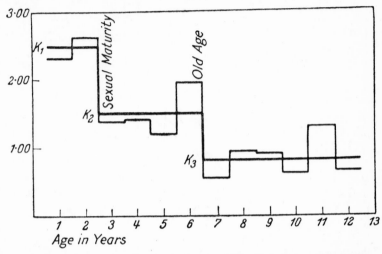

Fig. 24.—Growth in weight of the bream (*Abramis brama*)—annual increments. The mean growth-coefficients at various stadia (youth, maturity, postreproductive life) are indicated by transverse lines $K_{1, 2, 3}$ (from Schmalhausen, 1928).

neatness with which its growth can be controlled by varying the food intake and living space.

By combining restricted space with restricted diet, female *Lebistes* can be kept at a length of about 2 cm. for as long as 600 days. In this state they are reproductively mature (unlike the rats subjected to retardation by McCay—p. 199) and capable of resuming growth. There are 'specific sizes' characteristic of each size of container and each level of nutrition—or, alternatively, of each population-density in a tank, when a fish is promoted from one such container to a larger, or when fish are removed from a tank population, a new plateau is rapidly reached. The curve given by Wellensieck represents only one such equilibrium. The growth capacity also appears to decline somewhat throughout life, and there is a practical limit, as might be expected, to the size of guppy which can be produced

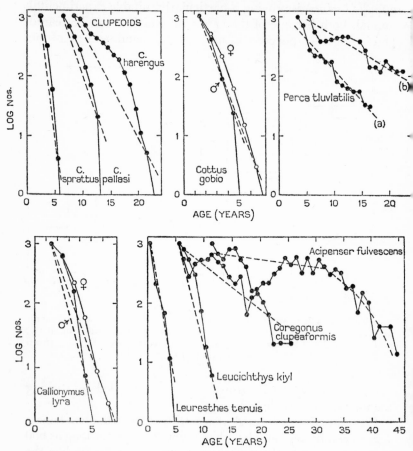

FIG. 25.—Some examples of survival curves in relatively unexploited fish populations (from Beverton and Holt, 1959).

at maximum food intake and maximum living space. The combination of variables in *Lebistes*, and the fact that the life-span of the non-growing males is not, upon present data, grossly different from that of the growing females, suggest that a great deal about growth and senescence in fish can be learned by the collection of actuarial data for guppies subjected to different programmes of growth.

A population study of guppies (*Lebistes reticulatus* Peters) was

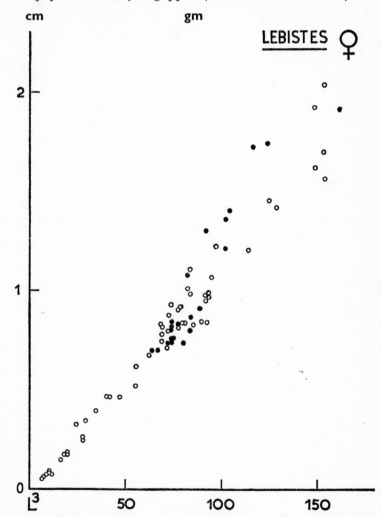

FIG. 26(*a*).—Weight-length relationship in female *Lebistes*: uninterrupted growth (open symbols) and checked and restarted growth (solid symbols). Scatter at higher ages is due to the presence in some fish of retained eggs.

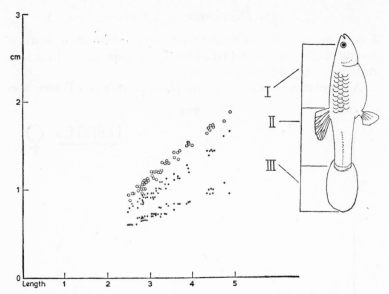

Fig. 26(b).—Isometry of rebound growth in checked female *Lebistes*. Abscissa—total length (cm) ordinate—mid-eye to anterior border of dorsal fin (circles), anterior border of fin to tail root (small circles), and tail-root to tail-tip (dots).

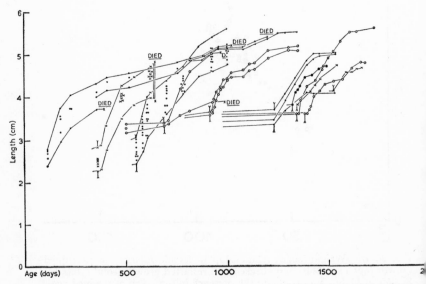

Fig. 27.—Growth of checked *Lebistes* females fully fed at the points marked λY.

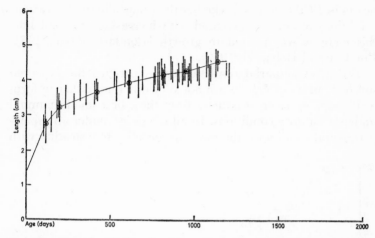

Fig. 28.—Growth of *Lebistes* females under 'normal' aquarium regime permitting slow continuous growth. Columns indicate range in individual tanks, curve indicates mean of whole sample (48 invididuals).

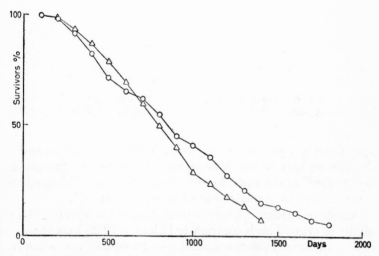

Fig. 29.—Combined survival curves of all tank-bred females (circles, $n = 351$) and all tank-bred males (triangles, $n = 312$).

begun in 1950 to find out whether their mortality under various conditions of culture increased with increasing age, and how this increase was related to growth (Comfort, 1960b, 1961; Comfort and Doljanski, 1959).

The main actuarial result appears clear-cut: the observed survival curves of *Lebistes* are not very different, either in form or in response to environment, from those of a small mammal under laboratory conditions. In all the series, under all the experimental conditions, the force of mortality rose steadily with

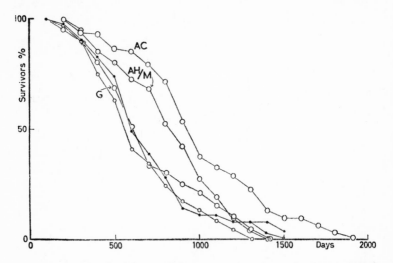

FIG. 30.—Survival curves of male guppies kept in tanks (large circles), 600-ml. jars (small circles) and 250-ml. milk bottles (small solid symbols).

age; there is a progressive squaring-up of the L_x curve and a decrease in variance with bettering conditions, but the curves are 'pegged' at the ends, forming the typical 'parallelogram of survival' seen in animals of fixed life-span (Fig. 32).

Ageing in guppies appears to take place in the presence of the ability to grow. This is contrary to Bidder's (1932) hypothesis—in the absence of evidence that all cells are equally renewable, it does not negative theories based on cell loss—renal degenerative changes, for example, do not appear histologically to be being made good, whether somatic growth is continuing or not.

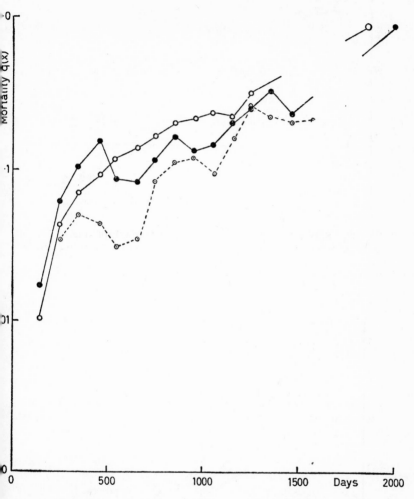

Fig. 31.—Mortality of guppies (q_x) against age: tank conditions. Circles—males; solid symbols—females; dotted line, epidemic 'incidents' treated as individual lives.

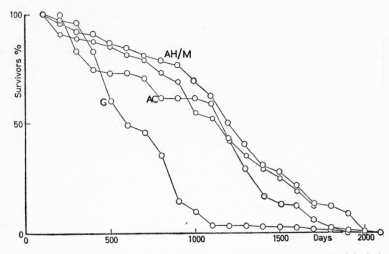

FIG. 32.—Survival curve of female guppies of 3 series kept in tanks (circles) and of breeding females transferred at various ages from tanks to 2-litre jars (hexagons).

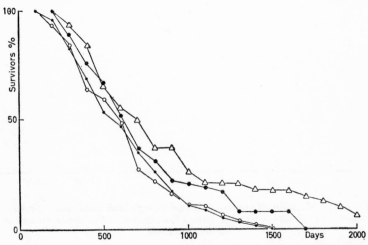

FIG. 33.—Survival curves of female guppies kept in 2-litre jars (triangles), 600-ml. jars with full feeding (large solid symbols), 600-ml. jars with restricted feeding (circles) and 250-ml. milk bottles (small solid symbols).

Whether what holds good for the growth of the guppy in relation to ageing is equally true of long-lived fish such as the sturgeon is a matter for speculation. In Beverton and Holt's (1957) terminology, the female guppy under favourable growth conditions has reached 75 per cent of its eventual limiting size $L \infty$ by about 700 days of age, and its limiting age λ appears to be about 2000 days, our oldest fish so far having reached 2200 days. The corresponding value of $L \infty$ for plaice is reached about 14 years (Beverton and Holt, 1957, page 284),

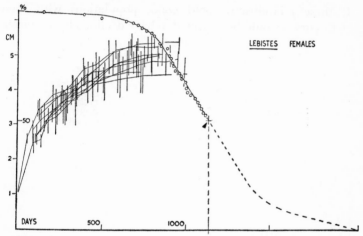

LEBISTES FEMALES

FIG. 34.—*Lebistes* females. Growth and survival. Compare Fig. 35.

giving an extreme longevity of 40 years if the same relationship holds. The growth curve of the sturgeon shows no sign of flattening by the age of 30 years (Schmalhausen, 1926). Assuming that it reached 75 per cent of the length asymptote by 45 years, we might on this basis expect a value of $\lambda \infty$ approaching 128 years. A record of at least 82 years has been claimed for sturgeon on the basis of fin sections (Milne and Milne, 1958).

Taking the data of *Lebistes* it is possible to construct curves for other species, showing what would happen to ability to survive if their growth and survival were in the same proportion. Fig. 34 gives the growth curves of 87 tank-bred female *Lebistes* by batches with the observed survival curve for the whole sample to 1100 days.

111

In Fig. 35 the growth curves of 4 species in the wild (*Gastero-steus*; cod, plaice; hake) are plotted on time-scales which bring their growth in length within the limits of the curve for *Lebistes*. The conversion factors for time are as follows:

$$500 \text{ days } (Lebistes) = 1{\cdot}37 \text{ years}$$

Gasterosteus	1·25 years	× 0·91
Cod	5·0	3·65
Hake	10·0	7·3
Plaice	15·0	10·95

If these relationships hold good, populations with these growth curves would be expected to have declined by a quarter,

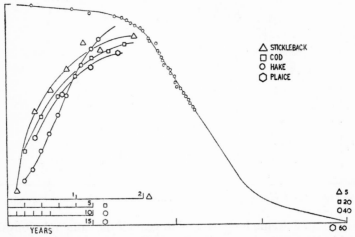

Fig. 35.—Growth and survival (extrapolated). △, Stickleback; □, cod; ○, hake; ◇ plaice.

from senescence alone, by 2·5, 10, 20 and 30 years respectively, and the four species would have limiting ages of 5, 20, 40 and 60 years respectively. *Gasterosteus* in the wild does in fact live 2–3 years, with a few individuals surviving longer. In the other species, if senescence were related to growth as in the guppy, senile mortality would not be significant within the normal expectation of life in fished populations—the modal age of plaice at catching being about 5 years. The limiting ages seem likewise reasonable, except that on a basis of size one might expect the extreme life of cod to be more than 20 years.

112

There seems accordingly to be no reason from existing data to postulate a different pattern of mortality for small as against large fish.

It seems probable that there is as much variation in 'senescence' as in growth-patterns among teleosts. Some forms apparently resemble monocarpic plants, mortality being linked to reproduction. Some, in captivity, have a life-span determined by senescence, their mortality increasing with age on a curve closely similar to that of mammals. Some forms, however, may conceivably have an effectively indeterminate life-span, though this may well mean only that their 'determinate' maximum, as in wild birds, comes so late in relation to mortality as never to be reached in practice.

2·4·2 REPTILES AND AMPHIBIA

There are no published reptilian life-tables, but a number of careful studies of reptilian growth have been made (Sergeev, 1937; Townsend, 1931, 1937; Cagle, 1946). By collating these with maximum age records, a good deal of significant information can be obtained. Sergeev found that while, in all reptiles, early growth depends on environmental conditions, being sometimes very rapid, and growth-rate declines with increasing age, there are a number of forms where both sexes have an effective specific size which is reached early in life, and after the attainment of which no further growth occurs. The cessation of growth in these forms is apparently as definitive as that in mammals, and its timing does not appear to depend on the arrival of sexual maturity. There appears to be no close correlation between either of these two patterns of growth and the length of the life-span.

Among chelonians, both patterns of growth are known to occur. Continuous growth at a decreasing rate appears to be general in tortoises, the large species having inherently higher growth-rates throughout. Townsend (1931, 1937) found that early growth in 100 specimens of the large *T. vicina*, kept in captivity, was potentially very rapid, and continued after the age of sexual maturity (about 20 years of age). Flower (1945) observed continuing growth in a 39-year-old specimen of *T. graeca*. The age of sexual maturity in the male *Terrapene carolina* appears to lie between 12 and 15 years (Nichols, 1939). All these are known to be long-lived forms. On the other hand, the majority of terrapins exhibit specific size. In *Emys* Sergeev (1937) found that growth-cessation by the fifteenth year of life was as complete as in the adult mammal (Fig. 36) although *E. orbicularis*, like *T. graeca*, is apparently capable of living 70–120 years and probably of breeding throughout life (Flower, 1937). Rollinat, however, on whose observations Flower's records were based, considered that growth in this form might continue for 30–40 years (Rollinat, 1934). Hildebrand (1932) studied the longevity and growth of over 1000 specimens of *Malaclemmys*

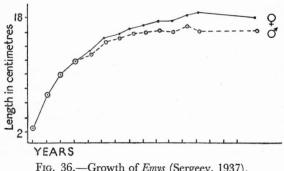

Fig. 36.—Growth of *Emys* (Sergeev, 1937).

centrata in captivity—an investigation which is the nearest published approach to a chelonian life-table, but which was unfortunately continued in detail for only 10 years. He found the age of maturity much more variable than in mammals, some individuals being full grown in 8–9 years, others requiring 12–15. The oldest specimens in captivity were 21 years old, and 'showed every appearance of being young animals', but other wild specimens taken when full grown had been kept for 20 years without decline of vitality or reproductive power. Hildebrand placed the maximum life-span for this species at 40 years or more, but evidence from other small terrapins suggests that this may be a considerable underestimate. Although the only aquatic species which is known to have reached an age comparable with that of the land tortoises is *Emys orbicularis*, it would be very difficult to argue upon the existing evidence that specific size and determinate age are correlated in chelonians. Contrary to Bidder's hypothesis, specific size here seems to be an adaptation to carnivorous life in small pools, while continuing growth is found in land tortoises and marine turtles (Parker, 1926, 1929).

Crocodiles have also been credited with indeterminate growth —'Crocodili perhibentur esse admodum vivaces, atque grandescendi periodem itidem habere insignem; adeo ut hos solos ex animalibus perpetuo, dum vivunt, grandescere opinio fit. . . . At de aliquo testaceo genere, nihil certi, quod ad vitam ipsorum attinet, reperimus' [1] (*Hist. Vitae et Mortis*). Claims of longevity are based on the exceptional size of some specimens. Large alligators have been observed in captivity to remain for 25 years in a non-growing state, e.g. *Alligator sinensis* (Dathe, 1935), though the difficulties of accurate length-measurement are evident.

There is only one long-term study of ageing in amphibia, but the result is theoretically important: in *Xenopus*, Brocas and Verzar (1961b) found that collagen contractility changes steadily with age as in mammals, both in females, whose growth continues, and in males, which have a fixed size. There was no difference in the rate of collagen ageing between the sexes, up to 13 years of age.

2·5 *Distribution of Senescence in Invertebrates*

Among invertebrates not only is there a demonstrable variety, greater than in vertebrates, in the nature of the preponderant senile process, but we have also the full range, from indeterminacy to very sharply defined determinacy of life-span. The gaps in our knowledge of life-cycles are so large that we cannot yet picture the distribution of senescence in invertebrate phylogeny: papers entitled 'The life-history of . . .' only very exceptionally include reference to the senescence of the species under study—an extraordinary deficiency, which is a measure of the equally extraordinary lack of interest in age processes. It

---

[1] 'Crocodiles are held to be very lively, and to have a notable span of growth—so that they alone of beasts, so opinion runs, grow so long as they live. . . . But of any hard-skinned beast, as pertaining to their length of life, we find nothing certain.'

is fairly evident, however, that the distribution both of senescence in general and of any one process of senescence, such as depletion or mechanical deterioration, is quite discontinuous in phylogeny. This evolutionary discontinuity is what we should expect if 'exhaustion of programme' is the common basis of adverse age changes.

Senescence in some shape or form probably occurs in every group where the power of regeneration or fissile reproduction is less than total, or where body-cells are not continuously and 'indeterminately' replaced. Some forms which 'degrow' under adverse conditions appear to be capable, in all probability, of unlimited alternate growth and degrowth, at least in the laboratory, while in a few, such as actinians, the adult can remain indefinitely *in statu quo*, though with a changing population of cells. Senescence is most striking in forms such as rotifers where determinacy of cell number is very highly developed and the power of regeneration is negligible. There do not appear to be any invertebrate cells (except possibly pelecypod neurones, of whose longevity and renewability we know little) which are called upon to remain for 100 or more years in active function, like a human neurone, or for still longer, like the neurones of the tortoise. The distribution of senescence in invertebrates suggests that in spite of the general argument against the selection of long-lived forms, relatively great longevity is sometimes an evolved adaptation, and that if some cold-blooded vertebrates age extraordinarily slowly, that, too, is likewise a specialized mechanism and not a primitive or an 'inherent' mechanism which has been lost with increasing somatic complexity.

2·5·1 PORIFERA

Bidder infelicitously cited 'the sea anemone, the bath sponge and the water-vole' as three organisms insusceptible to senescence. The only serious study of senescence in Porifera appears to be that of Arndt (1928) who concludes that it does not occur, although some sponges are fatally disrupted by their own larvae. Aquarium specimens have an effectively limited life, as in so many other groups, but sponges seem ideally able to conform to Bidder's expectation of them.

2·5·2 COELENTERATES

In hydromedusae, Child (1918) observed a progressive decrease in metabolism and pulsation rate with increasing size, which he regarded as evidence of senescence. His work on the processes of ageing and rejuvenation in hydroids (1915) depends on the criterion of resistance to cyanide as evidence of 'physiological age'—one which is hardly acceptable in this context. Child's results with *Pennaria*, using this test of age, were in any case less consistent than those he obtained with planarians, where cyanide resistance rose steadily throughout life (Child, 1915).

Evidence that the life-span of sea anemones is 'indeterminate' is probably stronger than for any other metazoan group. Dalyell's (1848) celebrated specimens of *Actinia* lived for 70 years in captivity without any sign of deterioration. An even more famous batch of sea anemones were collected 'some years prior to 1862', and were first identified as *Sagartia troglodytes* by Ashworth and Annandale (1904), later by Stephenson as *Cereus pedunculatus* (1935). They remained in the aquarium of Edinburgh University Department of Zoology until 1940 or 1942, when they were all simultaneously found dead. Budding continued freely throughout life, and the animals underwent no obvious change during eighty to ninety years of continuous observation (Warwick, 1954, personal communication). Whether gametogenesis likewise continued throughout life is not known.

Hydra. The long-standing controversy over the senescence of *Hydra* illustrates some of the difficulties of placing a gerontological interpretation on life-tables and histological appearances. *Hydra* was a favourite organism, earlier in the century, in the argument over the 'potentielle Unsterblichkeit' of metazoa. Differences in culture conditions almost certainly account for the very irregular results obtained.

Early workers (Hertwig, 1906; Boecker, 1914; Berninger, 1910) on this question found it impossible to keep *Hydra* for long periods without the onset of 'depression', evidenced by cloudy swelling and cytolysis. With better cultural methods Goetsch (1922, 1925) kept individuals of *Pelmatohydra oligactis*, *Hydra attenuata*, and *Chlorohydra viridissima* alive for 27 months. Goetsch considered that like the actinians *Hydra* was capable of remaining indefinitely *in statu quo*. Gross (1925) working with *P. oligactis* failed to keep any individual alive for more than 349 days, 'senescence' being evidenced by irregular and hypertrophic budding or by the animal becoming smaller and smaller in the presence of abundant food. 'Senile' changes in Gross's material began after the fourth month of life. A life-table, drawn from Hase's (1909) data by Pearl and Miner (1935), extending over only 148 days, indicates some increase in mortality with age, but is closer to the log-linear than to the rectangular contour (see Fig. 6c, p. 26). Hartlaub (1916) had already described experiments on Syncorinae in which he concluded that the power of producing gametes was lost relatively early in life, while that of budding persisted.

David (1925) kept isolation records in cultures of *P. oligactis* and satisfied himself that in this form the individual animals tended to die between 20 and 28 months in approximate order of individual age—an important observation which has not been repeated. According to Schlottke, however (Schlottke, 1930), the material in David's histological sections was heavily parasitized. Schlottke's own observations suggested that all the tissues of *Hydra* are continuously replaced throughout life, from a subjacent reserve of interstitial cells. This view is supported by the work of Brien (1953), who showed by marking experiments that there is continuous growth in *Hydra* from before backward, the marked zone travelling down the animal and being ultimately rejected at the base: a case, in other words, of 'indeterminate growth' coexisting with a final specific size. For the most recent discussion of this matter, see Strehler (1961, 1962).

In colonial hydroids, however, it seems to have been shown beyond reasonable doubt that the life-span of each hydranth is physiologically determinate. The resorption and involution of hydranths was described in full by Huxley and de Beer (1923); the hydranth shrinks, the gut becomes filled with cellular debris, and the degenerating material is returned to the colony by the contraction of the hydranth itself. In *Obelia* and *Campanularia* Crowell (1953) has now shown that regression takes place strictly in order of age, each hydranth having a life of 4 days at 21° C. and 7 at 17° C. When regression is accelerated by starvation or adverse culture conditions, the age order is still preserved.

Existing observations are scattered rather thinly over a number of groups. Child (1911, 1913, 1914, 1915, 1918) carried out exhaustive studies upon the regeneration of planarians, and upon their capacity for de-differentiation, to which subsequent research has been able to add little or nothing. Here again, as in *Pennaria*, he employed the increase in resistance to dilute cyanide solutions as a criterion of senescence, on the assumption that this change reflected a decrease in metabolic rate. While susceptibility decreased as a function of age in the growing animal, planarians kept for several months at a constant size showed no such increase, and planarians undergoing shrinkage under adverse food conditions showed a decrease in susceptibility. Child also demonstrated the 'rejuvenation', partial or entire, of regenerating fragments of planarians. This further observation, using the same criterion of resistance to toxicity (1915), that a gradient of 'rejuvenation' exists in *Stenostomum* (Rhabdocoela) during the production of new zooids has been confirmed by Sonneborn (1930) using direct-life-table studies. Sonneborn's experiments showed that the regenerative effects of fission were markedly unequal in the two halves, since the head portions, which required only to regenerate tails, underwent typical senescence, and died after a limited number of divisions, while tails, which required to regenerate most of the body and nervous system, could be propagated indefinitely. Some authors have detected signs of senescence (chiefly somatic distortion) even in planarians (Balasz and Burg, 1962), but, as in *Hydra*, it is hard to distinguish age changes from the pathologies inherent in prolonged culture.

In *Aeolosoma* (Oligochaeta), Haemmerling (1924) found that the anterior end of the body appeared to undergo eventual senescence, new worms being produced from the posterior end. Stolč (1902) had already given a circumstantial histopathological account of 'senile' death in *Aeolosoma* as a whole, but the appearances observed might have resulted from almost any environmental cause. In *Nais* (Annelida), Stolte (1924, 1927) found extensive histological changes with age, with disappearance of the normal zones, degeneration of the visceral ganglia, and the cessation of reserve-cell production from the embryonic tissue persisting in the posterior end. The significance of these changes is again obscure, and no attempt was made to determine actuarially the mortality rates at different ages. Rhabdocoelians have (Bresslau, 1928–33) been observed to be increasingly susceptible to protozoan parasites the longer they live.

How far the capacity for 'degrowth', which is found in planarians, is evidence of a potentially indeterminate life-span is not evident, but it seems likely that forms such as *Lineus* (Nemertinea), which revert on starvation over a period of years to a mass of cells resembling an embryo (Dawidoff, 1924), might be maintained indefinitely in alternate growth and degrowth until the patience of the investigator was exhausted.

The evidence in fissile worms at present suggests that non-senescence depends upon fairly active replacement of cells, and that any organ which fails to take part in the regenerative process is liable to undergo senile change. Harms (1949) considered that the senescence of Serpulids was due primarily to changes in the nervous system, and rejuvenated old specimens of *Protula* by grafting young heads. Some further work on this subject as careful as that of Child and Sonneborn would probably be well worth undertaking.

Morphogenetic loss throughout life of the power of regeneration in a nematode of determinate cell-number was actually demonstrated by Pai (1928) in *Anguillula aceti*. Amputation of the tail with nuclear removal kills the animal at any age. In young individuals, provided the nucleus is left intact, wound healing and cytoplasmic regeneration can take place. In mature animals there is wound closure but no cytoplasmic regeneration, while in senile animals amputation is fatal. In *Anguillula* senescence follows a pattern very similar to that of rotifers (see below) and occurs at about 44 days. The degenerative cellular changes in ovaries, gut and nerve cells have been described: these appear in the two or three days preceding death (Pai,

1928; Bürger, 1954). A life-table prepared by Goodbody (1962) for *Ascidia nigra* shows definite senescence with a limiting age of 94–96 weeks (Fig. 53).

2·5·4 ROTIFERS

The ageing of rotifers is one of the most spectacular examples of endogenous senescence in animals. It is also one of the most thoroughly studied, at least from the descriptive point of view. The life-span varies in different species from a few days to several months, and each species tends to exhibit very sharp specific age. After a period of growth, which takes place by increase in cell size, the nuclear number being fixed, and adult vigour, rotifers enter a period of senescence, with conspicuous loss of activity, degeneration of cells, deposition of pigment, and ultimate death in extension. In some forms the senescent phase is genuinely post-reproductive, but in the majority it occurs while egg-laying is still occurring at a diminished rate, and may be accompanied by the production of malformed eggs, or eggs of varying size.

The external appearances of rotifer senescence have been vividly described in several forms (*Callidina*, Plate 1886; *Pleurotrocha*, Metchnikoff, 1907; *Proales*, Noyes, 1922; Jennings and Lynch, 1928; *Hydatina*, Plate, 1886; *Lecane*, Szabó, 1935; Miller, 1931; *Rotifer vulgaris*, Spemann, 1924). The animal becomes sluggish in behaviour and reaction to jarring, the tissues and cuticle shrink and become opaque or granular in appearance, swimming is replaced by creeping, pigment accumulates in the gut, digestive gland and mastax. The movements of the pharyngeal cilia are the last signs of life to persist.

It seems clear that this is an endogenous process of degeneration. A number of attempts have been made to correlate it with other features of rotifer organization. Plate (1886) considered that senescence in *Hydatina* occurred typically when the activity of the ovary, and the supply of germ-cells, failed. This is not the case in all rotifers, however. In *Lecane inermis* Miller (1931) found that the mictic females cease egg-laying early in life and have a relatively prolonged post-reproductive period, while amictic females show signs of age before the last egg is produced, and all are dead within two days thereafter; the life-span of males is even shorter (Fig. 37). In this species, fertilization of the mictic females does not appear to influence longevity. Miller attributes the difference in life-span between mictic and amictic females directly to the difference in fertility, but this is not fully borne out by her life-tables, the chief difference being in the longer post-reproductive period of the mictic females. In *Hydatina senta* it is the amictic females which are the longer lived (Ferris, 1932). In both these species, however, the form having the higher reproductive rate in early life dies younger, an obser-

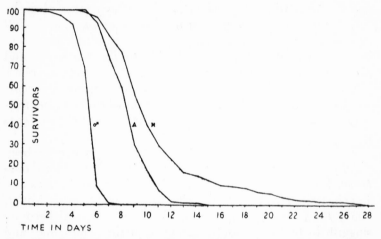

FIG. 37.—Survival curves for males, mictic (M) and amictic (A) females of *Lecane inermis* (from Miller, 1931).

vation which supports Miller's suggestion that death results from 'exhaustion'. Egg-laying in *Apsilus vorax* continues until death (Cori, 1925) and in *Proales*, appears itself to be adversely affected by somatic senescence, the egg-substance failing to enter the eggshell, and eggs of bizarre size and shape and of low hatchability being produced (Jennings and Lynch, 1928). Old populations of *P. sordida* consist of two types of senile individuals, some thick and opaque, and others abnormally transparent, with pigmentation of the gastric glands. There is considerable individual variation in the length of survival once senescence is established.

Impairment of function in all the species which have been studied is so general during senescence that it is not possible to identify a pace-maker organ in the process, though in some cases it appears to be the digestive system which first deteriorates. The pattern is fully consistent with some or all of the somatic cells having a fixed survival-time under normal metabolic con-

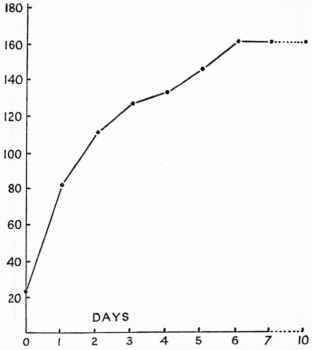

Fig. 38.—Growth in length of *Philodina citrina* (Lansing, 1948).

ditions—a highly important precedent for the study of other types of metazoan senescence. The senescent change depends directly upon metabolism—encysted rotifers can survive for very long periods (59 years—Rahm, 1923) and display enhanced reproductive performance on emergence from diapause (Dobers, 1915).

It is particularly interesting that this dramatic senescence in rotifers accompanies a very strict determinacy of cell number, a lack of regenerative capacity, and in most species a very limited power of repair. Nuclear division after hatching has not been described in any rotifer. In many forms wound healing is confined to young animals—older animals die after amputation (Pai, 1934) but in young *Asplanchna brightwelli* (Pai, 1934) and

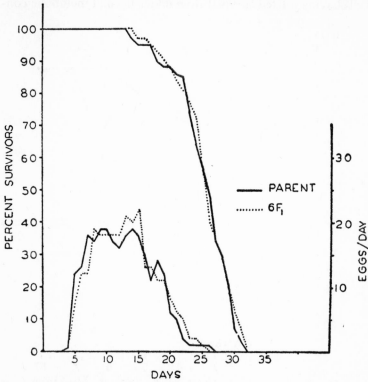

FIG. 39.—Life-span and egg-laying of *Philodina citrina* (Rotifera) over 6 generations in normal culture (from Lansing, 1952).

Stephanoceros (Jurszýk, 1926, 1927; Ubisch, 1926) the cytoplasm of the coronal lobes can be regenerated, as can parts of the coronal funnel in *Cupelopagis* (Huhnerhoff, 1931; references from Hyman, 1951).

The somatic growth of rotifers has been studied by several workers. *Rotifer vulgaris* shows little or no change in size throughout life (Spemann, 1924). The growth curve of *Apsilus vorax* is a parabola, with shrinkage before death (Cori, 1925), while in *Philodina citrina* growth ceases by the sixth day (Lansing, 1948). (See Fig. 38.) Lansing also made the striking observation that if these rotifers are propagated in each generation from eggs laid at or after the fifth day of maternal life, the rate of development becomes progressively greater and greater from generation to generation, and the longevity of the individual less and less, so

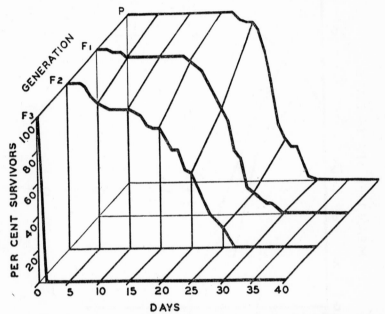

Fig. 40.—Progressive decline in life-span of a strain of *Philodina citrina* (Rotifera) raised in each generation from eggs laid by old mothers (from Lansing, 1952).

that clones propagated in each generation from old mothers invariably become extinct (Figs. 39, 40, 41). Jennings and Lynch (1928) had already noted that the offspring of very old rotifers are less viable than those of vigorous adults. Lansing's results suggested that the effects of maternal age are cumulative from generation to generation: they were also reversible, the eggs laid by young members of such a clone being capable of giving rise to normally long-lived individuals. Lansing also found that clones propagated in each generation from the eggs of very young mothers showed an increase in longevity over the control stock. In *Euchlanis triquetra*, the 'young' orthoclone could not be maintained, however, because within a few generations it gave rise largely to male-producing eggs. Lansing regards his

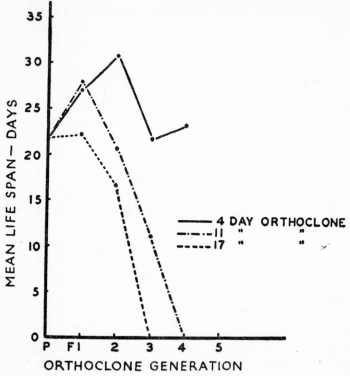

Fig. 41.—Life-span of successive generations of *Philodina* reared in each generation from the eggs of 4- 11- and 17-day-old mothers (Lansing, 1948).

ageing-factor as a product of growth-cessation, since it appears in the individual animal at the point where the negative specific acceleration of growth is greatest.

The susceptibility of rotifer eggs to external influences affecting the life-cycle of the progeny has been much studied in forms which give rise periodically to mictic generations. The literature on sex-determination in rotifers is reviewed by Hyman (1951).

The Distribution of Senescence

The longevity of the two types of female differs considerably; 'somewhere in the ontogeny of the females, it must be determined which kind of egg they are destined to lay. The determination occurs during the maturation of the egg from which the female comes, that is, during the last few hours before the egg is laid' (Hyman, 1951). Both internal and environmental factors of great complexity appear to operate in different forms. 'The conclusion from numerous researches seems to be that, in addition to an inherent rhythm as regards male production, monotony of conditions suppresses mictic females, whereas any sudden change, especially of diet and of physiochemical composition of the water, induces the appearance of mictic females' (Hyman, 1951). The reason for the difference in longevity between Lansing's old and young orthoclones is not, it should be noted, entirely comparable to that between mictic and amictic females. It does not seem to represent a difference in specific age due to a shortening of that part of the survival curves which, owing to the low early mortality in rotifers, is usually horizontal, but rather a 'breaking away' of this plateau by the introduction of a higher and higher early mortality, the curve becoming less and less rectangular and more and more oblique. If conclusions are to be drawn upon the effect of maternal age upon senescence, this difference is important.

It is possible that the uniform specific age of rotifer populations is due to *depletion*. Reproductive exhaustion has already been discussed. It is also known that the limited regeneration observed in *Stephanoceros* takes place at the expense of reproduction and of somatic growth. Little is known of the metabolic capacity of rotifers—they apparently store glycogen, but may be incapable of assimilating carbohydrate (Hyman, 1951). Sudden senescence might well represent the exhaustion of a metabolic substrate, or of a non-renewable system. *Accumulation* has also been suggested: pigment certainly does accumulate, probably secondarily to the ageing process. Lansing (1942) demonstrated the accumulation of calcium in old rotifers, and succeeded in prolonging their life by immersion in dilute citrate solution—it is not clear how often this process can be repeated. A more curious factor influencing the life-span was observed by Edmondson (1945) in *Floscularia conifera*, where individuals

127

growing in aggregation reach twice the length, twice the age, and a higher level of fertility as against solitary specimens.

The peculiarities of rotifer organization are so numerous that some, if not all, of the mechanisms controlling their longevity are likely to be peculiar to the group. On the other hand, their short life-span makes them a suitable object for study, and they provide an unequivocal example of senescence coupled with cellular non-renewal which calls for further investigation.

2·5·5 ARTHROPODS

Senescence in arthropods is widespread and probably universal. Those forms which have wings, jaws, bristles, and other chitinous tegumentary structures not renewed by moulting are particularly liable to genuinely 'mechanical' senescence. In the forms which moult as adults, the time of ecdysis is a particularly arduous one, judged by the mortality, and many of these, such as *Daphnia* and large spiders, appear very often to die in the attempt to carry out a final moult.

'Physiological' senescence, in the sense in which nineteenth-century biology used the term, also appears in a convincing form for the first time in arthropods, since, as Metchnikoff first pointed out (1907, 1915), a non-feeding imago *must* be regarded as expendable from the evolutionary point of view. The evolution of short sexual life as a modification in some groups is balanced by the evolution of a very long sexual life in specialized individuals of other, social, species, as part of the adaptive development of a group-existence—the longest life-span being reached in one or both sexual forms among true ants and termites.

There is no known case of arthropod indeterminacy comparable with that of actinians. Growth in most insect imagines is more or less rigidly limited, although the capacity for continued cell division persists in varying degrees. According to Harms (1959), somatic mitosis in many arthropod imagines is virtually confined to the mid-gut. Mitotic capacity has not been shown to bear any relationship to longevity, except perhaps in forms producing queens, where the relation of continued reproduction to long life might be either a direct example of cause and effect, or the result of two parallel adaptations. Some solitary arthropods are capable of very long life (20 years in tarantulas, Baerg 1945, possibly 50 years in lobsters, Herrick, 1896).

Crustacea. The small crustacea (Cladocerans, Copepods, Isopods) generally show very sharp specific age. In *Daphnia*[1] this appears to be definable in terms of instars, *D. longispina* living

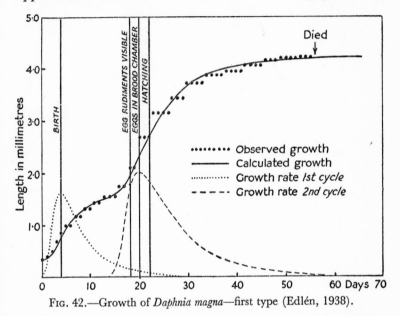

Fig. 42.—Growth of *Daphnia magna*—first type (Edlén, 1938).

for 19–22 instars, the duration of which depend upon the conditions of culture (Ingle, Wood and Banta, 1937) and *D. magna* for 17 instars (Anderson and Jenkins, 1942). Detailed studies upon factors which retard or accelerate the rate of development

[1] There is a striking lack of unanimity in the literature over the 'normal' life-span of various species of *Daphnia*, even when grown in apparently similar media. Fritsch (1953) has shown that this variation depends to some extent upon the amount of available pantothenic acid. Where Daphnids are fed upon living cultures of protozoans or algae, the food organism itself may metabolize and remove pantothenic acid. It is highly questionable in view of Fritsch's findings how far the life-tables obtained by workers using different culture techniques, or even by one worker at different times, are comparable. This is unfortunate, as Cladocerans are most useful organisms to gerontologists—further standardization of culture techniques seems essential if they are to be used in this way, however.

and life-span in *Daphnia* have been carried out. (McArthur and Baillie, 1926 *seq.*; Ingle, Wood and Banta, 1937; Anderson and Jenkins, 1942; Fritsch, 1953, 1959; Fritsch and Meijering, 1958; Meijering, 1958, 1960; von Reden, 1960, etc., see pp. 194 *seq.*). In view of the availability of life-tables for *Daphnia*,

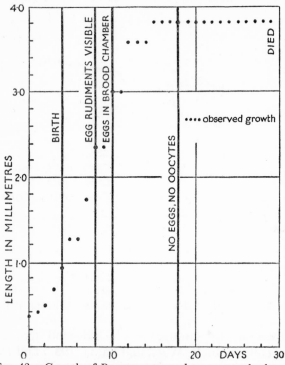

Fig. 43.—Growth of *D. magna*—second type: growth-phases superimposed (Edlén, 1938).

the pattern of its normal growth is of particular interest. Edlén (1938) showed that the growth of normal daphnids takes place in two cycles, the first levelling off after three or four instars, and the second coinciding with the development of the gonad. He found three types of pattern in the growth of individual *D. magna*. In the majority of specimens (Fig. 42) the two cycles of growth followed one another, the growth-potential in the second cycle falling almost to zero with increasing age; this fall is accompanied by a decrease in egg size and number, and the animal finally dies after a short period in which growth has almost ceased. In individuals of the second type (Fig. 43) the two growth-cycles were superimposed—in these growth was very rapid, there was no prepubertal 'shelf' in the curve of body size, and fertility was lost early, although the life-span appeared to be normal. The third type (Fig. 44) showed only the first cycle of growth, but no gonadal function developed,

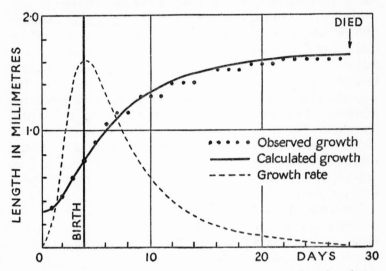

Fig. 44.—Growth of *D. magna*—third type. One growth-cycle only (Edlén, 1938).

and adult size was not attained. These forms died early. Edlén considered that the developing ovary exerts a hormonal control over growth, and possibly over the maintenance of life-processes generally.

The chief senile changes in *Daphnia* appear to be in the fat body, intestinal epithelium and musculature (Schulze-Röbbecke, 1951). This author found no evidence of the 'cerebral death' which was once widely accepted as the general cause of invertebrate senescence (Harms, 1926; Muhlmann, 1900, 1911), and which was described by Walter (1922) in *Cyclops*. Withdrawal of ovarian activity does not seem to be the direct cause of senescence in *Daphnia*. Schulze-Röbbecke's oldest specimens still showed considerable ovarian activity, and continued to lay eggs, though in reduced numbers, up to the time of death. Oocytes at all stages of maturation remained in the ovary to the last. Schulze-Röbbecke attributed the death of *Daphnia* in old age to failure of nutrition following degenerative changes in the gut.

Walter's work on *Cyclops* (1922) dealt with *C. viridis*, which has a life-span of about 9 months, 'senile' change in gut epithelium and in the cerebral ganglia being evident from the fifth month. Somatic mitosis in adult life occurs only in the mid-gut of *Cyclops*, and in this region 'senile' changes were not found (Harms, 1949). The most striking degenerative changes in *Cyclops* were found in the chromatin of the ganglion cells, with the appearance of large inclusion bodies suspiciously reminiscent of virus inclusions or fixation artefacts, and in the antennules. Gut degeneration occurred later in life, about the eighth month, and was confined to the anterior gut, mitosis continuing in other parts of the gut epithelium until the end. It is difficult to know what connection, if any, these changes have with the process of senescence.

Needham (A. E. Needham, 1950) has studied the growth-rate of limb regeneration in *Asellus aquaticus*; growth in crustacea, on Needham's figures for *Asellus* and *Carcinus*, is determinate and the curve sigmoid, the arithmetic rate of growth rising to a maximum and declining asymptotically thereafter to zero. The geometric rate of growth declines monotonically with age from the outset, and the rate of decline itself declines with increasing age. The specific regeneration rate decreases progressively with age, owing to the progressive increase in the duration of each instar; the rate of decline is much less than that of the normal growth-rate, and itself declines with age. 'In some crustacea the limiting size is attained at an age beyond the mean expected life-span. Growth is indeterminate in Crustacea only in this sense. They are not potentially immortal.' This investigation illustrates once again the difficulty of characterizing the growth-behaviour of real organisms mathematically: the decline of arithmetic growth may be asymptotic, or tangible size increase may continue; in crustacea there is the additional difficulty that growth is discontinuous, being interrupted by stadia, which superimpose a 'quantal' effect on the smooth ideal curve. The conclusion of Needham's studies is that the growth of crustacea follows a convergent series, and must cease, presumably, for practical purposes in any form which lives long enough. But the relation between such cessation and determinacy of life-span is still entirely conjectural.

Insects. It has long been recognized that several separate types of senile change may occur in insects. Mechanical damage to the cuticle (Blunck, 1924; Wigglesworth, 1945), depletion of reserves both in feeding and non-feeding imagines, accelerated in some cases by reproduction (Krumbiegel, 1929a, b; Bilewicz, 1953), accumulation of urates (Metchnikoff, 1915), deterioration of the nervous system (Hodge, 1894–95; Pixell-Goodrich, 1920; Schmidt, 1923; Weyer, 1931, etc.) and 'general senile decay' have all been demonstrated by more or less satisfactory evidence. The vast majority of holometabolous imagines give every evidence of having a sharp specific age, and this is a group in which we are unusually well equipped with life-tables. The nature of the processes which limit imaginal life seems, however, to vary widely, but they have the common property of being processes operating in a cellular system where little or no renewal, and no further morphogenetic development, are occurring.

One of the best general descriptions of insect senescence is given by Blunck (1924) for *Dytiscus marginalis*: he describes the main signs of advancing age as diminution in activity and deterioration of the epicuticle, with the growth of colonial protozoa on the dorsal shield, legs and mouth parts, which the animal cannot any longer clean effectively. The cleaning secretions seem to be reduced, and the chitin appears brittle, whole legs or antennae being occasionally snapped off in swimming. If pygidial gland secretion fails, air enters the subalar air chamber and the beetle drowns. In the beetles dissected by Blunck, the gonads had almost disappeared during the third year of life, the fat-body was increased in size, almost filling the body cavity, but chalky and full of concretions. In some individuals there was almost complete atrophy of the wing muscles. The extreme life-span is under 3 years, females living longer than males: sexual activity usually ceases in the second year but may persist in individuals into the third. A number of senile processes, which may not be mutually dependent, can be detected in this description. The balance between mechanical, depletive and 'morphogenetic' senescence must vary considerably from species to species, and even from individual to individual. Blunck's description is of interest in providing not only an account of such a mixed senescence, but one of the very few instances where the 'change in inert structures', so popular with colloid chemists investigating senescence, really seems to occur—in the progressive hardening and weakening of the chitin of *Dytiscus* elytra, which Blunck found to be a reliable rough measure of the age of specimens taken in the wild. On the other hand, a considerable part of this change, as Blunck himself suspected, may represent failure to secrete the normal lubricant coat—a cellular rather than a mechanical deterioration.

In many insects, especially lepidoptera, there is evidence that the fat-body contains a definite reserve of materials, which are not replaceable during imaginal life. In females of the moth *Ephestia elutella*, longevity and fecundity are both functions of body weight at eclosion (Waloff, Norris and Broadhead, 1947). Longevity is also greater in virgin females, possibly owing to the sparing of reserves through egg-rudiment resorption (Norris, 1933, 1934). Exhaustion of the fat-body is characteristically found in *Ephestia* which appear to have died of old age. Norris (1934) found evidence that the fat-body contains two types of store, one needed for the maintenance of the ovaries and the other for the maintenance of life. The second appears to be supplemented by feeding the imago, but not the first (Norris, 1933). Similar deterioration of the fat-body has been described as a sign of senescence in *Carabus* and *Drosophila* (Krumbiegel, 1929) and *Sitodrepa panicea* (Janisch, 1924) in which the period of depletion is apparently hastened by exposure to CO_2. This type of 'depletion senescence' is, in fact, in one sense an extension of morphogenetic senescence, if in the transition from larva to imago the organism loses the power of synthesis or assimilation of some material which it is able to store during larval and pupal life. How far depletion of larval reserves is a general feature of insect senescence it is difficult to say. The non-feeding or the starved imago is necessarily dependent upon what stores it has, although Metchnikoff (1915) from a careful study of *Bombyx*, favoured an 'accumulative' rather than a 'depletive' mechanism to account for imaginal death. Other imagines probably vary a great deal in their biochemical accomplishments. Some lepidopteran imagines feed on nectar and are known to

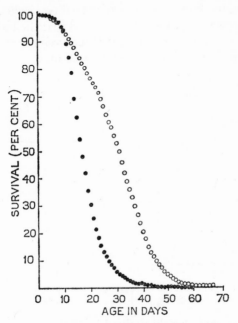

Fig. 45.—Survival curves of male and female house-flies. ●, Males; ○, females (Rockstein and Lieberman, 1958).

absorb water and sugars. Frohawk (1935) kept *Nymphalis antiopa* alive for three months from eclosion by feeding sugar solution. On the other hand, robust Coleoptera, such as *Blaps*, are fully capable of living on their intake and stores for ten years, while the mole cricket has been thought able to live much longer. Activity reduces the life-span: Camboué (1926) greatly prolonged the life of butterflies by decapitating them. The correlations between pre-imaginal and imaginal life-spans have been discussed by Balász (1960).

The influence of reproduction on life-span is equally variable, but it often seems to involve inroads upon stored and irreplaceable reserves. Unmated females of *Periplaneta* lay fewer eggs than mated females and live longer (Griffiths and Tauber, 1942). The life-span in both male and female *Drosophila* is substantially decreased by mating (Bilewicz, 1953). Krumbiegel found that the reserves in the fat-body of Carabids decreases after first copulation, but increases again with feeding (1929). In the moth *Fumea crassiorella* Matthes (1951) found that the longevity of the female was halved by copulation if egg-laying was allowed, and slightly reduced by it if egg-laying was prevented (Fig. 46).

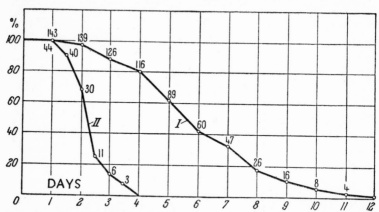

FIG. 46.—Survival curves of 145 isolated virgin females (I) and 44 isolated fertilized females (II) of the moth *Fumea crassiorella* (from Matthes, 1951).

The theory of 'cerebral death' (*Gehirntod*) in insects arises chiefly from some long-standing work on bees. Hodge (1894, 1895), Pixell-Goodrich (1920) and Schmidt (1923) all described cerebral degeneration, reduction of cerebral cell-number, and disorganization of the nervous system as characteristic and probably causal mechanisms in the senescence of worker bees. According to Hodge, the cell-number in the brain of old workers was reduced by three-quarters. Pixell-Goodrich found that in diseased, and therefore inactive, workers, the cerebral architecture was more normal than in healthy workers. Schmidt attributed the reduction in cell size and cell-number to direct 'wear by use', the amount of work done by the insect being a fixed quantity. Holmgren (1909) found a similar deterioration in the supraoesophageal ganglia of old termite primaries: the brain of old physogastric queens of *Eutermes* was reduced to two-thirds of the volume usually found in virgin queens. Another instance of *'Gehirntod'* in insects was described by Hansemann (1914) in *Bacillus rossi* (Phasmidae).

Quite apart from the fact that they have been indiscriminately transferred to mammals, these findings themselves have been open to intermittent criticism.[1] Smallwood and Phillips (1916) were by no means satisfied that the changes in relative nuclear size described by Hodge in worker bees resulted from ageing or were in any way pathological. Weyer (1930) regarded the cerebral ganglion changes as secondary, since the supposedly senile degeneration appears remarkably suddenly, and only after evident deterioration in other organs. In a 5-year-old queen, Pflugfelder (1948) found some disturbances of cerebral histology especially in the corpora pedunculata, but no significant cerebral change in old drones and workers. Rockstein (1950), however, found a decline in cell-number in the brain of worker bees from a mean 522 at eclosion to 369 at 6 weeks. The complex behaviour of worker bees deteriorates suddenly just before death.

In some lepidoptera this change in behaviour before death is very marked—so much so that it may have an adaptive function (Blest, 1960), there being aposematic species which, when no longer fertile, become behaviourally conspicuous to predators through over-activity.

Schulze-Röbbecke (1951) made a careful search for evidence of 'cerebral death' in *Dixippus* and *Melolontha* and found no signs of it whatsoever, the primary senile deterioration being most evident in gut and musculature. 'Vielleicht hat v. Hansemann bereits töte Tiere untersucht, was sehr leicht vorkommen kann, da bei den Stabheuschrecken infolge ihrer Reaktionsträgheit der Übergang von den letzten Lebensaüsserungen zum Tode nicht ohne weiteres festzustellen ist.' The amount of senile change described either as a result of fixation-artefacts or the

---

[1] The large literature of neurone loss with increasing age in mammals, especially in the cerebellum, is reviewed by Andrew (1955).

sectioning of 'that which dies of itself' has yet to be assessed in the literature.

A considerable amount of work has been done upon the physiological factors which influence longevity in worker bees. Winter bees are known to be considerably longer lived than the summer brood even when they are kept under similar conditions

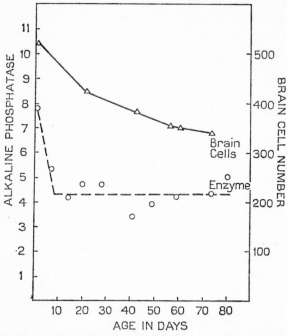

Fig. 47.—Alkaline phosphatase in whole body homogenates and brain cell-number in the adult worker honey bee (Rockstein, 1953).

of temperature and activity. Maurizio (1946) found that caged winter bees had a mean survival of 36 days from eclosion compared with 24 days in caged summer bees. The life-span of summer bees can be prolonged in two ways—by feeding pollen to caged bees (Maurizio, 1946), or by removing all the sealed brood regularly from the colony, so that the same bees continue with brood-rearing throughout life—under these conditions bees may live as long as 72 days (Moskovljević, 1939; Maurizio, 1950).

The Distribution of Senescence

Two factors appear to influence the longevity of workers. One of these is certainly activity. Ribbands (1950) found that anaesthesia with CO_2 had the effect of causing young bees to begin foraging earlier than usual: in bees which forage early, expectation of imaginal life is less ($30 \cdot 1 \pm 1 \cdot 2$ days), but expectation of foraging-life is greater ($15 \cdot 0 \pm 1 \cdot 2$ days) than in late starters ($37 \cdot 1 \pm 0 \cdot 6$ and $10 \cdot 8 \pm 0 \cdot 8$ days). The second appears to be dietary. 'Winter bees differ from summer bees in the greater development of their pharyngeal glands and their fat-bodies. This development results from autumn consumption of pollen, in excess of the requirements for immediate brood-rearing. In queen-right colonies in summer, prevention of brood-rearing can produce similar consequences, and in pre-swarming colonies temporary interruption of brood-rearing produces conditions different only in degree.' In all these cases the increased expectation of life is associated both with enhanced development of the pharyngeal glands and fat-body, and with decreased activity (Ribbands, 1953). It appears that worker bees have a life-span which is partially expressible in 'flying-hours', and that this life-span, and the total output of work per life, can be increased by increasing pollen consumption (Maurizio, 1950), but summer bees only increase their life-span in this way if they are deprived of brood. There is also ground for believing that the activity of worker bees is reduced by the possession of internal food reserves. In winter bees, then, absence of brood leads to repletion, which in turn induces both quiescence and inherently greater longevity at a time when both are beneficial to survival. (See the review of bee nutrition and longevity by Maurizio, 1959.) The expectation of foraging-life decreases in proportion to the age of the bee when it begins to forage—endogenous senescence therefore appears to play a part in limiting the life of workers, and they do not all die from accident alone (Ribbands, 1952). Queenless 'indoor' bees, which are not carrying out normal hive activities, live about 10 weeks (Rockstein, 1959). Whatever the facts concerning *Gehirntod*, this process of senescence appears to contain a major depletive element, combined, in all probability, with an element of mechanical damage. In this respect the senescence of worker bees conforms to a pattern which seems to be widespread in insects. Bees are, of course, a special case in that the far greater longevity of queens depends upon the developmental consequences of having been fed on 'royal jelly'. This substance has lately proved very effective in prolonging the life of pharmaceutical firms: there is no reason to think that it is otherwise effective in man.

2·5·6 MOLLUSCS

Pelseneer (1934) divides molluscs in the wild into annual species, pluriennial species with a short reproductive life, and pluriennial species with a long reproductive life. In some members of this last group, indeterminacy of life-span cannot be excluded. Most of the evidence is obtained from wild material. The combination of patterns appears analogous to that found in fish. Like fish, molluscs include short-lived forms, forms with a longer but apparently determinate life, and forms, especially among the larger pelecypods, which appear to have no maximum size.

The annual forms include many nudibranchs (Pelseneer, 1934, 1935) and probably most of the smaller freshwater species (*Paludestrina jenkinsi*—Boycott, 1936; *Ancylus*—Hunter, 1953). According to Boycott (1936) *Planorbis corneus* is the only British freshwater pulmonate which is not normally an annual. Many of these annual forms die immediately after reproduction. In *Viviparus contectoides* (van Cleave and Lederer, 1932) and *V. bengalensis* (Annandale and Sewell, 1921) the wild males live one, and the females up to three years. In captivity Oldham kept male *V. contectus* for $4\frac{1}{2}$ and female for 5 years (Oldham, 1931), and living embryos were present at the time of death. Growth, judged by length, ceased in the second or third year of life. A number of other forms live for a maximum of 2 or 3 years in the wild, breeding during one or two seasons (*Lioplax*—van Cleave and Chambers, 1935; *Carychium*, 18 months, Morton, 1954; *Bithynia*—Boycott, 1936; Lilly, 1953; *Fossaria*—van Cleave, 1935; *Sphaerium*—Foster, 1932; *Teredo navalis*—Grave, 1928). Specimens of *Limnaea columella* kept in captivity under good conditions give a life-table showing a typical senile increase in force of mortality similar to that in *Drosophila* (Winsor and Winsor, 1935; Baily, 1931). The growth of *Limnaea* has been studied by Baily (1931) and Crabb (1929). Among rather longer-lived forms, Pelseneer (1934) found a complete cessation of shell growth and a decline in fertility with age in *Gibbula umbilicalis*, complete infertility being general at about 54 months, and the extreme life-span 4½–5 years. In *Eulota fruticum*, the relation of egg-laying to age has been determined. According to Künkel, death takes place in captivity 'when the germinal glands are exhausted' (Künkel, 1928) (Fig. 48). In *Physa gyrina* De Witt (1954) found a distinct post-reproductive period, amounting to

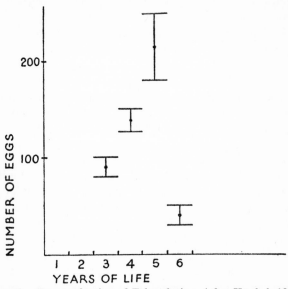

FIG. 48.—Egg production of *Eulota fruticum* (after Künkel, 1928).

as much as 49 per cent of the total life-span in mass culture, or 36 per cent in isolation culture, the overall mean life-spans being 211 and 143 days respectively, while an individual *Limapontia*, normally an annual, lived a year in captivity after breeding (McMillan, 1947). Szabó and Szabó (1929–36 *passim*) published a number of studies upon the 'senescent' changes observable in the digestive gland and nervous system of *Agriolimax*: these, however, were inconstant from species to species, and a life-table (Fig. 6c, p. 26) constructed from their data by Pearl & Miner (1935) shows a steady high mortality: it is probable that none of these slugs reached their maximum potential age.

Incidence of parasitic infection increases with age and size (*Bithynia*—Schäfer, 1953; *Littorina*—Moore, 1937). Wasting of the body tissues and fibrotic changes in the digestive glands are also described. Szabó and Szabó (Szabó, I., 1932, 1935; Szabó, M., 1935; Szabó and Szabó, 1929, 1930a, b, 1931a, b, 1934) found degenerative changes and pigment deposition in ganglion cells of old specimens of *Helix* and *Agriolimax*. The most evident histological changes with age were in the digestive gland, which underwent fibrosis and loss of cells, but these changes were not consistent from species to species. Künkel (1928) wrote that *Eulota* dies 'when the germinal glands are exhausted' and in old *Agriolimax* oöcytes had almost wholly disappeared (Szabó and Szabó, 1935) perhaps as part of a progressive change to predominant maleness: in *Limnaea stagnalis appressa* under laboratory conditions 'autopsy of senescent snails invariably discloses a badly atrophied liver, and the remaining organs, with the exception of the reproductive organs, are badly emaciated' (Noland and Carriker, 1946). There is evidently no basis here for any generalization.

Where there is a sex difference in the life-span of molluscs it appears to be in favour of the female, as in almost every other phylum (*Viviparus bengalensis*—Annandale and Sewell, 1921; *V. contectoides*—van Cleave and Lederer, 1932; *V. malleatus*—Niwa, 1950; *Lioplax*—van Cleave and Chambers, 1935; *Littorina scabra*, *L. obesa*—Sewell, 1924). But in *Chiton*, under wild conditions, Crozier (1918) found a progressive deficit of females in the higher age-groups. The growth rate and final size of males are also more commonly the less, where a difference exists (*Hydrobia*—Rothschild and Rothschild, 1939); *Spirula* (Bruun, 1943) is an exception.

Very little evidence exists to relate the apparent senescence of short-lived molluscs in the wild to their growth pattern, or to their potential life-span in isolation. Van Cleave (1935) and Hoff (1937) considered that the snails *Fossaria* and *Viviparus* continue to grow throughout life; in these forms, according to van Cleave, the maximum size which is characteristic of the facies of any colony is secured by a combination of environmental effects on the growth rate and an endogenous process of senescence which kills the animal after the completion of its life-cycle, irrespective of its general somatic growth. In the large *Trochus niloticus* Rao (1937) found no evidence of senile mortality, the upper limit of age being about 12 years in a wild population, and growth continuing at a decreasing rate throughout life. On the other hand, in spiral gastropods with an elaborate lip armature, growth must be *effectively* determinate so far as shell size is concerned. It has been suggested that in *Polygyra* growth

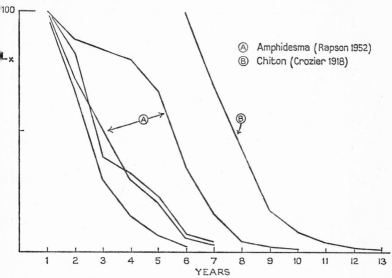

Ⓐ Amphidesma (Rapson 1952)
Ⓑ Chiton (Crozier 1918)

Fig. 49.—Survival curves of four wild populations of *Amphidesma ventricosum*, drawn from the data of Rapson, 1952—(A); and of *Chiton tuberculatus* from the age of 6 years, from the data of Crozier, 1918—(B) (from Comfort, 1957a).

in size ceases at lip formation, but body weight and shell thickness continue to increase (Foster, 1936). Przibram (1909) quoted observations by Taylor and de Villepoix that the gland-cells of the mantle disappear in fully-grown specimens of *Helix aspersa*, *H. nemoralis* and *Clausilia perversa*. The growth of molluscs is seasonal, and the development of the gonad appears in some forms to compete with, or inhibit, body growth—in oysters, the periods of shell growth occur in each year before and after spawning (Orton, 1928) while in *Hydrobia ulvae* parasitic castration leads to gigantism (Rothschild, 1935). The life-span

143

of such giants was unfortunately not recorded. On a small series of *Limnaea columella* Baily (1931) found that shell growth ceased at or soon after sexual maturity, and that the shortest-lived individuals were those with the highest growth rates. A life-table was constructed for this species by Winsor and Winsor (1935) (Fig. 50). Species whose life-cycle rarely exceeds 2 years may be capable of much longer life in captivity. Oldham

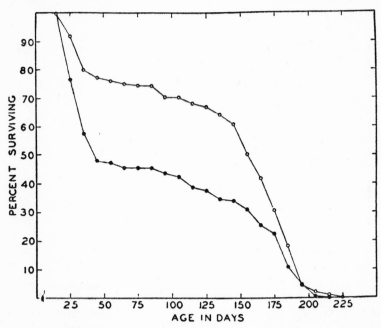

Fig. 50.—Life-span of the pulmonate *Limnaea columella* at two different population densities (from Winsor and Winsor, 1935).

(1930) kept *Planorbis corneus* in active reproduction up to 6 years of age. Many Helicidae, especially the smaller forms, have been regarded as annuals in the wild (Lamy, 1933; Pelseneer, 1935): the potential life of helicids and medium-sized land snails in captivity (excluding diapause, aestivation and so on) may, however, reach or exceed 10 years (*Rumina decollata*, 12 years, *Helix spiriplana*, 15 years—Vignal, 1919; *Helix pomatia*, 6–7 years—Künkel, 1916; 6–8 years—Cuénot, 1911; *H. hortensis*, 6

years, hybrid *H. hortensis* × *nemoralis*, 10 years—Cuénot, 1911),
while *Oxystyla capax* has been revived from diapause after 23
years (Baker, 1934).

Even less is known about the longevity and liability to senescence of most marine gastropods. In *Acmaea dorsuosa* Abe (1932)
found that growth continued in 15-year-old specimens from
some localities, while in other localities an apparent specific size
was reached at 5 years. Apparent specific size in certain colonies
was also found by Hamai (1937) in *Patelloida grata*. The most
suggestive evidence of a determinate life-span in limpets comes
from Fischer-Piette's (1939) observations which showed a definite inverse relationship between longevity, judged by growth
rings, and rate of growth in different stations (Fig. 51). This
strongly suggests that a process of morphogenetic ageing is oc-
curing at different rates depending on the rate of growth.

No increase in mortality with age has been demonstrated in
many of the longest-lived pluriennials, the decline in their numbers being gradual, without any evidence of a sharp specific age.
Crozier (1918, Fig. 49) obtained a survival curve for *Chiton
tuberculatus* between 5 and 13 years which is approximately
logarithmic, and showed no sign of an age-increase in mortality
(younger ages could not be sampled on account of their habits).
Rao (1937) found no increase in the mortality of *Trochus niloticus*
up to 12 years. But in other species the specific age is well
defined, and lies within the wild survival-period. Some of these
have a strikingly low adult mortality compared with small
vertebrates. *Nucula turgida* shows only a very gradual decline in
numbers until the 7th year, dying off thereafter to a limiting
maximum age at about 11 years (Allen, 1952): *Amphidesma ventricosum* begins its senile decline under favourable conditions at
$4\frac{1}{2}$ years and reaches a maximum age of about 10, 80 per cent
of yearlings surviving to 4 years (Rapson, 1952, Fig. 49). The
large Helices probably have survival curves both in the wild
and in captivity of this type, which is that characterized by
Teissier (1934), with a long initial plateau. *Eulota fruticum* has a
specific age of about 6 years in captivity (Künkel, 1928).
Welch (1901) collected 40 specimens of *H. aspersa*, some of
which were already adult; in captivity all survived at 15 months,
36 at 38 months, and 20, including two collected as adults, at 72

months. Deaths occurred chiefly in summer. The final intervals of this table do not seem to have been published, but Taylor (1907) states that specimens kept by Welch lived 8 or even 10 years; *Cepaea hortensis* was kept by Lang (1904) for over 9 years. Lamotte (1951), who carried out marking experiments, gives the mean wild longevity of *C. nemoralis* variously as 6–7 years and as 2–3 years (Lamotte, pp. 16, 100), but found that it was necessary to mark at least 1000 specimens to be certain of recovering 10 after the lapse of two years.

In monocarpic forms, especially short-lived nudibranchs, there is some evidence that adult death is a normal sequel of spawning. 'Parental death' due to the effects of reproduction occurs widely in insects and fish, though its physiology is not always plain. As in annual plants, death can in some cases be postponed indefinitely if reproduction is prevented. In female eels the life-span is determinate if the mating migration takes place, but not otherwise (Bertin, 1956), while non-spawners among minnows which normally die after breeding may live for a further year as unusually large specimens (Markus, 1934). Szabó (1932) found that mating shortened the life-span of *Agriolimax*: the effect of self-fertilization was less severe since fewer eggs were laid. There are no other experimental instances where the longer life of aquarium-bred snails can be shown to result from failure to breed. The amount of diversion of body-activities into reproduction varies from species to species. Shell-growth may be slowed or permanently stopped at maturity— Baily (1931) found that in the laboratory growth ceased with the onset of egg-laying in *Limnaea columella*. In other species the annual growth-check coincides with spawning (*Pecten maximus*, Tang, 1941). It is more interesting from this point of view that parasitic castration produced by trematode infection of the gonad regularly induces gigantism in some species (*Hydrobia*, Rothschild, 1935; *Littorina neritoides*, Rothschild, 1941; *Zebrina detrita*, Boettger, 1953, 1953a). It has not been shown whether this is a hormonal effect, a sign of competition between somatic and gonadal requirements, or a specific growth-stimulation by a product of the parasite. The life-span of such giants has not been described, and would be well worth noting. In general, heavily parasitized animals have their lives shortened, but any exception would have important epidemiological consequences. The power of inducing longer life might have evolutionary advantages to the parasite, equal to those of inducing large size and a consequently improved chance of being picked out by the secondary host.

The growth of the long-lived pluriennial lamellibranchs is in most cases indeterminate, in that it does not cease at a fixed adult size. There is however evidence that where mortality increases with age it may in some cases be size-dependent, both in these forms and in some gastropods. In wild populations of annual and biennial molluscs there is no 'plateau' at the end of the growth curve, and no relative accumulation of individuals in the large size groups. Death occurs consistently in adults at an age when growth is apparently still in progress. Van Cleave (1935) first suggested that in *Fossaria modicella* attainment of a critical size might in itself lead to death from environmental causes. Hunter (1953) considered that relatively simple factors such as rate of stream flow and the growth of attached algae might determine the size at which adult *Ancylus* die. There is also a size-effect in *Physa* and *Lymnaea* (Hunter, 1961).

Something similar occurs in several long-lived species, and in both cases it is open to a different interpretation. Fischer-Piette (1939) collected figures for the age and size of *Patella vulgata* from different sites, and found a definite inverse relation between growth-rate and final age, judged by ring counting, in the different samples. Hopkins (1930) found that the oldest individuals of *Venus mercenaria* were usually not the largest. Some small specimens had as many as 40 growth-rings, and appeared to have grown abnormally slowly, while large shells rarely had more than 20 or 25. Colonies of *Siliqua patula* in California show twice the growth-rate, but only half the final life-span, of the same species in Alaska (Weymouth and McMillin, 1931); Rapson (1952) found an abnormally high natural mortality in his fastest-growing colony of *Amphidesma* (Fig. 49). This behaviour closely resembles the results of experiment on animals which display 'endogenous' senescence. It suggests that the life-span is fixed in terms of developmental programme, rather than size alone, and that the rate of ageing is being modified by changes in nutrition and temperature. Although losses from selective predation often depend on size, the demonstration of any other environmental form of senescence due to pure size would be of great interest, for there is already a classical example of such a process in those fossil *Gryphaea* which finally became incapable of opening the shell (Westoll, 1950). A purely size-dependent effect does not seem the most probable general explanation of molluscan senescence, and the facts constitute strong evidence against regarding the life-span of any pluriennial molluscs as 'indeterminate' in the same sense as that of actinians.

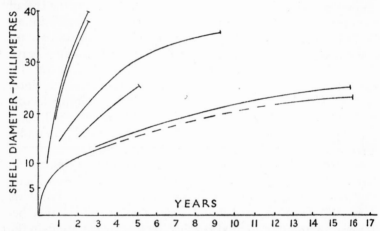

Fig. 51.—Growth and longevity of *Patella vulgata* in various stations, showing the short life of rapidly-growing populations (from Fischer-Piette, 1939).

Growth continuing actively to the maximum recorded age has been found in many forms (*Cardium*, 16 years—Weymouth and Thompson, 1930; *Venus mercenaria*, 40 years—Hopkins, 1930; *Siliqua*, 14–16 years—Weymouth, 1931; *Pecten jessoensis*, 8 years—Bazykalova, 1934; *Mya*, 7–8 years—Newcombe, 1935, 1936). The larger freshwater pelecypods, which have fewer enemies and are not subject to tidal disturbances, reach even greater ages.

The life-span of these freshwater mussels calls for special discussion. It has been widely studied because of their economic importance and depletion by fishing, but with inconclusive results, most of the argument turning on the interpretation of growth-rings. There are apparently large differences in growth-rate and wild longevity between species and in different stations. Some mussel populations show a combination of extremely slow and prolonged growth, long life-span and low adult mortality which is perhaps unique in biology, but much of the evidence is inferential, especially for the European forms, and more experiment seems to be needed.

In several North American species annulus counts have been shown, on evidence already quoted, to be reasonably acceptable measures of age (Coker, Shira, Clark and Howard, 1919; Isely, 1931). Washboard mussels (*Megalonaias gigantea*) with 53 and 54 such rings have been described, and even larger specimens exist, measuring as much as 280 mm. in length. In the smaller species the growth-rate has often declined so much by the twelfth or fifteenth year that subsequent annuli cannot be counted satisfactorily (Matteson, 1948; Saldau, 1939).

It has long been suspected that *Margaritana margaritifera* has by far the longest life-span of any European species; ages of 60 or even 100 years in the wild have been inferred from its growth-rate (von Hessling, 1859; Geyer, 1909; Israel, 1913; Korschelt, 1932). It forms rather ill-defined growth rings. Israel's estimate of 100 years is based in part on the extreme slowness of adult growth, but it also leans heavily on the finding of a shell marked '1851' which was still alive in 1911. This evidence gains a little credit from the habit among German pearlers of marking shells after partially opening them with a 'key'. Rubbel (1913) made a careful study of the growth of marked specimens over a two-year period. He failed to detect consistent rings: the growth-rate in length fell regularly with increasing size, from 1 mm./year in shells 60 mm. long to 0·4 mm./year in shells 100 mm. long. Assuming a 60-mm. specimen to be at least 10 years old, Rubbel concluded that it should take another twenty years to reach 80 mm. and a further forty years to reach 100 mm. On this basis the natural life-span could not be less than 70–80 years.

The growth-rate and size of *Margaritana* have been shown, however, to vary from place to place. Altnöder (1926) found that specimens from one locality bearing 20 annuli measured 11·6 mm. in length, while from another they measured 12·4 mm. with 60 annuli, and size relative to annulus number increased in a downstream direction. Altnöder accepts growth rings as a serviceable measure of age, having found that annuli produced during one year's observation in previously-measured mussels agreed in breadth with the recently-deposited 'annual' rings.

Saldau (1939) from data obtained in the European part of Russia found that while growth in *Unio* continued in some waters after the 8th year, *M. margaritifera* was growing steadily without any evident falling-off in rate at the 13th year. Her age estimations also were based on rings, determined by transillumination. If the ages so obtained are correct, mussels in some rivers had reached 60 mm. in length by 10 years of age and 70 mm. by 13 years, while 13-year-olds in other rivers measured less than 50 mm. Ages over 13 years were not estimated, since 'after this age the rings become too close'. Latterly Brander (1956), while making no attempt to judge their ages, records a specimen of *M. margaritifera* 154 × 63 mm., and several others not much smaller.

If the 100-year estimate of longevity in *M. margaritifera* is correct, it is the longest-lived invertebrate known, exceeding under wild conditions the 80–85-year record for the actinian *Cereus* in captivity (Ashworth and Annandale, 1904; Stephenson, 1935; Comfort, 1956). A life-span of this order in the wild would imply an exceedingly low adult mortality. Freshwater mussels are known to be attacked by rodents and birds, and *M. margaritifera* has also been fished for many centuries by man, often in a destructive manner. A direct determination of age-group mortality in marked shells does not seem to have been undertaken, either in fished or unfished rivers.

The upper limit of life-span in other European Naiades cannot be determined with certainty from shell sculpture, because of the falling-off of growth at high ages. In some stations a virtual plateau of size is probably reached. In general large shells represent a high growth-rate rather than extreme age: from the counting of rings, the normal maximum (in *Unio* and *Anodonta*) is probably not much more than 20–30 years. Haranghy (Haranghy, Balász and Burg, 1962) has described senile involutional changes in the gonad of *Anodonta*.

The Distribution of Senescence

The supposed longevity of *Tridacna* has already been mentioned, together with the fact that nothing whatever is known about its real life-span. The same applies to many large marine pelecypods, whose probable age can only be discussed when we know something of their growth-rate.

The pelecypods also illustrate the risks of purely ideal and mathematical representations of growth-pattern. Pseudo-specific size from environmental causes is common. In *Siliqua* (Weymouth, 1931), some populations reach an apparent limiting size, cease altogether to grow thereafter, and die early: this, like Fischer-Piette's observation on limpets (1939), might suggest that a senile process is at work. Wild limpets apparently die while in active growth, but those which grow fastest die earliest (Fig. 51). Other molluscan populations have growth records which, though fitted for practical purposes to an asymptotic curve, actually give observed readings in the highest age groups which lie well above such a curve, and indicate that in these groups growth is continuing (Weymouth, 1931). There is an obvious objection to the use of growth-rings to measure age, however, if conclusions are then to be drawn about continuing growth—arrest of growth lasting for years would leave no record of itself in this system of notation. The results obtained by the use of the ring method in pelecypods have so far been reasonably consistent (see Newcombe, 1936). The validity of growth-rings as annual markers requires careful confirmation in each population examined, however (Haskings, 1954). Hopkins (1930) found that in *Venus mercenaria* growth was continuing actively at 20 years. The oldest specimens aged by growth-rings were in general not the largest shells. Some small examples had reached an estimated age of 40 years, and appeared to have grown abnormally slowly. This observation, like Fischer-Piette's (1939) and Weymouth's (1931) findings, should lead to a great deal of caution in regarding the life-span of any mollusc as indeterminate in the same sense as that of actinians.

2·6 *Senescence in Wild Populations*

Senescence as a potential part of the individual life-cycle is, as we have seen, widespread: in discussing the evolution of senile processes, however, it is important to know how far it really occurs in wild animals. The weight of evidence suggests that senescence in the wild is rare but not unknown. Its commonest form is undoubtedly the pseudo-senescence which follows reproduction, but genuine senescence analogous to that of man is occasionally reached, at least by individuals, while there are probably some forms in which it is normally reached. If our observation of animal life-cycles were confined to small birds and mammals in the wild, however, we should probably not recognize senescence as an entity except in ourselves.

2·6·1 VERTEBRATES

Although data from bird and small mammal populations have perhaps led to an overstatement of the case against 'natural' senescence, old age is undoubtedly a relatively rare or very rare termination to the life-cycle of vertebrates studied in the field—as it is for man in societies where medical and economic conditions are bad. For large numbers of animal species, the typical curve is one in which a high or very high infant mortality-rate is succeeded by a high adult mortality-rate which does not increase with age. These species, even when they are capable of senescence, never reach it. This type of curve has been repeatedly demonstrated in population studies (see Lack, 1954). Whereas in voles kept in the laboratory the survival curve approximates to that of man (Leslie and Ranson, 1940, Fig. 52), in wild voles (Hinton, 1925, 1926; Elton, 1942) and in *Peromyscus* (Burt, 1940) senescence is never observed, judging from the state of the teeth and bones of recent and fossil animals. In some populations the vole must be regarded as an annual (Elton, 1942). Tooth wear is a reliable index of age in short-tailed shrews, those over 2 years of age being edentulous, but age limitation by this mechanical form of senescence is more potential than actual since few survive to exhibit it. They may survive in captivity up to 33 months (Pearson, 1945).

The log-linear pattern of decline in survivorship is highly characteristic of birds. It has been demonstrated in the blackbird, song-thrush, robin, starling and lapwing (Lack, 1943a, b, c), redstart (Buxton, 1950), American robin (Farner, 1945) and herring gull (Marshall, 1947). In a series of robins ringed by

Lack (1943a), 111 out of 144 leaving the nest (77 per cent) died in the first year. This compares with a maximum recorded age of 11 years, which is occasionally reached in the wild state. The succeeding annual mortality was at a steady rate approaching 50 per cent. A survivorship curve for lapwings (*Vanellus vanellus*) calculated from 1333 birds is closely fitted by a line

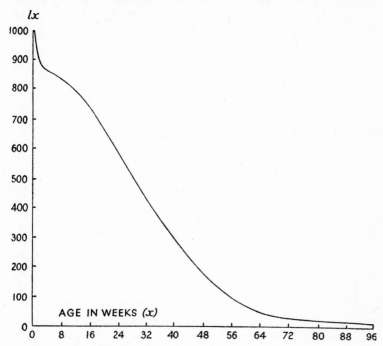

FIG. 52.—Smoothed survival curve for the vole *Microtus agrestis* in captivity (from Leslie and Ranson, 1940).

corresponding to a constant mortality of 40 per cent per annum (Kraak, Rinkel and Hoogerheide, 1940; Lack, 1950). The rates of mortality for most birds which have been studied appear to fall between 30 and 60 per cent per annum. Very much lower figures have been recorded for large sea birds such as cormorants (Kortlandt, 1942) in which the mortality was found to decline from 17 per cent before fledging to an annual rate of 4 per cent between the third and twelfth years. The annual mortality in one species of albatross (*Diomedea epomophora*) is only 3 per cent. Such birds may well live to reach senescence, if their life-span is 50 years. But considerable evidence has accumulated, chiefly from ringing studies, to show that the expectation of life of some wild birds actually increases with age. Although the total of ringed birds recovered in Europe does not exceed 10,000 per year, a few individuals are known to have survived for longer than could be expected if the early mortality were maintained. R. Perry (1953) gives records of this kind (redwing—*Turdus musicus*, 17+ years; goldfinch—*Carduelis carduelis*, 16+ years; meadow pipit—*Anthus pratensis*, 13 years) all of them in species which have mean annual survivals of the order of 50 per cent (Lack, 1950). A ringed starling (*Sturnus vulgaris*) has been re-taken after 18 years. The probability of such records being obtained as a result of chance, bearing in mind how few birds are ringed, is very low indeed. An almost exactly similar situation has been observed in the human population of the Punjab, where, in spite of a very heavy early and adult mortality, very old individuals are not uncommon, and those who survive beyond middle life have an expectation of life comparable to that in Western Europe (Yacob and Swaroop, 1945).

In lizards, the wild mortality-rate declines with increasing age (Sergeev, 1939): this result agrees with the ecological studies of Stebbings (Stebbings and Robinson, 1946; Stebbings, 1948) on *Sceleporus graciosus* in the wild. A very high proportion of the population was found to consist of lizards 6 to 9 years old (30 per cent), and there were signs of a decreasing force of mortality with age. In some cases the decrease may be even steeper. In some vertebrates the enormous infant mortality would completely overshadow subsequent trends in any life-table based upon a cohort at birth: in the mackerel, for instance (Sette, 1943), survival to the 50 mm. stage is less than 0·0004 per cent.

There are a certain number of apparent instances where senescence occurs as a regular phenomenon in wild populations of animals, both vertebrate and invertebrate, quite apart from occasional records of 'old' individuals (Bourlière, 1959). Murie (1944), from the examination of the skulls of 608 mountain sheep (*Ovis dalli*), constructed a life-table in which the death-rate was minimal between 1½ and 5 years of age, and climbed thereafter. The main deaths in old and young sheep appear to have been due to predation by wolves. The Arctic fin whales studied by Wheeler (1934) appeared to undergo an increase in mortality after the fifteenth year of age (in females); the apparent increase may however have been the result of the failure of the older specimens to return from their winter quarters to the regions where they can be caught and recorded. A good many larger carnivores and herding animals probably survive occasionally into old age in the wild state, though death must as a rule occur very early in the process of declining resistance. It is evidently impossible, in population studies, to assume either a constant mortality with age or a mortality increasing with increasing age, without some prior evidence of the behaviour of similar forms.

The 'normal' or 'wild' pattern of mortality in man is, of course, an abstraction, since even man in modern urban society is, biologically speaking, living 'in the wild', albeit after much social and behavioural adaptation. Early and primitive human societies almost certainly resembled in their ageing behaviour those populations of animals which occasionally reach old age, and in which the force of mortality shows some decrease during middle adult life. This is the pattern one would expect in social animals, where the survival of certain experienced individuals has probably a positive survival-value for the group, although in man the adaptation has been expressed in increasing capacity for abstract thought and social organization, rather than in increasing longevity *per se*. Although one may guess that early man occasionally reached the point at which his powers of homoeostasis began to fail through age, he must have died through environmental pressure, like Murie's sheep, very early in the process. Out of 173 palaeolithic and mesolithic individuals whose age could be determined, only three (all males) appeared to have been older than 50 years, and none much older (Vallois, 1937). Palaeolithic man in the Chinese deposits normally died from violence at a presenile age (Wiedenreich, 1939). In rather more civilized societies, the fall in mortality with increasing age becomes more evident: according to Lack (1943a, 1954) the curve of mortality based on the ages given in Roman funerary inscriptions (Macdonnell, 1913) is much like that for birds. Hufeland's (1798) and Silbergleit's (Vischer, 1947) figures (Fig. 9) illustrate further stages in the transition to the rectangular survival curve of modern societies in privileged countries: many other examples have been collected by Dublin and his fellow-actuaries (1949).

2·6·2 INVERTEBRATES

Senescence also occurs in the wild in some invertebrates, though it is often probably of the type of the 'parental' deaths of shotten

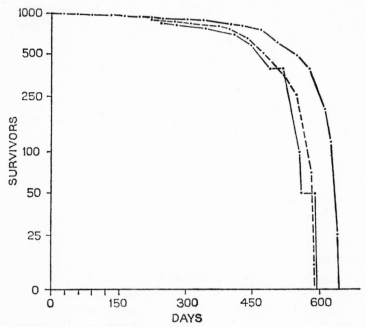

FIG. 53.—Corrected survival curves for three groups of ascidians which first appeared in August, September and October, 1957. · ——————— · : Group A, appearing in August. · - - - - - - - - - - - · : Group B, appearing in September. .... : Group C, appearing in October. For the sake of clarity curves B and C have not been carried back to the origin (from Goodbody, 1962).

eels. Senescence in one form or another has been invoked to account for the fixity of size and life-span in some freshwater gastropods (Sewell, 1924; van Cleave, 1934, 1935). The figures of Fischer-Piette (1939), relating longevity inversely to growth-rate in *Patella*, also suggest the operation of senescence. It very probably occurs in the long-lived sexual forms of social insects, such as termite primaries, and has been found to contribute to the mortality of worker bees (Ribbands, 1952). Among other insects, Jackson (1940) observed a factor of senescence in tsetse flies (*Glossina*) occurring only during the rainy season, when the life-span of the flies is longer. Dowdeswell, Fisher and Ford (1940) infer the possibility of a decline in the viability of butter-flies (*Polyommatus icarus*) throughout imaginal life. The position in insects is considerably complicated by the existence of specialized overwintering forms. Overwintering Gerrids show changes in the muscles which appear to precede natural death—mechanical wear of the rostrum, which occurs in old insects, is never far enough advanced to explain their decease (Guthrie, 1953). Cladocera and Amphipoda, together with other small crustaceans, tend to exhibit constant specific age in the laboratory, and may also do so in the wild state. In a natural population of *Corophium volutator* (Watkin, 1941) the mortality in females rose sharply after maturity.

Several genera of rotifers also exhibit well-defined specific age in culture (Pearl and Doering, 1923; Pearl and Miner, 1935; Lansing, 1942, 1947a, b, 1948) and almost certainly undergo senescence with significant frequency in the wild state. A population of the tube-building *Floscularia* marked in the wild with carmine underwent a linear decline, followed by a steep increase in mortality in the final survivors (Edmonson, 1945): the curve obtained in this marking experiment was not far different from those obtained in laboratory populations of rotifers.

~ 3 ~

SENESCENCE IN PROTOZOA

3·1 *Individual Cells*

MUCH theoretical study was devoted during the last century to the 'immortality' of protozoans, and their insusceptibility to senescence, following the concepts put forward by Weismann. It was considered that in unicellular organisms generally, and in populations of metazoan cells undergoing division without differentiation, the product of a cell's division is always a pair of daughter cells having the same age status, and destined each to lose its identity in another division. This theory makes very important assumptions about the nature of the copying processes which underlie cell division. In the majority of cases to which it was applied, the assumptions are probably correct, although there seem to have been no direct experiments designed to show whether, in a given protozoan population, the diagram of lineages shows any tendency to segregate the deaths of individual cells towards its edges, as in a metazoan genealogy.

Weismann had been impressed (1882) that in protozoa there is no death because there is no corpse. 'Natural death' of individuals (often apparently from strictly endogenous causes) does occur in protozoa, as Jennings (1945) has shown (see below); and the assumption that there is no unrenewable matter at cell division is not universally true; in many forms, especially those producing swarm spores, there may be a substantial corpse, at least as tangible as the rejected parental shell of the dividing radiolarian. This is less often demonstrably the case in somatic cells, and the analogy between strictly acellular organisms and tissue cells cannot now be whole-heartedly maintained: it is still generally held, however, that the outcome of a protozoan cell division is a pair of rejuvenated and infant cells rather than ? mother and a daughter of different seniority.

Senescence in Protozoa

The indeterminacy of cell lineages has lately been attacked with some ferocity, though on grounds of political philosophy rather than experimental evidence (Lyepeschinskaya, 1950). The question legitimately arises, however, particularly but not only in ciliates, how far the renewal of structures at mitosis is evenly distributed between the resulting cells. (Taylor, 1958; Mortimer and Johnston, 1959). Child (1915) noticed that in *Stentor* one of the progeny retains the old, while the other forms a new, peristome. From experiments he concluded that this made no difference to the age status of the inheritors, both being equally 'young'. The criterion of 'youth', however, was high susceptibility to cyanide poisoning. The critical experiment of making a genealogical table to determine the order of death of the fission products over several generations on the pattern of Sonneborn's (1930) *Stenostomum* experiments does not appear to have been carried out.

True senescence, and a marked difference in age status between mother and progeny, certainly appears to occur in suctorians. Korschelt (1922) noticed this in several forms (*Acanthocystis, Spirochona, Podophrya*, etc.), while in *Tokophrya* the parent organism's life-span can be measured, and is increased by underfeeding (Rudzinska, 1952). In a far greater number of cases there are signs that the copying process at division only produces a new structure additional to one which already exists, not two new, or one new and one manifestly renovated, structure. The theoretical interest of this process (in *Euglypha*) and its bearing on protozoan 'age' has been noticed before (Severtsov, 1934). In such cases, either the structure does not deteriorate with time, or it is maintained continuously during life, or its possession must ultimately confer a disadvantage on one or other of the division products.

Whereas in some protozoa organelles, axostyles, flagella and cilia are visibly resorbed or shed at fission, and new ones produced for each fission product, in others, especially in ciliates, maternal organelles, flagella and other structures are shared between the progeny, being taken over by one daughter cell while copies are developed in the other. Of two closely-related species of *Spirotrichonympha* infesting termites, for example, one divides longitudinally in the normal flagellate manner, while in the other division is transverse, the anterior daughter receiving all the extranuclear organelles of the parent cell except the axostyle, while new organs are formed for the posterior daughter. The axostyle is resorbed (Cleveland, 1938). The possibility that the 'inheritance' of organelles may modify the age status of the inheritor certainly merits re-investigation.

3·2 *The 'Senescence' of Clones*

A large part of the literature included in the bibliographies of senescence deals with the presence or absence of 'ageing' in protozoan clones. Maupas (1886) appears to have been the first to draw an analogy between somatic ageing in metazoa and the behaviour of protozoan populations. He predicted that such populations would display a life-cycle including a phase analogous to metazoan senescence, and ending in the death of the population, unless nuclear reorganization by conjugation, or some similar mechanism, brought about the 'rejuvenation' of the stock. For many years a vigorous competition was conducted between proto-zoologists in seeing how many asexual generations of *Paramecium, Eudorina*, and similar creatures they could rear. In the course of this process much nonsense was written about 'potential immortality', but a great deal was learnt about protozoan reproduction and culture methods. It became evident that some clones deteriorate and others, including somatic cells such as fibroblasts in tissue-culture, do not. Calkins (1919) in a classical study showed that strains of *Uroleptus mobilis* kept in isolation culture without conjugation underwent senescence characterized by falling-off of growth-potential, degeneration of nuclei, and ultimate loss of micronucleus. These strains ultimately became extinct. Conjugation at any stage of the process, and probably also endomixis, produced an immediate reversion to normal, regardless of whether the conjugates came from old or young isolation strains. Sonneborn (1938) succeeded, by selection of strains of *Paramecium* in which endomixis was long delayed, in breeding a race which no longer exhibited any kind of nuclear reorganization. These strains invariably died after 4 or 5 months. Rizet (1953) has recently reported similar results with an Ascomycete kept in continuous vegetative reproduction.

On the other hand, Bélár (1924) maintained *Actinophrys sol* in isolation culture, without the occurrence of paedogamy, for 1244 generations over 32 months, and observed no decline in the rate of cell division. Beers (1929) kept *Didinium nasutum* for 1384 generations without conjugation or endomixis. Hartman (1921) kept *Eudorina elegans* in active asexual reproduction for 8 years. Woodruff's oldest culture of *Paramecium aurelia* persisted for over 15,000 generations but was undergoing autogamy. The conclusion must be that some clones are stable while others are not.

More light is thrown on this problem by the work of Jennings (1945) upon clones of *Paramecium bursaria*. He found that in this species the life-cycle fell into well-defined phases of growth, sexual reproduction by conjugation with other clones, and decline. The length and character of these phases differed substantially from clone to clone. In the decline phase the death of individual cells, and especially of the progeny of conjugation between old clones, becomes very common. The vitality and viability of the progeny of conjugation, even when the conjugant clones are young, varies greatly, and a very high proportion of ex-conjugants normally die. This mortality is highest among the progeny of conjugation between related clones. Of 20,478 ex-conjugants, 10,800 (52·7 per cent) died before undergoing their fifth successive cell division, while 29·7 per cent died without dividing at all. Most conjugations produced some nonviable clones, some weakly clones capable of limited survival, and a few exceptionally strong clones, some of which appeared capable of unlimited asexual reproduction. It is from these strong races that the population of laboratory cultures is normally obtained.

Jennings concluded as follows: 'Death did not take origin in consequence of organisms becoming multicellular . . . it occurs on a vast scale in the Protozoa, and it results from causes which are intrinsic to the organism. Most if not all clones ultimately die if they do not undergo some form of sexual reproduction. . . . Rejuvenation through sexual reproduction is a fact . . . yet conjugation produces, in addition to rejuvenated clones, vast numbers of weak, pathological or abnormal clones whose predestined fate is early death. The rejuvenating function of conjugation is distinct from, and in addition to, its function as a producer of variation by redistribution of genes. Among the clones produced (by conjugation) there are seemingly, in some species, some clones of such vigour that they may continue vegetatively for an indefinite period, without decline or death' (Jennings, 1945).

Some authors have regarded the increased proportion of weak and non-viable conjugants of old clones as the outcome of an accumulation of unfavourable mutations. Comparable effects (Banta, 1914; Banta and Wood, 1937) have been described in clones of *Daphnia*. This was long since suggested by Raffel (1932) on the basis of *Paramecium* experiments. The type of lineal 'senescence' which occurs in *Paramecium* is in some respects analogous to the processes which are familiar in inbred stocks reproducing sexually, from *Drosophila* to domestic cattle (Regan, Mead and Gregory, 1947), and described under the general title of inbreeding depression, but differs from it in that in clones the accumulation of mutations, rather than the segregation of existing genes and the loss of the advantages of heterozygy, have been held to be involved. The mortality among the progeny of autogamy in *Paramecium* is directly related to the length of time during which autogamy has been previously suppressed (Pierson, 1938). The time scale of the group 'life-cycle' is modified by a great many physical and chemical agents—on the other hand, methylcholanthrene, normally a mutagenic agent, delays the decline of *Paramecium* clones (Spencer and Melroy, 1949). Sonneborn has found (Sonneborn and Schneller, 1960a, b) that clonal senescence in *Paramecium* depends, as other workers have foreseen (Fauré-Frémiet, 1953), on the peculiar mechanism in ciliates whereby the germinal and vegetative functions of the nucleus are divided between two separate structures. When *Paramecium* divides after a sexual process, the new nucleus of each daughter cell again divides into two. One of these products, the micronucleus, which reaches the anterior end of the cell, has the normal diploid number of chromosomes, and is apparently concerned solely with conveying the genotype: it is, in other words, the 'germ-plasm'. The other portion, the macronucleus, controls the metabolism of the cell. It becomes highly polyploid, and at subsequent cell divisions, while the micronucleus divides evenly in the normal manner of nuclei, the macronucleus distributes its chromosomes at random to the daughter macronucleus arising from it. Because of the enormous number of sets which it contains, every cell in the earlier divisions has a fair chance of getting its quota, but with the passage of time more and more daughters receive an unbalanced set and a reduced physiological repertoire, and a chromosome once lost cannot be restored from the micronucleus except by sexual division—conjugation or autogamy. In the later stages of clonal senescence even sexual division is affected and abnormal or non-viable products increase. Sonneborn suggests that this is not due to the accumulation of mutations, since it can be prevented by periodic autogamy, even though this does not alter the genotype: it appears to be due to injury inflicted upon the micronucleus itself through the abnormal intracellular conditions produced by the defective macronucleus. In ciliates the germ-plasm has to live in the cell where the processes of somatic maintenance are carried out, and it is therefore unusually exposed. This is probably a unique situation—it does not even apply in other ciliates—and the division of function between vegetative and germinal nuclei is confined to this group. The existence of presumed cytoplasmic mutations, although there is no evidence to relate them to metazoan senescence as such, might be far more relevant to it than studies of protozoan clones. A kindred subject, that of somatic aneuploidy, is discussed in 6.1.3 (p. 222). It is in any case probably misleading to identify the decline of protozoan cultures with the metazoan senescence which it superficially resembles; it is doubtful if analogies can properly be drawn between acellular organisms and metazoan cells, and the only relevance of the whole question of 'ageing' in protozoan clones to ageing in the metazoan body lies in the light which it might possibly throw upon the effects of cell division in renewing expendable enzyme systems. There is no special reason, upon the present evidence, why the 'senescence' of *Paramecium* should continue to figure as extensively as it has done in treatises devoted to gerontology.

The 'senescence' of some lines of plants in vegetative propagation apparently depends on the accumulation of exogenous viruses which hamper vigour (Crocker, 1939)—other agriculturally important varieties have been propagated vegetatively for years or centuries without deterioration. The accumulation of exogenous viruses itself raises interesting questions in regard to the possible accumulation of other, endogenous, intra- or extranuclear self-propagating materials.

Not all senescence or degeneration in clones, however, can be put down to the peculiarities of protozoa or to the action of viruses. A striking example of such a degeneration has been studied at Oxford by K. G. McWhirter, to whom I am much indebted for his unpublished observations on it. This is the condition called 'June Yellows', which affects strawberry plants propagated by runners, and impairs the formation of chloroplasts. It appears simultaneously in all plantations of a clone, even when they are geographically separated, and progresses in jumps, all the plants of the same clonal (but not individual) age passing synchronously from stage to stage. Usually in the end the clone dies out. The condition cannot be transmitted to adult plants by grafting. Transmission to seedlings is ambilinear through both egg-cell and pollen. In the progeny of crosses between clones at different stages of degeneration it is matroclinous: seedlings of very degenerate 'mothers' deteriorate most rapidly. As a clone degenerates, the tendency to transmit 'yellows' to its offspring increases. The factor or factors remain latent in some clones, but 'yellows' may appear after varying intervals in some of the selfed or crossed seedlings obtained from these clones, thus showing a latency reminiscent of that of the presumed oncogenic plasmagenes. This similarity has been pointed out before (Darlington, 1948; Darlington and Mather, 1949).

The behaviour of this degeneration is like that of a mutation which is in part cytoplasmically controlled. Such conditions are characterized by a lag-phase, by simultaneous appearance in all the members of a clone, non-infectivity, passage through a series of stable phenotypic stages, and interaction with growth and reproductive hormones. In some of McWhirter's material, 'yellows' appeared to be aggravated during the flowering period, although it may occur in seedlings long before flowering.

4

THE INFLUENCE OF GENETIC CONSTITUTION ON SENESCENCE AND LONGEVITY

4·1 *Inheritance of Life-Span*

4·1·1 GENERAL

IT is evident in any comparison of laboratory stocks that differences of specific age are to some degree 'inherited' (Pearl and Parker, 1922; Gonzales, 1923; Gruneberg, 1951, Fig. 54), but detailed genetic knowledge of the manner of their inheritance is not plentiful. Much variation in life-span occurs between inbred lines. This variation is often related to a single heritable predisposition to die of cancer, renal disease, or some other single cause: in these cases it is often short life, not long life, which is capable of genetic selection in the homozygote. Bittner (1937) showed that in some cases it is possible to transpose the longevities of strains of mice by cross-suckling. In other cases, secondary causes, such as restricted capacity for activity in deformed stocks, affect the life-span. In a stock of mice bred by Strong (Strong, 1936; Strong and Smith, 1936) longevity increased the apparent incidence of disease by allowing animals to reach the cancer age. Two factors appear at first sight to be involved in inherited longevity—absence of genetic predisposition to specific causes of death, and a less definite quantity ('vigour') which contributes to Darwinian fitness because it is usually expressed both in fertility and in longevity. It is by no means certain that these factors are distinct. 'Vigour' itself may in fact represent either the covering-up of deleterious recessives by heterozygosis, or a state of over-dominance, in which the heterozygote is inherently more vigorous than either homozygote.

165

Hereditary factors in human longevity have often been sought. Pearl and Pearl (1934a, b) found, for instance, that the summed ages at death of the six immediate ancestors of centenarians and nonagenarians were significantly greater than in a control series of the relatives of individuals not selected for longevity. 86·6 per cent of long-lived (> 70) subjects had at least one long-lived parent, while 48·5 per cent of nonagenarians

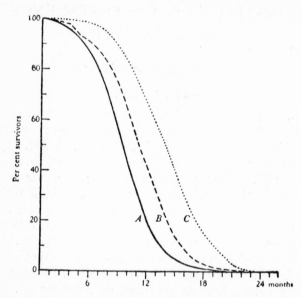

FIG. 54.—Survival curves of mice in laboratory culture—breeding females. Curve A based on 241 *dba* females, curve B on 730 Bittner albinos, curve C on 1350 Marsh albinos (from Gruneberg, 1951).

and 53·4 per cent of centenarians had two such parents, all these figures being significantly higher than in the control series. Kallman and Sander (1948, 1949) found that in 1062 pairs of twins the mean difference in longevity between dizygotic twin individuals was twice as great as in monozygotics. These and other studies indicate that longevity is 'hereditary', but unfortunately give little light on its genetics. When mares were grouped by parental longevity, the calculated means show differences of less than twice the standard error in favour of the groups with one long-lived parent; 113 mares with two long-lived parents had a mean expectation of life at 4 years of $18 \cdot 07 \pm 0 \cdot 58$ years, which is significantly more than the global mean, or the mean for any other group (Comfort, 1958a). Beeton and Pearson (1901) studied the longevity records of Quaker families, and found that the sib-sib correlation of longevity was nearly twice the parent-offspring correlation, in those individuals who died at 21 years of age or later, but thas there was a far lower sib-sib correlation between those dying at minors. Haldane (1949) has pointed out that this is the type of correlation which would be expected where the heterozygote is fitter in the Darwinian sense than either homozygote: insofar as natural selection operates to eliminate homozygosis, not to promote it, such fitness must imply a higher correlation between sibs in an equilibrium population than between parent and child. In any case, the degree of parent-child correlation observed by Beeton and Pearson is only a quarter that between parental and filial statures in comparable studies.

Dublin and his colleagues (1949) have summarized most of the historic studies on the inheritance of longevity in man. They conclude that the popular idea of inheritance as a factor in longevity is probably correct, that the evidence from actuarial studies is heavily vitiated by all kinds of environmental influences, and that the order of advantage to the sons of long-lived fathers is small compared with the secular increase in life-span during recent generations. The difference in life expectation at 25 years between those with better and poorer parental longevity records is between 2 and 4 years—this compares with a gain of $6 \cdot 7$ years in the general expectation of life at 25 years in the U.S.A. between 1900 and 1946. 'It may be well, as has been suggested, to seek advantages in longevity by being careful in the choice of one's grandparents, but the method is not very practicable. It is simpler and more effective to adapt the environment more closely to man' (Dublin, 1949).

It does not follow from these considerations that longer life cannot be obtained in a given population by selective breeding, and in mice this has, in fact, been done (Strong and Smith, 1936). There may well be single-gene characters where the homozygote is significantly longer lived. 'Vigour', on the other hand, which is a correlate of both longevity and fertility, and hence of Darwinian fitness, is likely in most cases to be an expression of heterozygosis, and one would not expect to be able necessarily to produce abnormally long-lived animals by inbreeding long-lived parents.

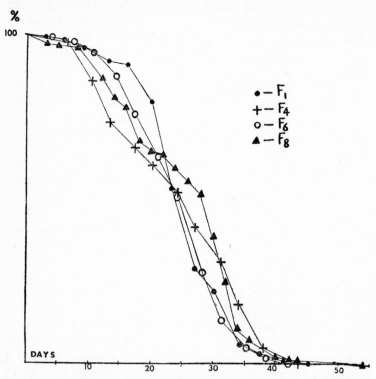

Fig. 55.—*Drosophila subobscura*. Strain K. Survival curves of flies raised in each generation from eggs laid by adults which had passed the thirtieth day of imaginal life (Comfort, 1953). Compare Fig. 56.

Agricultural genetics, like natural selection, has for the most part attempted to increase lifetime production averages by increasing early output of eggs or offspring. Greenwood (1932) found that the fertility and hatchability of hens' eggs decline with age of the parent to such an extent that attempts to improve the stock by breeding from long-lived birds were economically impracticable. Apart from the obvious difficulty of breeding for long life in any animal with a substantial post-reproductive period, which involves rearing all the progeny of large numbers of animals throughout life, the consequence of inbreeding *per se*, and the tendency of inbred laboratory stocks to reach a very stable equilibrium life-span (Pearl and Parker, 1922) militate against any such experiment. In Pearl's own experiments (Pearl, 1928) the long- and short-lived *Drosophila* segregates were identified in the F_1 by subsidiary, anatomical characters known to be associated with the desired lines. In *Drosophila subobscura* of the structurally homozygous Küssnacht strain, which had been in culture for about three years, and had reached an equilibrium life-span considerably shorter than that of wild-caught flies, breeding for 8 generations over 1 year exclusively from eggs laid after the thirtieth day of parental life produced no significant alteration in mean imaginal longevity (Comfort, 1953) (Fig. 35).

The inheritance of long life in man is presumably bound up with the inheritance of 'general health' (Pearson and Elderton, 1913; Pearl, 1927), an element which is not more susceptible to analysis than 'vigour', though it has been partially described in terms of response to stress (Selye, 1946). Robertson and Ray (1920) found that in a population of mice the relatively long-lived individuals formed a stable sub-group, displaying the least variation and the highest resistance to disturbing factors. In such a group the growth-rate tends to be a measure of 'general health', and rapid rather than retarded growth correlates with longevity. In other studies on groups of animals living under standardized conditions, rate of growth and length of life have been found to vary independently (Sherman and Campbell, 1935). The relation between growth-rate and vigour in a mixed population requires to be distinguished from the effect of growth retardation by dietary means in a homogeneous population; here the retarded growers live longer. As McCay (1952) points out, much early work on the relation between growth-rate and longevity was vitiated by this confusion in experimental planning.

4·1·2 PARENTAL AGE

The *age of the mother* is known in certain cases to modify the longevity of her offspring. This influence apparently includes a wide range of dissimilar effects, some strictly 'genetic', and others operating at various stages in the process of embryogenesis, or, in mammals, on into lactation. Certain of these effects appear only in the F_1, while others, like the factor described by Lansing in rotifers, which leads to a decreasing life-span in successive generations of clones propagated exclusively from old individuals, appear to be cumulative and reversible (p. 125).

The general question of maternal age effects in genetics is beyond the scope of this book. It has been reviewed (Miner, 1954) in a valuable symposium. In mammals the age of the mother exerts an influence on the vigour of the progeny which appears to vary greatly in direction and extent, even within a species. Sawin (in Miner, 1954) found that in one strain of rabbits, the early (< 6 months) mortality was lowest in the progeny of young mothers, and increased throughout maternal life, while in another, larger, strain it reached a minimum in the progeny of mothers 18 months old. These changes were not correlated with any differences in lactation or maternal weight. Suntzeff, Cowdry and Hixon (1962) found that in mice there was no decline in longevity on repeated breeding from old mothers, but there was a significant increase in the age at which daughters became pregnant. Jalavisto (1950, 1959) found evidence that in man the expectation of life decreases with increasing maternal, but not paternal, age. The percentage of abnormal offspring is greatest in litters born to young guinea pigs (Wright, 1926) and elderly women (Murphy in Miner, 1954). It is possible that the association of mongolism with high parental age is a reflection not of increasing foetal abnormality, but a decrease to the point of viability in an abnormality which, at younger maternal ages, is lethal (Penrose in Miner, 1954). In some celebrated experiments upon mouse leukaemia, McDowell and his co-workers have shown that when susceptible males are crossed with resistant females, the age of onset of leukaemia in the hybrid F_1 is significantly retarded in mice born to, or suckled by, old as compared with young mothers. At the same time, the mean longevity of mice which die of causes other than leukaemia is also greatest in the progeny and nurslings of old mothers (McDowell, Taylor and

Broadfort, 1951). Strong (in Miner, 1954) has described a factor influencing the latent period of sarcoma production after injection of methylcholanthrene into mice, which appears, like Lansing's rotifer longevity factor, to be cumulative—a line derived from seventh to ninth litters in each generation had a significantly increased and increasing latent period compared with a line derived from first and second litters. Unlike Lansing's effect, this increase has not been shown to be reversible in the progeny of young members of the 'old' line. There is at present no evidence in mammals of any cumulative disadvantage in longevity accruing to 'youngest sons of youngest daughters'. In this connection Strong has however stressed, on a number of occasions, the need for further information on the relation between longevity and cumulative parental age in human genealogies. Such information is unfortunately hard to come by, and no large-scale study has yet been published. Comfort (1953) failed to find a comparable effect in *Drosophila*; but in houseflies the 30-day mortality of females rises from 50 per cent among offspring of 4-5 day old parents to 90–95 per cent in offspring from eggs laid at 27 days of age (Rockstein, 1958). The longevity of males was not affected. In *Drosophila*, Parsons (1962) found that variability in egg length and bristle characters increases with high maternal age. Lansing's effect has also been sought in the parthenogenetic Cladocera. The age of the mother affects the rate of development, and probably the longevity, of young *Daphnia*. Green (1954) recently found that the size of *Daphnia* at birth determines the instar in which maturity occurs, the largest becoming mature earliest. The birth size itself depends upon maternal age, being highest (in *D. magna*) in the third brood. Since the pre-mature phase is the part of the life-cycle in which most variation occurs, the mature phase being usually of fixed length, early developers might be expected to be significantly shorter-lived than late. Fritsch (1956) has compared the longevity under carefully standardized conditions of successive generations of *Daphnia* raised wholly from first, third, and sixth hatchings, and finds no significant trend in any of the orthoclones, the mean life-span in all remaining at about 30 days.

The critical issue with regard to mutational theories of ageing is the presence or absence of a *paternal* age effect. The Stud Book could be expected to yield useful material for such studies. The search for parental age effects on the life-span of man is complicated by the high correlation between ages of spouses (Sonneborn, 1960; Jalavisto, 1959); there is no such correlation between ages of sire and dam in horse-breeding, and both mares and stallions commonly remain at stud to advanced ages.

Vitt (1949) has claimed that the longevity and racing performance of thoroughbred horses are substantially influenced by the age of both dam and sire, and that impairment of vigour by the use of old breeding stock is cumulative. He found that in a sample of 100 mares from vol. 1 of the General Stud Book, the progeny of dams 12 years old or less developed more slowly, judged by the age at first foaling, and lived longer $(e_{x=4} = 19 \cdot 5$ years) than the progeny of dams aged 13 or more $(e_{x=4} = 16 \cdot 4$ years). Absolute figures and standard errors are not cited, and it is not clear whether the estimates are corrected for losses or based on the distribution of recorded deaths alone. Vitt also compared the fertility and racing form of foals by old and young stallions, and concluded that there was an equally marked paternal age effect, the optimal performance being reached by the foals of stallions 8–16 years old out of mares 6–13 years old. Rather similar views have been expressed by other Russian mammal-breeders (Eidrigevits and Polyakov, 1953; Isupov, 1949; Ponomareva and Spitskaya, 1953; Pospelov, 1952; Zamyatin, Stolbova, Chugaeva and Kuznetsova, 1946).

In a large series of Stud Book figures, the lives of mares were distributed (a) by age of dam at foaling, (b) by age of sire at covering, one year earlier, (c) by age of dam at foaling and sire at covering, where these fell in the same grouping interval. Of 1492 lives, 1342 were scored and grouped by age of dam, 1355 by age of sire, and 719 by both. (Comfort 1958a, b; 1959b, c). There was no significant difference in expectation of life between foals of mares under and over 13 years of age (< 12, $e_{x=4} = 16 \cdot 89$: > 13, $e_{x=4} = 16 \cdot 86$ years). With further subdivision the progeny of the oldest mares had the shortest lifespans, but the largest difference was less than twice its standard error. Still smaller differences were obtained for the same lives grouped by paternal age alone. Of the 719 lives grouped by age of both parents, those whose dam and sire were under 13 years old lived slightly longer $(17 \cdot 39 \pm 0 \cdot 36)$ than those whose parents were over 13 $(16 \cdot 45 \pm 0 \cdot 48; t \neq 2 \cdot 3, 0 \cdot 02 > p > 0 \cdot 01)$, and the difference was greater in the extreme segments of these groups (dam and sire $< 9, 17 \cdot 91 \pm 0 \cdot 47; > 16, 15 \cdot 71 \pm 0 \cdot 83;$ $t \neq 2 \cdot 3, 0 \cdot 02 > p > 0 \cdot 01)$. This difference is much smaller than that described by Vitt (1949) from maternal age alone, and is of the order of the difference between cohorts.

In a second series, the longest-lived group were the progeny of parents of 16 years and over, but the standard error was very large $(17 \cdot 26 \pm 1 \cdot 09)$: the 220 animals which were the progeny of two young parents had numerically the shortest life-spans $(16 \cdot 51 \pm 0 \cdot 52)$: none of the differences was significant, and all were in the reverse direction to those in the 1875–1880 sample.

121 mares got during or after their sire's 20th year by 3 long-lived stallions had a slightly, but not a significantly, higher expectation than the global mean $(16 \cdot 65 \pm 0 \cdot 57)$. Only 41 mares were got by the 3 selected stallions in or after their 16th year upon dams 16 years old or more; these had a mean expectation of life of $16 \cdot 29 \pm 0 \cdot 94$ years. By combining these mares with all the progeny in other samples of parents 16 years old or over, we obtained 154 lives, with $e_{x = 4} = 16 \cdot 45 \pm 0 \cdot 62$ years, which is less than any of the 3 global means, but not significantly so. These results, taken as a whole, seem to afford no evidence of any consistent effect of parental age on the longevity of mares.

4·2 *Heterosis or Hybrid Vigour*

Abnormally long-lived animals can regularly be produced by crossing certain pure lines, not themselves unusually long-lived, the effect being greatest in the hybrid F_1 and their offspring and declining rapidly on subsequent inbreeding. This is, in fact, the simplest method of increasing the specific age in many already inbred laboratory and domestic animals. Striking examples of this effect (heterosis) in increasing longevity have been recorded in mice. Gates (1926) by crossing Japanese waltzing with 'dilute brown' strains produced a generation which was still actively breeding at 2 years of age. Chai (1959) gives details of the longevity of such crosses. 'Super-mice' produced by heterosis develop precociously, reach a large size, and remain in active reproduction much longer than their parents, thereby exhibiting a combination of rapid growth with increased longevity analogous to that of the rapid growers described by Robertson

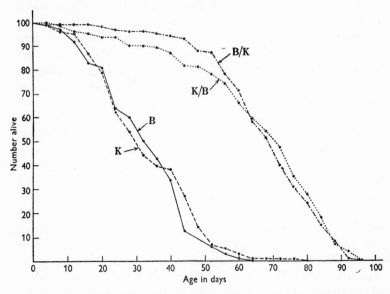

FIG. 56.—*Drosophila subobscura*—hybrid vigour and longevity. Survival curves for the inbred lines B and K, and for the reciprocal hybrids between them (sexes combined) (from Clarke and Maynard Smith, 1955).

and Ray (1920). An example of the same effect in *Drosophila* is shown in Fig. 56. The greater longevity of goldfinch-canary mules compared with the parent species is apparently well known to aviarists, and such techniques of crossing are of widespread agricultural and economic importance when applied to sheep or to plants. Vetukhiv (1957: Figs. 57–8) has shown that in *Drosophila* there is considerable heterosis in crosses between natural populations from different places.

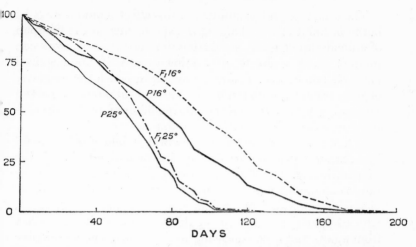

Fig. 57.—Survival curves of geographic populations of *Drosophila pseudo-obscura* and their hybrids. Summarized data for all parental populations and for all F_1 hybrids at 16° and at 25° C. Solid lines indicate parental populations, dashed lines—F_1 hybrids (from Vetukhiv, 1957).

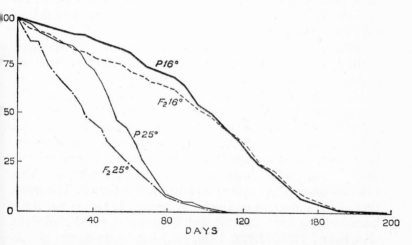

Fig. 58.—Survival curves of geographic populations of *Drosophila pseudo-obscura* and their hybrids. Summarized data for all parental populations and F_2 hybrids at 16° and at 25° C. Solid lines indicate parental populations, dashed lines—F_2 hybrids (from Vetukhiv, 1957).

The existence and magnitude of this effect should always be borne in mind in the planning of experiments on the life-span of animals drawn from closed laboratory stocks—such work can produce very seriously misleading results if unrecognized heterosis takes place. If an experiment in which the longevity of generations is compared begins with hybrid progeny, marked inbreeding depression can shorten the life-span of the succeeding generations if genetical precautions are not taken.

A fuller study of longevity in hybrids might provide useful information on the nature of 'constitutional vigour' in relation to growth-rate. The effect is variously explained. Some of the possible complications of heterosis in relation to the criteria of vigour are indicated by the findings of Rutman (1950, 1951), who compared the rates of methionine uptake in liver slices from a fast- and a slow-growing strain of rats. The methionine replacement rate in slices derived from the fast-growing strain was almost double that in the slow, but the growth-rate of the slow strain could be made to approach that of the fast by transposing the litters during suckling, and appeared to be controlled by a milk-borne factor. Interstrain hybrids at first showed a growth pattern like that of the mother, but later followed that of the faster-growing strain.

Although by a very elegant experiment J. and S. Maynard Smith (1954) have shown that in certain cases at least heterosis appears to result from orthodox heterozygy, the number of instances in which cytoplasmic and environmental factors also appear able to evoke vigour is increasing. This is largely a reflection of the very heterogeneous character of 'vigour'. Some years ago Borisenko (1939, 1941) reported an increase in vigour in the progeny of *Drosophila* matings where the inbred parents were reared under different environmental conditions. This observation does not appear to have been repeated. The question of the induction of vigour by non-genic means has since been most actively investigated by avowed anti-Mendelians (Kurbatov, 1951; Hašek, 1953, etc.) but by no means all the positive results come from this school. As far back as 1928, Parkes observed that mice suckled by rats exhibited an extraordinary overgrowth, which results simply from excessive nutrition. Marshak (1936) found evidence of a maternal cytoplasmic factor influencing the increase of growth-rate due to heterosis in mice. The increased vigour in progeny of pure-line ova transplanted to hybrid mothers (Kurbatov, 1951) is also found in transplanted foetuses (Venge, 1953). Hašek has claimed (1953) that when parabiosis is carried out between Rhode Island and Leghorn embryos in the egg, by an ingenious technique, the pullets occasionally show even greater vigour than the progeny of R.I.R. × Leghorn crosses. Without endorsing the sweeping theoretical claims based by the Russian school upon 'vegetative hybridization' of this type, it seems clear that the last word has yet to be said upon the nature of induced vigour, and that this can be of more than one kind. The whole problem is one which might be of considerable interest to gerontology, since in some cases 'vigour' appears capable of induction post-conceptually, or even post-natally. It is important to notice, however, that there is no clear evidence at present to show that the vigour and longevity obtainable by true heterosis are greater than those existing in *wild* strains. Heterosis should be regarded, in all probability, as the restoration of 'wild' vigour, whether by restoring heterozygy or by other processes, in lines which have lost that vigour through inbreeding. How far the results of heterosis can be superior to those of wildness, in longevity or otherwise, remains to be demonstrated.

4·3 *Sex Effects*

4·3·1 FEMININE ADVANTAGE

In most animals which have been studied, the male sex is the shorter lived. This is true in organisms as dissimilar as fish (Bidder, 1932; Wimpenny, 1953), spiders (Deevey and Deevey, 1945, Figs. 59, 60), *Drosophila* (Alpatov and Pearl, 1929; Bilewicz, 1953), *Habrobracon* (Georgiana, 1949), *Tribolium* (Park, 1945, Fig. 61), water-beetles (Blunck, 1924), houseflies (Rockstein and Lieberman, 1948) and man (Daw, 1961). In exceptional cases the preponderance of male mortality can be reversed. Thus Woolley (1946) found that in crosses between dba female and c57 male mice, the virgin females of the F_1 had a mean life of 27 and the males 29 months: in the reciprocal cross, the females lived 30 and the males 33 months. Males of *Rattus natalensis* outlive the females (Oliff, 1953). Darwin (1874) regarded the shorter life of the male as 'a natural and constitutional peculiarity due to sex alone'. Attempts have also been made to explain it in genetic terms (Geiser, 1924; Gowen,

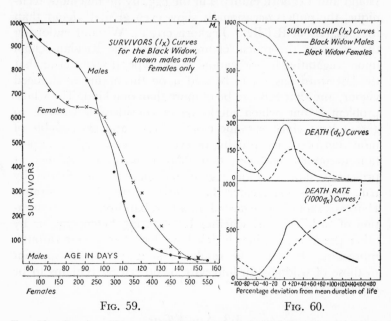

Fig. 59.

Fig. 60.

FIG. 59.—Survivorship curves for 82 males and 45 females of the black widow spider *Latrodectes mactans* (Fabr). Note that the male curve is shown to five times the time scale of the female curve (from Deevey and Deevey, 1945).

FIG. 60.—Survivorship, death and death-rate curves for the black widow. Note that the death curves are shown to twice the ordinate scale of the others (from Deevey and Deevey, 1945).

1931, 1934). Gowen constructed life-tables for *Drosophila* inter-sexes and triploids, and concluded from his results that chromosome imbalance in itself exerted an adverse effect on life-span. In inbred *Drosophila* lines any pattern of sex advantage may appear, depending on the genes present (Maynard Smith, 1959). In most of the forms where full life-tables have been made, the bias of mortality against the male follows the rule of greater vigour in the homogametic sex. McArthur and Baillie (1932) pointed out that if the lowered vitality of the male was due to greater homozygosis for adverse genes, the effect should be reversed in those forms where the female is heterogametic—notably lepidoptera and birds. From the studies of Landauer and Landauer on fowls (1931) and of Rau and Rau (1914) on saturnid moths, they could find no evidence of such a reversal. Adequate life-table studies are still very scarce in these groups. In crosses, the difference in vigour between homogametic and heterogametic sexes may certainly

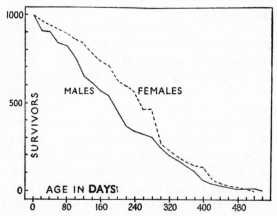

Fig. 61.—Survivorship curves for male and female *Tribolium madens* (radix of 1000 imagines) (from Park, 1945).

be so great that only the homogametic reaches maturity—thus Federley (1929) found that in certain interspecific crosses in hawk moths, only the males survived pupation, though in reciprocal crosses both sexes survived. Beside these studies, that of Pearl and Miner (1936) upon *Acrobasis caryae*, which is one of the few actuarially-constructed lepidopteran life-tables which have been published, and an extensive study by Woodruffe (1951) on the survival of the moth *Hofmanophila pseudospretella* under different environmental conditions both show a significantly higher female life-span. Alpatov and Gordeenko (1932), working on *Bombyx mori*, found no difference in longevity between unmated males and females, but a significantly longer male life in mated moths. Re-examining the results of Rau and Rau (1914) they concluded that in both *Samia cecropia* and *Calosamia promethea* the mated female had a shorter life-span than the male. This difference, however, might be due at least in part to the exhaustion of reserves by more frequent egg-laying in mated females. The life-span of the female *Aglia tau* is said to be the shorter (Metchnikoff, 1907).

Rey (1936) working on the non-feeding imago of the moth *Galleria mellonella*, found that the males lived up to twice as long as the females, the difference being unaffected by humidity but exaggerated at low temperatures. He assumes this to be 'the rule for lepidoptera'.

In poultry, it seems to be established that the female is the more viable and has the longer reproductive life (Pease, 1947) and observations such as those of McIlhenny on wild ducks (1940), which indicate an increase in the proportion of males with increasing age, are probably the result of differential risks. Male pigeons are reputedly the longer-lived sex (Levy, 1957). Longer life-span in males is also found in some other birds in the wild (Lack, 1954). In cyprinodont fishes, some of which have an atypical mechanism of sex-determination, evidence is inadequate, but Bellamy (1934) found no conspicuous sex difference in longevity in a small series. An example of longer life in the male teleost occurs in minnows (van Cleave and Markus, 1929) but this refers to a wild population. It seems altogether likely that where a sex difference in longevity is observed it arises from the sum of differences in metabolic rate and behavioural pattern—in other words, from physiological sexual dimorphism. A number of invertebrate metabolic studies support such a view (*Daphnia*, McArthur and Baillie, 1929a, b; *Drosophila*, Alpatov and Pearl, 1929), by indicating that the 'rate of living' in the male is in fact higher. The degree to which the inferior vitality of the male mammal results directly from the action of androgens has been discussed, and the whole question of male mortality reviewed at length, by Hamilton (1948). In man, the higher male mortality is present both *in utero* and in infancy. At later ages the question is, of course, complicated by social and occupational factors (Herdan, 1952). There are as yet no fully satisfactory human data upon the relative longevity of castrates, though their life-span is certainly not grossly inferior to that of normals. Many of the highest recorded ages in cats have occurred in gelt males (p. 61). The finding of Slonaker (1930) that castration produces a slight decrease in rat longevity was based on too few animals to be significant. Virgin and ovary-less *Drosophila* females live longer than normals, and sterilization increases the female life-span (Maynard Smith, 1958a, b).

Muhlbock (1959) finds that virgin mice live longer than spayed females, while castrated and entire males have closely similar curves. The oldest survivors of all are castrates, however. In rats, Árvay, Takács and Verzár (1963) found little difference between castrate and entire male longevity.

4·3·2 SEXUAL ACTIVITY: SHUNAMITISM

In some instances (*Drosophila*—Bilewicz, 1953) the life of the male is still further shortened by copulation or by egg-laying. In others (*Latrodectes*, Shulov, 1939–40) the male dies after a determinate short life-span, whether mated or not. While the mortality of Anglican clergy in England during the 1930's was only 69 per cent of the general male mortality, and that of other Protestant clergy 74 per cent, the mortality of Roman Catholic clergy was 105 per cent (Registrar-General's statistics, 1938). This observation is complicated by a variety of factors: in rats, however, regular mating improves the condition and longevity of the male (Agduhr, 1939; Agduhr and Barron, 1938). Though there may be other reasons for the fact that married persons live statistically longer than unmarried persons (Sheps, 1961), this might tend to support the view that the virtues of 'continence' in man, *vis-à-vis* longevity, have been over-praised by interested parties.

One particularly odd finding is the vast excess of deaths from most causes, including tubercle, accident, and cardiovascular disease in the young widowed group of both sexes (Kraus and Lilienfeld, 1959). It has been variously suggested that the healthy widowed soon marry and leave the group, that assortation leads to a 'mutual choice of poor-risk mates', that the survivor and deceased shared an unfavourable environment, and that early death—possibly psychogenic—is a direct effect of surviving a spouse. Between these interpretations a complete absence of facts leaves us freedom of choice at present.

One must here distinguish between the effects of sexual inter-course and *shunamitism*, the beneficial effect on old males of the proximity of a young female. Though it is an old notion of magical origin, Muhlbock (1959) has shown that this actually occurs in rats—old males live materially longer if one young female is introduced to groom them. After citing the opinion given by the Dutch physician Boerhave (1668–1738), who 'recommended an old Burgomaster of Amsterdam to lie be-tween two young girls, assuring him that he would thus recover strength and spirits', Hufeland (1798) remarks 'We cannot refuse our approval to the method.' It would seem by tradition to be applicable only to the male.

Apart from King David and the Burgomaster aforesaid, the *locus classicus* of magical shunamitism is the treatise *Hermippus Redivivus* of Cohausen (1742), which contains much engaging nonsense. The influence technically responsible was the physical proximity or the 'heat' or 'breath' of a young virgin, coition being specifically excluded as dangerous to the failing constitu-tion ('the King knew her not'), but the process was semi-parasitic and took from the young what it gave to the old. In the Indian tradition, where the revivifying contact is specifically sexual, it was held particularly dangerous to lie with an old woman (see the *Ratimañjarī* of Jāyadeva).[1]

The magical idea of shunamitism might now be transferred *mutatis mutandis* to mere social contact, but there may well have been greater scientific value in the techniques adopted by the mediaeval Indian kings of Chandella, builders of the Khajurāho temples, who successfully pursued both longevity and proximity through industrious ritual coition with specially-instructed maidens (see Zannas and Auboyer, 1960), and in the popular notion of 'grinding young': 'while the miller grinds the old man's

---

[1] Bālā tu prāṇadā prottrā taruṇi prāṇahārinī/Prauḍhā karoti vṛddhatvaṁ vṛddhā maraṇamādiśet

  'the young girl gives the breath of life,
  the young woman takes the breath of life,
  the grown woman hastens age,
  the old woman brings death'

(Ratimañjarī, v. 24).

corn, the miller's daughter grinds the old man young again'. Failing this, according to Marsilio Ficino (1498) 'he should find a young, healthy, gay and beautiful girl, attach his mouth to her breast, and drink her milk while the moon is waxing: and thereafter take *pulv. foeniculi* with sugar'. This advice has perhaps some psychoanalytical virtue in acting out the regression seen commonly in old age.

The mean age of ceasing regular coitus works out at 68 in married and 58 in unmarried men (Holland; Braadbart 1961): Newman (1959) found that 70 per cent of married American couples in his sample were sexually active at 60, many continuing into the late 80's. Regular coitus with mutual orgasm is recorded between a man of 103 and his wife aged 90 (Kinsey, Pomeroy and Martin, 1949) and fatherhood at 94 (Seymour, Duffy and Koerner, 1935). Contrary to popular belief, there is little or no decline in woman's libido with age—in fact, it more often increases, up to at least the age of 60 (Kinsey, Pomeroy, Martin and Gebhard, 1953).

Continued sexual activity is apparently a correlate of continued vigour: as Hufeland dutifully puts it, 'The power of procreating others seems to be in the most intimate proportion to that of regenerating and restoring one's self: but a certain regularity and moderation are necessary in the employment of it, and marriage is the only means by which these can be preserved . . .' (1798). For life-tables of monks and nuns, see Madigan (1959) and Josephina (1955).

4·4 *Progeria*

Although the rate of senile deterioration varies between individuals, the specific age of genetically homogeneous animal lines is very stable; even in human populations the range of apparent variation is not very great, and the few descriptions of racially-distributed 'premature senility', as in Eskimos (Brown, Sinclair, Cronk and Clark, 1948), are not actuarially supported, though such variation, genetic or environmental, may occur.

Sporadic cases of syndromes having some of the general characters of premature old age occasionally occur in man. It is not clear how far any of these syndromes can be regarded as genuine accelerations of the timing mechanisms which determine senescence. They are apparently pleiotropic genetic defects, occurring commonly in sibs, and are most conveniently mentioned here. They have been regarded as pluriglandular endocrine disturbances, but they affect many ectodermal structures and look in most respects much more like an inborn error of metabolism —possibly the deficiency of an enzyme system, or a chromosomal abnormality.

Infantile progeria (Hutchinson-Gilford syndrome) (Thomson and Forfar, 1950; Manschot, 1940, 1950) occurs in childhood. After an apparently normal infancy, the child begins to show retarded growth, with dwarfism and progressively increasing physical abnormality. The appearance becomes senile, the skin atrophic, and there is hypertension with extensive atheroma and calcification. Death usually occurs from coronary disease before the thirtieth year. The mental development of these children may be retarded, but is more typically precocious. Cataract may occur. The endocrine appearances at necropsy are inconstant, but pituitary eosinophiles are reported to be reduced (Manschot, 1940).

Adult progeria (Werner's syndrome) was first described by Werner (1904) in four sibs. It bears some resemblance to a delayed infantile progeria, occurring after growth has been wholly or partially completed. The subjects are short and of unusual appearance. The symptoms begin in the third or fourth decade, with the development of baldness, greying, skin changes, cataract, calcification of vessels and occasionally of tissues, osteoporosis, hypogonadism, and a tendency to diabetes (Thannhauser, 1945). This seems in general a more promising source of analogy with normal senescence than does the infantile progeric syndrome. Extensive bibliographies of progeria are given by Thannhauser (1945) and by Thomson and Forfar (1950).

Other less generalized conditions with rather similar symptomatology have been described. 'Senile' change may be limited to the extremities (acrogeria). The main interest of these conditions is in providing examples of mechanisms which may mimic the deteriorative changes of human old age. The conditions are all rare, and no parallels have been described in laboratory animals. In infant progeria, pituitary growth-hormone deficiency appears to play some part, though the condition differs markedly from straightforward dwarfism. The deficiency of oxyphil cells in some reported cases bears a resemblance to that which follows castration (Wolfe, 1941, 1943). Walford (1962) draws the analogy with autoimmune diseases.

Pearce and Brown (1960) have described a progeric familial syndrome in the rabbit—this appears to represent the incomplete manifestation of a character which, in its severest form, produces *infant* death, since it occurs in a strain liable to produce non-viable young with parchment-like skin. The 'senile' changes are loss of coat, loss of weight, ulceration, cachexia and ophthalmia, and the range of acute and chronic types is reminiscent of the range of human progeric syndromes. It does not appear to be identical with these, however, and calcification is not prominent. A much more human-looking animal 'progeria' has lately been produced in rats by a type of experimental calcium hypersensitivity (Selye, 1962).

Sudden 'senescence' in adults, a great standby of the nineteenth-century dramatist, is an uncommon endocrine, or possibly hypothalamic, reaction to severe emotional shock or accident which, although not genetic, can conveniently be considered here because of its superficial affinity with progeria. In the interest of literary effect, the preliminary phase of sudden baldness is usually not stressed. The hair may fall out within twenty-four hours, to be replaced when it grows again after an interval, by white or structurally defective hair—impotence, depression and cachexia are described as concomitants. The condition is recoverable, and appears to have more connection with Simmonds' disease than with senescence. A case was reported by Greene and Paterson (1943) in a railwayman who fell from a locomotive and suffered head injury and severe shock. In another case, a policeman rang the doorbell of a gas-filled house and was severely shocked by the explosion which followed (*Evening Standard* 18.12.61). A few cases are alleged to have followed intense fear, as in battle. The pituitary may well be the endocrine chiefly responsible.

The Influence of Genetic Constitution

4·5 Choice of Material for Experimental Study of Age Effects

Research on the senescence of man and most large mammals necessarily involves work on genetically diverse populations. Where closed laboratory stocks are used, or the subject is a 'genetical' domestic animal such as the mouse or *Drosophila*, genetic precautions are essential in ageing experiments, especially if comparisons are to be made between the life-spans of different groups or different generations. The size of the effect which can be produced in such stocks by heterosis has already been mentioned. The presence or absence of uniformity in the experimental population is also particularly important in research involving life-tables, since in many inbred lines the form of the life-table depends entirely on one cause of death which is not typical of the species, or even the phylum.

In non-genetical experiments (nutrition, biochemistry, growth-rate and so on) the choice lies between *inbred*, *hybrid* and *random-bred* material. *Inbred* lines commonly have a life-span which is rather low for the species, and this may be advantageous. Their vigour is often low, though inbreeding depression is more evident in some species than others. Inbred lines are often chosen by non-genetical workers for bioassay, in the belief that they have the advantage of uniformity. This, however, is not so. Grüneberg (1954) has stressed two important characters of such lines: they cannot be relied upon to remain constant in their heritable properties with the passage of time, and may diverge rapidly when split into separate colonies; and they do not constitute phenotypically uniform material, but may, on the contrary, be strikingly more variable than F_1 hybrids between strains, and even than random-bred material (McLaren and Michie, 1954).

Hybrid material, bred in each generation by crossing inbred lines, suitably chosen, has a number of important advantages for general work upon ageing. In such crosses the life-span approaches the maximum for the species under the experimental conditions. Vigour is high, so that 'background' losses due to temperature change, infection, operative mortality and accident are much reduced, and variation between individuals is minimal. This uniformity is itself probably a reflection of vigour, in the form of better homoeostasis (Robertson and Reeve, 1952). Hybrids can, like inbreds, be employed for transplantation experiments. Like inbreds, too, they may all die of a single cause, and will do so as a rule with greater unanimity in regard to age.

Random-mated material, when mating is genuinely random, and not occurring within an already highly-inbred colony or between such colonies, produces animals, the strongest of which exhibit a vigour and life-span approaching that of hybrids, more variable than hybrids, unsuitable for transplantation experiments, showing a variety of causes of death more closely resembling that in human populations, and, in general, resembling such populations more closely than hybrid or inbred lines.

The choice of inbred, hybrid, or random-bred material, when it is not dictated by the fact that no pure lines are available, will depend upon which of these attributes are most useful. The type of material must, however, be correctly stated, since it greatly affects the interpretation of results. Probably the most valuable approach to the comparative study of ageing, though not always a practicable one, would be a scheme of research carried out in parallel upon all three types of strain, in an animal which is already genetically familiar.

~ 5 ~

GROWTH AND SENESCENCE

5·1 *'Rate of Living'*

THE idea of the life-span as a fixed quantity is an old one. In a great many organisms it has long been recognized that the contrast, perhaps originally moralistic, between a long life and a high 'rate of living' had valid biological applications. The phrase 'rate of living' we owe to Pearl, and it conveys the concept very satisfactorily without making too many assumptions. In many organisms the life-span, like the rate of development, is a function of the temperature over a considerable range. In such forms it appears that a fixed quantity of *something*, which, for want of a better term, we have called 'programme', must run out and be succeeded by senescence. The organism must pass through a fixed sequence of operations, metabolic or developmental, the rate of its passage determining the observed life-span.

The period in which the kinetics of metabolism were being discovered expressed this 'programme' in directly chemical terms. Life had an observable temperature-coefficient. Growth, in the classical conception of Robertson (1923), followed the same course as a monomolecular autocatalytic reaction. Loeb (1908) attempted to answer by the determination of temperature coefficients a fundamental question about the 'rate of living' in relation to ageing—what is the nature of the 'programme' which has to be fulfilled before senescence begins? Is it a programme of differentiation, or growth, or maintenance metabolism, or of all three? Loeb's experiments showed that the temperature coefficient of the rate of 'ageing' in echinoderm ova differed greatly from that of their respiration. Later work has shown the relationship between development and temperature to be too complex for simple estimation of coefficients.

188

Morphogenesis depends upon a large number of simultaneous and occasionally contrary processes. We should almost certainly now be inclined to interpret the programme fulfilled by an animal during its life-cycle in terms drawn from experimental morphology and from the study of control systems, rather than directly from physical chemistry.

The postulation that senescence always accompanies, or follows, the cessation of growth, which certainly appears to fit many of the observed facts, we owe originally to the work of Minot (1908). It is, in fact, no more than a postulation, since, as we have seen, there may be organisms in which senescence occurs hand-in-hand with growth, and there are certainly organisms, such as terrapins, which have a virtual maximum size but are not known to exhibit senescence. Senescence in man, judged by the life-table, commences while active growth is in progress: Minot himself considered that the rate of senescence was actually greatest when growth-rate was at its maximum. If the relationship between senescence and growth-cessation is real, it might mean (1) that that which 'causes' the cessation of growth also causes senescence—implying that growth-cessation results from an active and inhibitory principle, (2) that that which no longer grows, senesces, (3) that growth-cessation and senescence are parallel phenomena, both arising from the process of differentiation.

The dissociability of growth from development was first shown by Gudernatsch's researches upon the action of thyroid in the developing tadpole (1912). Metabolism, measured by respiration, is dissociable from both. 'The fundamental mechanisms are not separable only in thought: on the contrary, they can be dissociated experimentally or thrown out of gear with one another' (Needham). The fundamental problem in relation to the 'rate of living' lies, therefore, in determining which of these processes, and in what proportions, make up the essential sequence of operations through which the organism must pass before senescence makes its appearance. In its crudest form the question is: given that these processes, though dissociable, are normally interdependent, does this organism undergo senescence (1) when it reaches a particular stage of cellular differentiation, (2) when it has exhausted a particular store of 'growth energy', whatever the nature of such a store, or (3) when it has carried out a certain stint of metabolism—a life-span measurable in calories or in litres of oxygen consumed? It is immediately evident that the programme in real organisms is complex, that since senescence is a diverse process the pacemaker differs in different forms. In some cases, when (1) above has been satisfied, the further life-span of the *differentiated* cells may depend upon their metabolism, as in (3). All concepts based on 'wear and tear' in neurones or other cells postulate a similar sequence: loss of regenerative power followed by mechanical or chemical exhaustion. In the rotifer the normal sequence of differentiation produces an organism which is almost incapable of cellular repair, and quite incapable of nuclear regeneration. The life-span of the adult, once this point in the programme has been reached, is inversely proportional to temperature and metabolic rate over a certain range. How this effect operates we do not know. The encysted adult, although unable to survive in the complete absence of oxygen (Rahm, 1923), may pass years in diapause. The life-span of many larvae can be enormously prolonged by underfeeding or shortened by heating: once metamorphosis has taken place the programme is resumed but still responds to changes in temperature by a change in pace. The longest-lived imagines, termite queens, do in fact increase in size after eclosion (Harvey, 1934). In mammals it has been postulated that, since the metabolic rate is held steady by various homoeostatic devices, the essential ingredients of the programme leading to senescence are growth and differentiation; that growth ceases as a result of some process or processes of differentiation, and that the absence of growth is a proximate cause of senescence.

We have already suggested that this is not wholly in accordance with the evidence. The observational test, that no vertebrate which continues to grow undergoes 'morphogenetic' senescence, and that all vertebrates which cease to grow are subject to it, is not satisfied, while the experimental test, the demonstration that the life-span of an adult vertebrate can be prolonged by keeping it artificially in continued growth, beginning after normal size and development have been attained, gave a negative result in Everitt's (1959) rat experiment with

190

growth hormone. We cannot yet identify any single process which, by its failure, produces the senile decline of homoeostasis in mammals. It is however possible to treat the developmental sequence leading to senescence, in its relation to growth and to differentiation, as an 'integrating system', of the type employed in various calculating and timing devices.

The most familiar example of such a system, functioning as a calculating device, is the taxi-meter. This machine records time when the taxi is stationary, and distance, or time and distance, when it is moving. The real taxi-meter does so upon an 'open-ended' scale, the amount of the fare which can be rung up on the dial being theoretically unlimited, since the dials after reaching £99 19*s*. 11½*d*. return to zero. For the purpose of our argument, the biological taxi-meter has been adapted by an anarchist to produce an undesirable result when a particular fare is reached —say £10; or, more correctly, an *increasing probability* of this result as £10 is approached and passed: an increasing impairment of the brakes and steering would be a suitable device. The meter records one shilling per minute, so long as the taxi is stationary and half a crown per mile plus one shilling per minute so long as it is moving. In this case, if the journey never begins, the impairment will take place eventually, though not for a very long time. For an extended biological analogy it is probably better to take the case in which the conditions of the impairment reaching a disastrous stage are, first, that the fare shall reach £10, and second that the taxi shall have travelled at least a short distance from its starting point.

The question we have to ask is this: does mammalian senescence effectively resemble such an integrating system, in which differentiation is the higher-scoring and the essential component, but in which retardation leading to continuance of growth directly or indirectly delays the point at which senescence appears; or does cessation of growth *itself*, whether it arises from some active mechanism of size limitation or through the attainment of an equilibrium state, directly cause the senile deterioration? The crude application of the calculating-machine or the time-fuse analogy has many objections, the chief of them being that the senile decline in resistance in mammals is not a sudden process, as it is in the rotifer, but a smooth rise in the

191

force of mortality beginning at an early stage. Mechanical timing devices produce as a rule a single event after a fixed programme, not an increasing probability throughout the programme, though this objection does not hold good for analogue computing systems: it is relatively simple to devise an electronic taximeter-bomb in which the *probability* of an explosion increases with the increase of time and distance, or a system in which the steering of the taxi becomes increasingly impaired as the 'programme' continues. A far more serious objection is that in ordinary taxi-meters time and distance are not normally interlocked, as growth and differentiation, though experimentally separable, are interlocked in the developing animal. It has been suggested that the two processes are in some degree mutually exclusive (Bertalanffy, 1933, 1941)—a conception which goes back to Minot. It seems probable that in most organisms it is the component of differentiation, not that of mere growth, which is responsible for senescence.

Analogies, in any case, are mostly of use as teaching-illustrations. In the final analysis, senescence, even if it never reaches the ideal state of being expressed as a sequence of chemical reactions and equilibria, must presumably be reducible to a series of definite processes—such-and-such a mechanism leads to the loss of dividing-power in such-and-such cells, which then have a life-span limited by the non-renewability of their enzymes to so many chemical operations, after which they deteriorate with the following consequences. We are nowhere near such a picture of any one senile or developmental process in any organism, let alone of mammalian senescence or morphogenesis in general. A certain amount of experimental evidence has, however, accumulated—enough to indicate the directions in which further research might profitably be directed.

One of its most important—and theoretically distressing—findings is that the decrease in longevity of *Drosophila* imagines at high temperatures is not a matter of simple thermal acceleration. Clarke and Maynard Smith (1951b) have kept *D. subobscura* at high temperatures and then transferred them back to lower temperatures, with a view to measuring the expected loss in life-span which the taximeter analogy would predict. Apart from the special case of females which are rendered sterile by heat and consequently live longer than usual, a period spent at a high temperature, provided it is less than the 'plateau' in the survival curve which precedes the onset of deaths, subtracts nothing whatever from subsequent survival at a low temperature. The rate of ageing in *Drosophila* is therefore temperature-independent: what appears to vary with temperature is the level of environmental attack (Maynard Smith, 1958; 1959c; Clarke and Maynard Smith, 1961a, b). The decline in *Drosophila* 'vitality' during the plateau, Neary's (1960) 'induction period', is not accelerated by heating: flies in hot conditions die early not because their vitality is more rapidly impaired by age, but because the vitality required for survival is higher than in cool conditions. This is a sobering conclusion for those who like to compare the curves of chemical processes and population decline and draw conclusions from the comparison. (See also Strehler, 1962; Shaw and Bercaw, 1962, however.)

5·2 *Experimental Alteration of the Growth-Rate*

5·2·1 INVERTEBRATES

In many invertebrates, the specific age is easily altered, either in response to temperature changes, to which it bears a simple relation, or by retardation of growth through the restriction of food. The total longevity of insects can be increased either by underfeeding the larvae, or by keeping any or all of the stages, from egg to imago, at low temperatures. The same applies to ticks—starvation will increase the life-span of some species from a few weeks to 2 years (Bishopp and Smith, 1938). Northrop (Northrop, 1917; Loeb and Northrop, 1917) kept *Drosophila* larvae for varying periods on a yeastless medium to delay growth and induce stunting: by this means the total life-span from hatching to death was increased. There is disagreement whether delayed growth of larvae leads to an increase in the life-span from eclosion. Northrop found no such increase in imagines reared from retarded larvae. Intermittent starvation of the imago of *Drosophila* shortens its life; retardation of the larvae of *Lymantria* also fails to increase the life-span of the imago, which cannot feed (Kopeć, 1924, 1928). Alpatov and Pearl (Alpatov and Pearl, 1929; Alpatov, 1930) found a slight increase in imaginal life-span in *Drosophila* when the larvae were retarded by development at 18°. This effect was less evident in males, and appeared to be reversed in some experiments: where the imagines were kept at 25–28° larvae reared at 28° gave longer-lived flies than those reared at 18°. The statistical significance of the differences was in any case small.

In insects in which metamorphosis is incomplete, the optimal intake of food, and particularly of protein, for rapid growth produces a shorter total life-span than a poorer diet; in *Blatta orientalis* and *Periplaneta americana* the optimal protein intake for longevity of all the stages is about half that which gives the fastest development (Haydak, 1953). In holometabolous insects, dietary slowing is confined to the larval stages, which can be extended by intermittent fasting (*Lymantria*—Kopeć, 1924) —with beetle larvae to many years: the life of imagines, on the contrary, usually seems to be increased by food supplements (butterflies—Frohawk, 1935) especially in females (*Musca domestica*—Rockstein, 1959), and still more by the prevention of egg-laying (*Musca domestica*—Rockstein, 1959; *Ephestia*— Norris, 1934; Köhler, 1940), since in both feeding and non-feeding adults the longevity is determined by stored reserves, particularly of protein. Bees present a special problem; here feeding controls development and the choice between two life-cycles, that of a queen, lasting up to 5 years (Pflugfelder, 1948) and that of a worker, which depends directly on how much pollen protein is kept back for individual use, rather than used for rearing brood. Broodless or 'winter' workers have a life-span of 300–400 days compared with 30–70 days when brood is present (Maurizio, 1959). Attempts have been made to increase the imaginal life-span of insects with vitamin supplements on the model of royal jelly, but with small effect (Gardner, 1948).

The life-span and final size of *Daphnia* (McArthur and Baillie, 1926) and *Moina* (Ingle, 1933; Terao, 1932, etc.) vary inversely with the temperature over a considerable range. Like *Drosophila*, *Daphnia* can be markedly retarded either by cooling or by underfeeding. A detailed study on the effect of retardation upon specific age and growth in *Daphnia* was carried out by Ingle, Wood and Banta (1937). By diluting the medium, it was shown that starvation of *Daphnia* for varying numbers of instars resulted in an increase of life-span approximately equal to the period of starvation, but that individuals starved only until the 11th or 17th instar lived longer than individuals starved throughout life. This prolongation of life was achieved by lengthening the duration of each retarded instar, the total

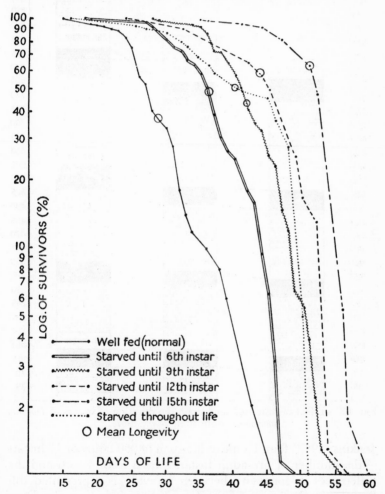

FIG. 62.—Effect of restricted food upon the longevity of *Daphnia longispina* (from Ingle, Wood and Banta, 1937).

number of instars remaining constant. In this species (*D. longispina*) the specific age appeared to lie between the 19th and 22nd instars, without reference to the chronological age which these may represent. (Figs. 62, 63.) In *D. magna*, Anderson and

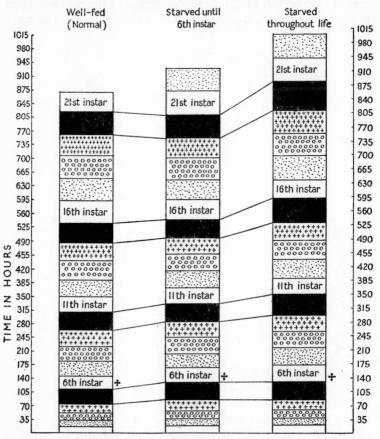

FIG. 63.—Effect of restricted food upon the duration of instars in *Daphnia longispina* (from Ingle *et al.*, 1937).

Jenkins (1942) found a mean life-span of 960 hours or 17 instars —the number of pre-adult instars varied from 4 to 6 and the differences in longevity between individuals represented differences in the length of the pre-adult period. (See also Dunham, 1938.) The finding of Fritsch (1953) that the pantothenic acid content of the medium is a major factor in determining the life-span of *Daphnia* complicates the interpretation of some of these studies of dietary retardation, however. For recent studies of the longevity and heart-rate of *Daphnia*, see Meijering (1958, 1960) v. Reden (1960) and Fritsch (1956, 1959).

5·2·2 INSECT METAMORPHOSIS AND SENESCENCE

A great many insects are capable of very long pre-imaginal life, the duration of which is largely determined by food supply. The 'rate of living', as a simple quantity treated apart from morphogenetic processes, does not give an entirely satisfactory picture of insect development. We might possibly make an experimental approach to the study of insect senescence on the following lines. Senescence, of course, occurs in the ordinary course of events only in the imago. The larval or nymphal stages must be regarded as a system which is self-maintaining but which tends towards ultimate metamorphosis. They are analogous to the young growing period of non-metabolous metazoa. The question arises how long, if metamorphosis could be indefinitely prevented, the metathetelic larva would remain self-maintaining as an equilibrium system. It might presumably do so indefinitely, or it might ultimately undergo a specialized type of senescence due to the suppression of development or to imbalance between continued, divergent growth processes; or it might nevertheless undergo senescence from the same cause, whatever that cause may be, which limits the life of the imago.

To ask whether a larva or a nymph would senesce if it did not metamorphose is not entirely idle speculation. The data which we have on the developmental physiology of *Rhodnius*, chiefly from the work of Wigglesworth, make it possible to contemplate interfering with the development of nymphs. The pre-imaginal phase of *Rhodnius*, during which growth takes place, is maintained by the so-called juvenile hormone. 'During larval life, imaginal differentiation is suppressed because in the presence of the juvenile hormone secreted by the corpus allatum the intracellular system which leads to the production of larval structures takes precedence over the system which leads to the formation of adult structures' (Wigglesworth, 1953b). The influence of temperature on larval development appears to act through this system, high temperatures or low O_2 tensions depressing the juvenile hormone and producing prothetely, low temperatures enhancing its effect and producing metathetely. This system lends itself particularly well to analysis in terms of control-mechanisms. The tendency of the cellular system in its 'free-running' state appears to be towards the imaginal form. Moulting hormone from a fifth-stage larva will cause a first-stage larva *Rhodnius* to metamorphose (Wigglesworth, 1934). Second-instar moth larvae will metamorphose to minute pupae and adults if the corpora allata are removed (Bounhiol, 1938) and isolated fragments from the integument of newly-hatched moth larvae tend to pupate (Piepho, 1938). The function of the juvenile hormone appears to be to moderate or prevent this free-running tendency, though as a standing bias, not as a negative feedback. The point to which the free-running system tends, moreover, is an unstable one, ending in eventual senescence. In the fifth-stage *Rhodnius* nymph the thoracic gland undergoes very rapid disintegration as soon as metamorphosis takes place, and the possibility of moulting and cuticular renewal is thereby lost, from lack of evocator, although the power of the dermal cells to respond to injected moulting hormone remains (Wigglesworth, 1953a). Long-term change in this system causes the bias to be overcome at the correct moment. The homoeostasis achieved by the juvenile hormone is not absolute, otherwise metamorphosis would never take place; the metamorphosis-producing hormone ultimately carries the day. But occasional nymphs of *Rhodnius* devoid of the thoracic gland cannot metamorphose, and appear to live for long periods without senescence. This mechanism offers an opportunity for the dissection of just such a system of partial homoeostasis, directed to act as a delay-mechanism, as appears to underlie so many life-cycles which end in senescence. Work on insect senescence is in many respects unpromising as a source of principles which can be extended to the biology of vertebrate old age; such research is frequently confined to the very special circumstances which exist in the imago—in other words, to a system which is already in a time-limited equilibrium. For measures of interference with the growing organism, however, and attempts to stabilize the system in its earlier stages, insect material may

198

prove the most manageable. Any example of indefinite stabiliza-
tion at an immature stage, in any organism, would be of great
biological interest. The degree of drift towards the unstable
state probably varies throughout development in different insects—Bodenstein has shown (1943a, b) that in *Drosophila* early
salivary glands implanted in late larvae are not immediately
capable of metamorphosis: 'Whether the organ discs respond
with growth or differentiation depends on a definite relationship between hormone concentration and organ responsiveness'
(Bodenstein, 1943b).

5·2·3 VERTEBRATES

The possibility of producing a long-lasting but recoverable
delay in mammalian growth and development by underfeeding
first arose from the studies of Osborne and Mendel (1915,
1916). The work of McCay on rats, which extended the results
obtained by underfeeding upon arthropod growth directly to
mammals, is well known, but still very remarkable. It also still
represents the only successful assault which has ever been made
on the problem of mammalian specific age, which is itself the
key problem of medical gerontology; and the rather exceptional
growth-pattern of rats in no way diminishes its interest. The
experiments, first described in 1934 (McCay and Crowell,
1934; McCay, Maynard, Sperling and Barnes, 1939; McCay,
Pope and Lunsford, 1956; Saxton, 1945), extended over years
and are fully reviewed in retrospect by McCay (1952). Groups
of rats were reared on a diet sufficient in all other constituents
but deficient in calories, and their growth thereby retarded.
After periods of retardation up to 1000 days, the calorie intake
was raised to permit growth. The animals then grew rapidly to
adult size, even though the longest-retarded group had already
exceeded the normal life-span for the strain, and continued to
live to approximately twice the maximum age reached by un-
retarded controls (Fig. 64). This long survival was accompanied
by a decreased incidence of many chronic diseases, which
appeared to represent a true diminution in senile liability to
death from random causes. The chief specific diminution was
in death-rate from pulmonary diseases and from tumours. 'In
general, the retarded rat remains active and appears young

whatever its chronological age. It is very alert. It tends to go blind in the second and third year of life. Its pulse rate of 340 beats per minute is about 100 below normal' (McCay, 1952). The basal metabolic rate of rats so retarded lay between that of normal young and normal old animals (Horst *et al.*, 1934). In rats retarded for 850 days, heat production per unit surface area was lower, but heat production per unit weight higher,

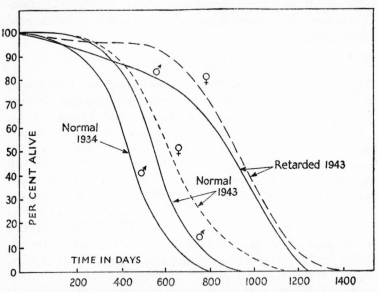

FIG. 64.—Survival curves of normal and retarded male and female rats, showing the effect of dietary restriction (from McCay, Sperling and Barnes, 1943).

than in normal controls (Will and McCay, 1943). The aorta and kidneys of retarded rats showed in general a higher level of calcification than those of controls (Hummel and Barnes, 1938) perhaps on account of the relatively higher mineral concentrations in the restricted diet (Barnes, 1942). A further series of experiments in the dietary restriction of animals which had already reached maturity was unfortunately complicated by the introduction of many groups of variables (exercise, casein intake, liver supplements, etc.)—in these experiments, underfeeding produced a significant increase in life-span compared with fully-fed controls, but the difference was far less conspicuous than in the retardation of young growing rats, and the factors which were most important in determining life-span were those which determined the degree of body fatness (McCay, Maynard, Sperling and Osgood, 1941; Silberberg and Silberberg, 1954). This difference was largely accounted for by the higher incidence of renal disease on a high protein diet and in obese animals (Saxton and Kimball, 1941); in contrast to the findings in animals retarded while young, the incidence of chronic pneumonitis and of tumours was not reduced by underfeeding in mature animals (McCay, Sperling and Barnes, 1943; Saxon, 1945).

Basal metabolism in restricted rats is intermediate between that of normal young and normal adult rats (Will and McCay, 1943). Their size restriction is a restriction in cell number, retarded animals having the cellular population appropriate to size group, not age group (Fukuda and Sibatani, 1953). The operative effect seems to be mediated by the pituitary—it is a dietary hypophysectomy (Samuels, 1946) and is antagonized by extraneous growth hormone (Hrůza and Fábry, 1957). Tissues from retarded animals have a shorter latent period in tissue culture (Holečkova, Fábry and Poupa, 1959) and the tail collagen in such animals is 'young' in its response to heat shrinkage (Chvapil and Hrůza, 1959). Evidence regarding food restriction in normally grown adult animals is less spectacular —gains in general seem to reflect the avoidance of overweight (McCay *et al.*, 1956).

Ross (1961) varied the components of the diet of rats separately—restriction of protein alone produced little gain in longevity; restriction of carbohydrate produced some gain, but less than when protein, calorie intake and carbohydrate were all restricted. Rats on an unrestricted diet low in protein and high in carbohydrate restricted their own intake, and lived longer in consequence than other unrestricted groups (Fig. 65).

In retarded rats the liver composition resembles that of much younger animals: the amount of RNA phosphorus in Edsall's reagent extractives is even higher at 12 months than in normal 1-month-old animals, and protein turnover appears to be enhanced compared with normals. On realimentation, these indices rapidly 'catch up' with the chronological age (Nikitin, 1962).

The results of these experiments indicate that at least some mammals are capable while immature of undergoing prolonged suspension of growth without any acceleration of senescence. The suspension is not complete, since deaths occur unless some increase in weight is allowed. The most important inference to be drawn from the work would appear to be that senescence itself is the direct consequence not so much of growth-cessation

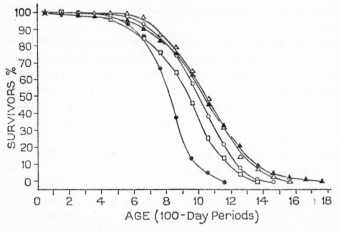

FIG. 65.—Percentage of survivors at successive 100-day periods of 4 groups of rats maintained on restricted intakes of semisynthetic diets and of one group of rats maintained *ad libitum* with a commercial diet. Key: ●, commercial laboratory chow; ○, high casein-high sucrose intake; △, high casein-low sucrose intake; □, low casein-high sucrose intake; ▲, low casein-low sucrose intake (from Rose, 1961).

as that of the attainment of a developmental stage, the timing of which is partially, but not wholly, linked to the growth-rate —there being no evidence that starved rats remain 'young' indefinitely. By 1150 days, moreover, only about half the retarded individuals were capable of resuming growth (McCay, Sperling and Barnes, 1943). There is some evidence from later work that prolongation of the life-span, though in a smaller degree, can be produced by intermittent dietary restriction without any evident effect on the growth-rate (Carlson and Hoelzel,

1946). Moreover most of the changes which ultimately fix the specific age appear to have occurred at the time of maturity, since the increase in longevity obtained by underfeeding adult rats is far less (McCay, Maynard, Sperling and Osgood, 1941).

In contrast to McCay's findings, retardation of rats *before* weaning leads to permanent undersize and tends to affect longevity adversely (Widdowson and Kennedy, 1962).

Less severe or intermittent restriction prolongs life, but chiefly by cutting early mortality, with less effect on the specific age. Riesen, Herbst, Walliker and Elvekjem (1947) found that in Wistar rats the gain was roughly proportional to the severity of restriction: starvation for 1 day in 3 or 4 produced a significant increase in mean life. The benefit from retardation is greater in rats on an omnivorous than on a vegetarian diet (Carlson and Hoelzel, 1947, 1948). By fasting 1 day in 3, increases in mean expectation of 20 per cent in males and of 15 per cent in females are obtainable without arrest of growth (Carlson and Hoelzel, 1946). Thomasson (1955) found that the survival curve of rats receiving 27 per cent fat in the diet in the form of butter was oblique, with little initial plateau. If rapeseed oil was substituted the plateau was prolonged by about 25 weeks, and the curve became more rectangular: growth was slower, chiefly because appetite was decreased, and there was a marked reduction in renal disease. By reducing food intake only moderately, to a level which did not inhibit growth or retard sexual maturation, Berg and Simms (1962) have increased the life-span of rats by 25 per cent (200 days) in females and 30 per cent (300 days) in males, with corresponding delay in the onset of diseases and tumours.

Experiments of the same type have been made upon mice, with very similar results. Both total and reproductive life-span can be increased by calorie restriction. On a diet containing half the calories (as lard and dextrose) in the standard mouse diet, C_3H females which are normally sterile at 11–12 months were still rearing litters at 21 months, the longest records being in mice restricted for 11–15 months and then fully fed (Carr, King and Visscher, 1949); fasting on 2 days out of 7, with or without addition of nucleic acid to the diet, produced an increase of

50–60 per cent in the life-span of albinos (Robertson, Marston and Walters, 1934).

Mice have the advantage of being available as inbred lines, which vary in life-span and predominant cause of death. They are also free of the enzootic lung infections which complicate rat-longevity studies. Several investigators have studied special effects of calorie restriction or of limiting intake of particular foodstuffs. Tannenbaum (1947) found that female DBA mice restricted to a weight of 19–20 g. showed a striking absence of spontaneous tumours, which were the chief cause of death in 30 g. controls. In YBR/Wi 'yellow' mice, a high-fat diet reduced the incidence of amyloidosis but greatly shortened life (Silberberg and Silberberg, 1955, 1957b), but a high-carbohydrate diet, though it produced obesity, did not affect lifespan; C57 mice responded to a high-fat diet by developing a high incidence of arthritis (Silberberg and Silberberg, 1957a). King, Lee and Visscher (1955) found that in C_3H mice given a diet containing the normal trace-element additives, there was a high incidence of sudden heart failure after about a year, and of foetal resorption, which could be prevented either by added tocopherol or by omission of trace elements. 'Obese' (*ob*, *ob*) mice whose weight was restricted by a diet low in calories have proved remarkably long-lived, reaching 1027 days (Lane and Dickie, 1958): the gain from restriction was greater than in the non-obese hemizygotes (*ob*, +). In a few instances vitamin supplements have been found to improve performance: vitamin A (Sherman and Trupp, 1940), pantothenic acid (Anonymous, 1949; Pelton and Williams, 1958), but the examples probably represent the remedying of deficiencies.

The mechanism of retardation by dietary restriction in growing mammals is partially known from other studies. Inanition lowers the gonadotrophic activity of the pituitary: this was clearly shown by the transplantation studies of Mason and Wolfe (1930) on female rats, and again in male rats by Moore and Samuels (1931). In rats, reduction of the protein content of the diet below 7 per cent produces anoestrus from gonadotrophin deficiency (Guilbert and Goss, 1932). In the 'pseudohypophysectomy' of malnutrition, pituitary growth hormone will re-initiate growth of the skeleton and decrease the rate of weight loss even without increase of food intake (Mulinos and Pomerantz, 1941). The subject was reviewed by Samuels (1946). The relationship between this 'pseudohypophysectomy' and McCay's results is not yet clear, but the effects of restricted food intake on the pituitary probably play a major part in the alteration of apparent specific age.

In C_3H mice, Carr, King and Visscher (1949) produced anoestrus by reducing the standard calorie intake by half: at 14 months of age, single cycles were readily induced by administering dextrose, though the dose necessary to bring this about varied from 0·15 to 1·0 gm. When the mice were permitted at the age of 21 months to feed at will, and mated, all became pregnant, and 10 out of an initial total of 17 were alive and sexually active at the age of 23 months.

We have no comparable observations in man. Malnutrition can produce gross retardation of puberty (as can disease or 'indirect' malnutrition—the effects of bilharzia are particularly striking) but such malnutrition is always total, and shortens life. In McCay's experiments the dietary restriction was confined to reduction of calories. The undernourished majority in the world at the present time derive no benefit in longevity from their circumstances. But it is not impossible, as Edmonds suggested in 1832, and as Sinclair (1955) and McCance and Widdowson (1955) have repeated, that adult life might be shortened by the pursuit of excessively rapid growth during childhood. Human puberty can be accelerated by overfeeding (Bruch, 1941), and there is already evidence that while the maximum mean height of Englishmen has not increased during the last century, it is now reached no less than five years earlier (Morant, 1950), and the loss of height with increasing age shows a parallel advance. The main objections to such an argument are that the present acceleration of puberty is probably a return to normal rather than a fresh development, the age of menarche in the ancient world having been what it is now: and that the evolved 'lag' in early human development, characteristic of the lengthened primate childhood, is likely to complicate any direct analogy with rodent growth and maturation (Tanner, 1955; Comfort, 1960c). Constitutional precocious puberty does not appear to shorten life (Jolly, 1955), cf. Fig. 67.

Growth and Senescence

In 1948, Evans, Simpson and Li confirmed with pure growth hormone Wiesner's (1932) original finding that rats could be kept in continuous growth throughout life by injections of pituitary growth hormone. Wiesner had reported some improvement in the condition of old male rats under the influence of growth hormone. The experiment of Evans, Simpson and Li was not designed to study the effect of growth on longevity, and they found that continued growth from hormone administration in rats itself leads to death from an increased incidence of tumours. The 12 animals in the original experiment of Evans, Simpson and Li were killed at 647 days for histological purposes. With small doses of the purified hormone, 'drug-resistance' to the growth-promoting and nitrogen-retaining effects develops (Whitney, Bennett, Li and Evans, 1948). In dogs, and cats, continued administration of growth hormone after growth-cessation produces not growth but diabetes, while in others (man) epiphyseal fusion prevents continued body growth after sexual maturity. Although the response of rats both to retardation and to growth hormone is apparently atypical, and certainly differs from that which might be expected in man, the possibility exists of comparing in a mammal the effects on rate of senescence of (1) retarded growth to the full specific size, (2) of accelerated growth up to, and beyond, the specific size, and (3) of growth beyond the specific size, but beginning in old age. Moon and his co-workers (Moon et al., 1952) found that massive administration of growth hormone (2 mg./day) to mice evoked tumours in only one of the tested strains. It appears, moreover, that growth hormone alone fails to induce tumours in hypophysectomized animals (Asling et al., 1952a, b). The resistance which develops to the heterologous (ox) hormone used in such experiments may perhaps be surmountable. The idea underlying this kind of investigation was already present in the work of Robertson (Robertson and Ray, 1919; Robertson, 1923) at a time when endocrinology was insufficiently advanced to enable it to be realized. The results they obtained in retarding growth with 'tethelin' were almost certainly non-specific. Work upon growth hormone in mammals whose epiphyses do not unite would appear to be one of the critical experiments in finding out how far growth and development are in integrating system tending to senescence at a fixed point, and how far mere growth, induced by one of many anabolism-stimulating factors, is capable of reversing or preventing senile change. Everitt (1959) has attempted this, and finds that growth hormone failed either to prolong life or to reverse indices of senescence in ageing rats.

Attempts to *accelerate* mammalian senescence have been surprisingly unsuccessful. While laboratory animals can be prematurely killed by a number of drugs or deficiencies, these do not in general affect the process of senescence, radiation and the radiomimetic drugs excluded. Experimental efforts to accelerate ageing in rats with dinitrophenol (Tainter, 1936, 1938) and thyroid (Robertson *et al.*, 1933) or retard it with thiouracil (Hartzell, 1945) have been uniformly unsuccessful in bringing about any change in the specific age. Petrova (1946) obtained evidence that induced neurosis at least shortens the life, if it does not affect the specific age, in dogs: it is significant that in man the most effective means of reducing the apparent rate of senile change, *ceteris paribus*, are psychological, social and occupational.

5·3 *Growth-Cessation and Mammalian Senescence*

Mammals in captivity under 'optimal' conditions exhibit both specific size and specific age, and these vary widely between related species, and between genetic races of the same species. The mechanism which determines specific size has long been believed by some workers to intervene more actively in mammalian development and to be more selective in its action on tissues, than the mechanism which leads to the more gradual decline of growth in some reptiles and fish. In these forms, according to this view, the die-away curve of growth, which is generally exponential in relation to body weight, suggests a far more general process of size-limitation affecting all the tissues approximately equally, and reaching the virtual limiting size without much alteration in the general physiology of the animal. 'It is the rule in fishes and other cold-blooded vertebrates that growth is asymptotic and size indeterminate, while in warm-blooded animals, growth comes, sooner or later, to an end. But the characteristic form is established earlier in the former case, and changes less, save for . . . minor fluctuations. In the higher animals, such as ourselves, the whole course of life is attended by constant alteration and modification of form' (D'Arcy Thompson, 1942). The form of the mammalian, and especially the human, cycle both of growth and of senescence has frequently been interpreted as an active process of negative feedback, which operates unequally, which may contribute to the relatively sharp arrest of growth at the level represented by the specific size, but which results in a 'morphogenetic' senescence depending in turn upon a rather limited number of key physiological changes.

With the hypothetical relationship between growth-cessation and senescence in mind, a number of attempts have been made in the past to interpret senile changes in terms of endogenous 'growth inhibitors', whether these are regarded as substances or as physico-chemical conditions (Baker and Carrel, 1926; Carrel and Ebeling, 1921; Simms and Stillman, 1936). The case for such an inhibiting system was stated by Bidder (1932) in the passage already quoted (p. 15). The nature of influences determining mammalian organ size is virtually unknown. Some of these appear to be extra-cellular and inhibitory. In cultures, e.g. of diatoms, growth may be arrested by the accumulation of a metabolite (Denffer, 1948). The most primitive types of morphogenesis, such as that found in hydroids, depend on the acquisition by certain zooids of inhibitory powers over the development of others (Summers, 1938), although the inhibited cells retain the potentiality of growth. It is also known that some 'old' tissue cells are capable of indefinite growth in cultivation.

The suggestions implicit in this type of reasoning are tempting, but there are evidential grounds for caution in postulating a simple 'toxic' senescence due to the existence of a growth-inhibiting senile principle. Such a principle is not readily demonstrated. Bidder once rashly located it in the pineal gland. Kotsovsky (1931) attempted successfully to retard the growth of tadpoles by feeding senile heart muscle—an improbable tissue for such a purpose—and Grimm (1949) obtained similar results with senile plasma. Picado (1930) enhanced the growth of young rats by transfusions of adult plasma. More serious data, however, exist.

The best experimental evidence concerning growth-limitation is probably that obtained from studies of mammalian liver. Although mitotic figures and binucleate cells decrease in mammalian liver throughout life, regeneration after hepatectomy occurs in senile rats, apparently at a rate not much lower, so far as replacement of cell number is concerned, than in young adults, though much less than in growing animals (Bucher and Glinos, 1950). As Minot pointed out (1908) the adult differs more from the infant than the old from the adult. The time-lag between hepatectomy and maximum mitotic count increases with age (Marshak and Byron, 1945), thereby paralleling the difference between the behaviour of tissues from young immature and young adult donors in tissue culture (Hoffman, Goldschmidt and Doljanski, 1937), and confirming the universal finding of increased growth-inertia, rather than decreased growth-capacity, as the most conspicuous character of cellular explants with increasing donor age (Cohn and Murray, 1925; Suzuki, 1926; Medawar, 1940). In regenerating rat liver at all ages, however, the lag reverts to the value characteristic of young animals (Glinos and Bartlett, 1951). In young, actively growing rats the restoration of liver mass after hepatectomy shows a considerable rebound phenomenon, reaching 145 per cent of the original weight in 7 days (Norris, Blanchard and Polovny, 1942). All the general characters of tissue behaviour during the attainment of specific size appear to be exemplified in liver. These include (1) negative specific acceleration of growth, (2) retention of growth-capacity after the limiting size has been attained, as demonstrated either by explants, or, in this case, following partial removal of the organ, (3) increased growth-inertia with increasing age and (4) 'post-inhibition growth rebound'. Medawar (1942) stresses the surprisingly wide distribution of this last effect, which is shown by tissue cultures (Spear, 1928) and *Amblystoma* larvae (Buchanan, 1938) retarded by cooling, and in rats or mice following brief restriction of diet (Osborne and Mendel, 1916; Clarke and Smith, 1938; Jackson, 1936).

Much is still being made of the decline in rate of wound

healing with age proposed by du Noüy (1916, 1932) as a criterion of senescence (Landahl, 1959). This entire theory was based on less than a dozen uncontrolled cases and should now be considered extinct. (Landahl, in citing it, appears to agree that it is probably wrong in fact—but what matter? It gives such a beautiful curve.) Experimental studies suggest that while actual cell replacement in wounded skin is highest in infancy, little difference in cell multiplication exists between adult and senile animals, though here again the time-lag in reaching the peak mitotic rate becomes longer with age (Howes and Harvey, 1932; Bourlière, 1950) though the actual mitotic rate increases (Thuringer and Katzberg, 1959). Delayed healing of skin wounds is not clinically very evident in old people (Elman, 1953). In male mice the mitosis curve for skin *in situ* is bimodal, with peaks in infancy and again in middle age (Bullough, 1949). One easily-measured growth-system which shows a steady decline throughout later life is that controlling finger-nail growth (Knobloch, 1951; Bürger, 1954; Hamilton, Terada and Mestler, 1955).

Attempts have been made in the specific case of liver tissues to relate organ size to the existence of a mitotic inhibitor or inhibitors. Studies on plasmapheresis (Glinos and Gey, 1952) and parabiosis (Bucher, Scott and Aub, 1950) after partial hepatectomy have yielded some evidence that a humoral inhibitor, of the kind envisaged by Carrel and Ebeling (1921), disappears from circulation after hepatectomy. These observations, though interesting, could provide a suspiciously simple picture of the dynamics of growth-limitation, and of consequent senescence.

An opposing view to the humoral school has been suggested by Medawar (1942). Both in whole animals and in specific organs and tissues the rate of growth declines throughout life. Medawar points out that it is not self-evident that this decline is the result of active growth-inhibition. 'We are so deeply influenced by the spirit of Newton's First Law that we tend to think that whenever a *rate* falls off, something is actively suppressing it. This is true of rates of motion, but it is not true in quite the same sense of the rates of a type of change which we may call changes in *probability states*. The rate at which heat is lost from a cooling body is initially high, and falls off as its temperature approaches that of the environment. The rate at which the distribution of molecules in a closed diffusion system tends towards uniformity is likewise rapid at first, and slower and slower thereafter. In these cases, and in others similar to them, we are dealing with rates that fall off "of their own accord", with systems that tend to a certain, most-probable state at a rate which depends upon how far they have yet to go to reach it. We may look in vain for inhibitors and controllers: they are not there. I do not know whether what I have called the "kinetic picture" of growth will be found to fall within the domain of statistical mechanics. . . . It is simply a picture which we should keep in mind when thinking of growth processes, lest we should come to regard the doctrine of growth-controlling factors as self-evident; which it certainly is not.'

This argument is graphical rather than explanatory, and the analogy which it contains must be approached with caution. It is evident that organ size has certain properties of an equilibrium state, in approaching which the cell number and growth-energy vary after the manner of potential energy in the process of redistribution. The equilibrating forces, however, manifestly arise, on the evidence of explanation, from the organ's and the cell's surroundings. Mathematically similar systems involving real energy loss, such as cooling, are in no real sense analogous, since they are examples of a process not subject to further analysis. The decline in human population-growth is as fair a comparison. Although morphogenesis is no doubt ultimately expressible as a redistribution of energy, 'inherent' decline of rate in approaching a most-probable state is only *explanatory*, in the sense of providing a satisfactory regression of causes to the limit of useful experiment, if 'growth energy' is itself a form of energy in the physical sense, analogous to heat in a kettle or electro-chemical energy in a battery—in the hypothetical case where a population of cells was restricted in growth by exhausting a particular energy source, employed only for growth and not for maintenance metabolism, such a system would apply, and would not only depict but 'explain' the course of events.

The great value of the approach from probability, as Medawar points out, is in preventing a facile assumption that if a growth-rate declines, this decline must result from the action of a specific toxin or inhibitor. This does not mean, however, that in a complex biological system we can avoid asking specifically *what* declines, since a decline in rate implies real quantitative and qualitative change in terms of chemical structure, and the investigation of these changes is practicable. It appears manifest that the reversion of explanted tissues to active growth is in fact caused by removal from their previous environment. It seems at least arguable whether the time-lag in multiplication which characterizes aged explants is inherent in the cell at all. Simms found that the lag in cell division of aortic explants from old fowls can be reduced by a number of non-specific procedures such as papain digestion, or washing with an ultra-filtrate of serum (Simms, 1936; Simms and Stillman, 1937). Such effects might even be purely mechanical. For most purposes it is probably also desirable to regard growth-energy less as a 'store', since, to maintain the analogy, such a 'store' must be almost immediately 'replenished' after hepatectomy or explanation, than as a 'space', with walls defined by the continuously-varying properties of any individual cell in the growing tissue, and by the continuously-varying properties of the 'environment', in which are included all the adjacent cells of the same tissue. Such a concept, and, in fact, any concept of limiting size as an equilibrium process, would seem incidentally to imply the continuous replacement of any deciduous cells. The chief criticism of the humoral theories of growth-limitation is their readiness to assume that the limiting factors derived from the 'environment' can (*a*) be treated in isolation and (*b*) necessarily correspond to substances rather than to physico-chemical states and gradients. That adjacent-cell effects need not depend upon molecular hormones is well shown by Whitaker's work on the mutual orientation of *Fucus* egg cells through a simple pH gradient (see J. Needham, 1942). The search for hormonal substances which can be isolated is abundantly justifiable, but the failure to find them should not be astonishing or discouraging. There is much evidence (reviewed by Stewart and Kirk, 1954) to suggest that the 'inhibitors' detected in old serum by Carrel and his associates were nonspecific materials, probably including the serum lipoproteins. This is not to say that such materials do not exert a growth-inhibiting effect *in vivo*, or that such an effect is without physiological significance, but most existing studies certainly support Medawar's conclusion (1942) that there is no simple extractable contact hormone in adult tissue which directly restrains the growth of cells. The 'inflection' in the curve of absolute growth (weight/time) is still occasionally quoted as evidence of active growth-inhibition, but this is a mathematical fallacy which has been repeatedly exposed (Minot, 1908; Schmalhäusen, 1929; Weymouth, 1931; Medawar, 1945).

The most interesting aspect of this question, in relation to senescence rather than morphogenesis, turns once again on the supposed absence of age changes in some reptiles and fish, though speculation is vain so long as we do not know whether this absence is real. The growth of the body, and of the individual organs, in some of these forms follows much the same pattern of decline as that described by Medawar in the growth energy of isolated tissues. If reptiles whose growth declines in this way, and whose degree of histological complexity is in any case similar to that found in mammals, do not exhibit senescence, then *this* general pattern of growth-decline with age, although it occurs in many mammalian tissues treated individually, is not the 'cause' of mammalian senescence. Equilibrium cessation of growth implies the probability of one-for-one replacement in tissues which are capable of continuing division, so that unless some other process intervenes, an organism in the equilibrium state as regards growth should remain indefinitely self-maintaining, except for tissues whose degree of differentiation precludes mitotic renewal. This seems a reasonable depiction of the state of affairs in long-lived cold-blooded vertebrates (at least there seems to be no good evidence to the contrary), but it does not appear to obtain in mammals.

We have already suggested that while we might have reason to expect senescence, or one form of it, in the total absence of cell division, either in the whole animal or in certain organs, it is not self-evident why, in order to avoid senescence, an animal should be obliged to increase constantly its total cell number or its overall body size. If this were the case, it would suggest, perhaps, not that growth prevents senescence, but that the capacity for continued growth reflects a type of morphogenetic physiology which does not produce senescence.

The possibility exists, then, that vertebrate growth-cessation might be of two kinds: that some cold-blooded vertebrates may cease to grow visibly when a cell-population of a particular size and composition is reached, and that this population thereafter remains substantially static, with replacement of all except such mechanically irreplaceable cells as neurones, while mammalian growth is arrested by a more active process—probably of differentiation rather than mere mitotic inhibition—affecting a few key points. This would resemble in its effects the difference between the behaviour of a society which voluntarily limited its reproduction to replacement level, and one which, when a predetermined figure was reached, summarily castrated a vital and hereditary profession. Such a difference, if real, would explain the apparently less catastrophic effects of growth-cessation upon those reptiles which exhibit virtual specific size, compared with the rapid post-mature decline in most mammals. Birds, significantly, occupy a midway position, since it is virtually certain that all species are subject to senescence in captivity, though at specific ages considerably higher than those of mammals of comparable size and activity: their period of growth, however, is proportionately much shorter. A serious investigation of the phylogeny of senescence is badly needed. The hypothesis put forward here would regard it, so far as mammals are concerned, not as the consequence of general growth-cessation, but of a particular *manner* of growth-cessation, involving, perhaps, selective non-renewal of certain important structures and changes in the specificity of the response in others; a genuinely morphogenetic senescence depending upon alteration of cell-responses, and having evolved, or re-evolved, within the phylogeny of vertebrates. The mammalian pattern of ageing, if it differs from that of other vertebrates, would in this case have evolved as a correlate, though not necessarily a consequence, of several fundamentally important physiological processes—homoeothermy, the development of a complex endocrine regulation centred in the pituitary, the avian-mammalian pattern of determinate growth, which is linked with this development, and the system of immune response and tissue specificity characteristic of higher vertebrates. The possible association between size-limitation and homoeothermy is interesting in view of the different relationships between pituitary and thyroid hormones in the determination of growth which have been found in mammals and in amphibians (Evans, Simpson and Pencharz, 1939; Scow and Marx, 1945; Steinmetz, 1954); at some point in vertebrate evolution, a balance-mechanism between thyroid and growth-hormone, which leads to gigantism in the thiouracil-treated tadpole, has become converted into a synergism such as normally operates in the rat or in man. Unfortunately for any phylogenetic theory, the pattern in fish appears to resemble that in mammals (Goldsmith *et al.*, 1944). This subject will be further considered in a subsequent chapter.

ᔕ **6** ᔕ

THE MECHANISMS OF SENESCENCE

THE two theories of mammalian ageing now chiefly fancied by gerontologists, and their recent allies the radiobiologists, are that it represents either (1) progressive loss or functional deterioration of fixed postmitotics or (2) progressive accumulation of faulty copying in clonally-dividing cells—attributed variously to somatic mutation aneuploidy, crosslinking effects in information-carrying molecules, or some other stochastic process which would enable natural ageing to be fitted with the findings concerning radiation-induced life-shortening. Either (1) or (2) could presumably act as a clock located, probably, in one or more key groups rather than in the generality of fixed or of non-fixed tissue cells and would initiate secondary types of mischief which would produce the exponential mortality-rise which we see in life-tables.

All theories of senescence are at present based on unwarrantable assumptions, in the absence of concrete answers to the essential questions of fact. The formulation which would receive, perhaps, the widest assent, at least in the matter of human senescence, is that morphogenetic processes lead to the differentiation of cells which have lost the capacity for division, such as neurones and skeletal muscle fibres, and to a suspension of division in others, and that processes of 'wear and tear', chemical, mechanical, or of a degree of biophysical subtlety depending on the taste of the investigator, thereafter bring about the decline of some or all of the tissues thus deprived of the power of self-renewal. This is plausible and probably true. On the other hand no satisfactory technique has been devised for the study of cell populations *in situ*, apart from the search for mitotic figures in sections; we do not, therefore, know the life-span of most tissue cells in their natural situation; many of the descriptions of senile change in fixed postmitotics, especially neurones, are based upon the assumption that the life-span of cells specialized to this extent is limited by their incapacity for division, as appears to be the case in rotifer and *Anguillula* cells. The striking differences in specific age between related species do not disprove the contribution of cell ageing to general senescence, but they cast a great deal of doubt on any assumption that the effect of wear and tear upon neurones (Bab, 1948; Vogt and Vogt, 1946) or any similar process is the prime mover in determining the senile decline. The powers of self-renewal possessed by neurones apart from cell division have almost certainly been under- rather than over-estimated. Neurone regeneration in adult fish and amphibia can involve actual cell replacement from a reserve of neuroblasts:[1] in adult birds and mammals it is usually held to be limited to axon growth (see Clemente and Windle, 1955 for a review of the large literature). Radioactive thymidine incorporation in rat brain is strictly limited to glia cells, which go on increasing throughout life—it does not appear in neurones (Smart and Leblond, 1961). The numbers of new glial cells appearing seems disproportionately high compared with the number of visible mitoses—some amitotic process may possibly be occurring to supplement them (Smart and Leblond, 1961). Cell division, however, may not be the only means of nuclear renewal—the appearance of 'binucleate' neurones in some old animals has been taken as evidence of a process of reconstitution (Andrew, 1955). Apart from this it is evident from observation that some neurones are capable of living and remaining in function for 100–150 years, unless we postulate a system of 'reserve circuits' which has so far no evidence to support it. The distinction drawn by Weismann between immortal germ cells and mortal soma still persists in many of these assumptions, in spite of the growing number of instances where differentiated somatic cells in invertebrates are thought to give rise to germ cells, or to structures having the potentialities of germ cells (Brien, 1953).

[1] It has even been claimed that the Purkinje cells of the mammalian cerebellum, the least likely of all such cells to do so, undergo a cycle of periodic replacement from such a reserve (Baffoni, 1954). This is surely either a fundamental discovery or an egregious error.

The Mechanisms of Senescence

6·1 Senescence in Cells

6·1·1 'IRREPLACEABLE' ENZYMES

There is no self-evident reason why morphogenetic forces acting upon cells, and inhibiting their free division, should lead to their senescence. Mechanical and 'colloidal' interpretations will not do—they fail to treat postmitotic cells as the dynamic systems which they certainly are A theory of 'mechanical ageing' in postmitotic cells could, however, be based upon the exhaustion of specific cell constituents. It is reasonable to ask how much of the senescence of such cells, if they necessarily undergo senescence, is due to the existence of 'expendable' enzymic or other intracellular structures which can be replaced only at cell division.

The concept of an expendable 'life-ferment' appears to have originated with Bütschli (1882), although he probably regarded it simply as a material undergoing distribution from the germ cells, where it is highly concentrated to the somatic cells in which it is increasingly diluted by subdivision. There are two essentials for our acceptance today of a system in which senescence depends on enzyme exhaustion in postmitotics—we have to postulate (1) a fixed quantity of enzyme present in the cell and exhaustible by use, and (2) the existence of an essential enzyme replaceable only at cell division. The first proviso appears already to be largely met, since it is known that the effective life-span of enzyme molecules is finite in terms of molecule turnover (McIlwain, 1946, 1949; Theorell *et al.*, 1951).

The existence of enzyme systems renewed *only at cell division* has not, it seems, been demonstrated as such, but with the single general and large exception of 'hereditary materials', nuclear and extranuclear, it has not been sought. Some direct evidence might be derived from the action of known selective blocking agents upon bacteria of protozoa. It will be evident, however, that the idea of an 'enzyme replaced only by mitosis' falls very close to some biochemical models of the gene, which has been invested, either directly or at one remove, with direct catalytic properties. McIlwain (1946) has shown that in some catalytic systems the number of enzyme molecules per cell is of the order of unity. The inference from his figures is that if genes are not themselves molecules acting as catalysts, each gene during its 'lifetime' (i.e. between one cell division and the next) produces one such molecule. McIlwain (1949) also calculated the life-span per molecule of the nicotinic acid co-enzyme component of *Lactobacillus arabinosus* as representing the production of $5 \cdot 8 \times 10^7$ mol. lactic acid. Theorell (1951) in tracer experiments demonstrated a very slow turnover of haemoprotein enzymes, the exception being liver catalase which has a molecule/life of only 4–5 days. The wastage of such systems is due, presumably, in part to side reactions and non-specific inactivation, and in part to competitive inhibition or blocking by metabolites partially resembling the correct substrate. If the determination of such a single-molecule system were a cause of cell senescence, and if the catalyst itself were to be identified with the gene, we would evidently need to postulate a copying mechanism at mitosis in which inactivation of the catalytic portion of the system (1) does not interfere with the production of a copy, and (2) is itself reversible: or, alternatively, one in which the products of division are two copies, not an original and a copy. It can, of course, be argued that when a differentiated cell in fact undergoes senescence, we cannot infer whether any system in it *would* be renewed by further division. Its failure to divide, even if that failure is a physiological one, leading to final differentiation, may be due to the loss of a copying mechanism. This type of problem has been encountered already; however, by workers attempting to explain some of the results of research on adaptive variation in *Neurospora* and yeasts. 'Unless gene reproduction and gene action are totally independent of each other, we have to reconcile the uniformity in the reproduction of genes with the enormous variation in what we believe to be their primary products' (Pontecorvo, 1946).

Classical genetics, although they allocate an equal proportion of nuclear genic material to every cell, have so far given little direct information about the activity of this material in cells of different kinds at any time except during mitosis, and a new category of study ('epigenetics') has had to be coined to cover this activity. Of the large number of subsidiary copying processes which have been inferred from adaptation experiments and work on anuclear portions of cells some apparently continue undiminished throughout the intermitotic period. The power of adaptive enzyme production persists in yeasts rendered non-viable by X-rays (Spiegelman, Baron and Quastler, 1951). In a neurone which may remain functioning in man for over a century, either the enzymic mechanism which maintains cell metabolism is continuously kept in repair, or it is of a kind which is almost invulnerable to incidental spoilage by use. The survival-time of non-dividing cells varies greatly, even between closely related organisms: thus in rotifers, the life-span reaches 5 months in *Callidina* (Zelinka, 1891) and even, perhaps, several years in certain bdelloids (Murray, 1910). If 'wear' is to be invoked in these cases where senescence occurs in the presence of cellular determinancy, then the susceptibility to it must vary enormously. Other cells—squamous epithelium, for example— have a function which depends on the progressive *change* in their structure and metabolism from formation to complete cornifica-tion. This implies a process of chemical heterauxesis within the cell, and all such 'open-ended' systems, if they continue, must eventually destroy homoeostasis. The development of histo-chemical methods of detecting enzymes in cells, and of selective blocking agents which irreversibly inactivate particular enzymes, already suggest experiments by which we might learn something of the limits of the postmitotic cell's power to regenerate its en-zymic complement, and detect long-term changes in this power.

A special case of limited survival in the non-dividing cell is provided by the mammalian erythrocyte. This is one of the few cell types for which a life-table can be constructed. The form of the curves obtained by a variety of methods indicates that the decay of circulating erythrocytes is a true 'senescence', i.e. that the probability of the destruction of a given cell increases markedly after it reaches a certain age. There is also, apparently, an 'infant mortality' among newly-formed red cells to make the mimicry of a metazoan survival curve even closer.

The cause of erythrocyte 'senescence' has been the subject of a good deal of study. Although it is probable that the proximate cause of erythrocyte destruction is a change in the physical properties of the stroma or the envelope of the cell, there is considerable evidence that the timing mechanism in this instance is the deleterious effect on other intracellular systems of the products of one particular oxidation-reduction system, in which methaemoglobin is formed from haemoglobin. The evidence for this view has been reviewed by Lemberg and Legge (1949). In this case we are dealing with a specialized, anuclear cell—in the nucleated avian erythrocyte, haemoglobin synthesis, and possibly other processes of renewal, continue in the circulation, but the life-span is, curiously enough, very much shorter (Hevesy and Ottesen, 1945; Hevesy, 1947) than that of the mammalian red cell.

6·1·2 CELL TURNOVER

It is necessary to point to a widespread impression among medical writers on senescence that cell turnover in the organ, of the adult animal is virtually confined to such tissues as skins and that the 'cause' of senescence resides in the exhaustion of endocrine cells which have accompanied the individual throughout life. This may be true of some invertebrates, many of which have a wholly determinate cell number throughout, or in certain organs, such as the corpus allatum of bees (Pflugfelder, 1948) and possibly also in man and other mammals; the most probable candidates in this case are neurones. Definite loss of muscle cells, which are not normally replaced, has been demonstrated by Yiengst, Barrows and Shock (1959). Although the rate of turnover in liver cells decreases with age, and mitotic figures become few, the mean mitosis rate in adult rats is such as to double the volume of the organ in the animal's lifetime, if there were no incidental wastage.[1] This figure suggests that some liver cells may accompany the animals from cradle to grave, but that the majority do not. They do, however, undergo a peculiar process of nuclear multiplication with increasing polyploidy: in post-operative regeneration only the diploids divide to supply new cells (Doljanski 1960; review, Falzone *et al.*, 1959; Tanaka, 1951, 1953). Adrenal cortical cells are said to be continuously replaced in the adult cat (Lobban, 1952). Mitotic activity does, however, appear to decrease with advancing age (Blumenthal, 1945; Townsend, 1946; Korenchevsky, Paris and Benjamin, 1950): in some other tissues, e.g. skin, it

[1] I am indebted to Professor M. Abercrombie, F.R.S., for this figure.

increases (Thuringer and Katzberg, 1959). The generation cycle of mouse duodenal epithelium lengthens with age, and individual variation increases (Lesher, Fry and Kohn, 1961). The adrenals of old rats show various degenerative changes (Jayne, 1953). Mitosis varying in frequency with the sexual cycle occurs in the anterior pituitary (Hunt, 1942, 1943, 1947) though it may not affect all cell types equally, since the population changes in composition with advancing age (Parsons, 1936). There is no direct evidence that the power of cell replacement is lost in any endocrine gland with age, though there may be more general involutional changes at both cellular and tissue levels. The pattern of mammalian endocrine cell behaviour is predominantly one of continual division and replacement, regulated in level by hormonal influences, and often occurring in cycles. It is impossible to say at present whether there is a single key exception to this pattern, but ageing is unlikely to be so simple a matter as the defection of one type of cell. It is significant that the syndrome of senescence cannot be produced experimentally by extirpating any one gland.

The morphological changes in endocrine cells with age have been widely studied, though here, as in all pathological studies or ageing, no line can be drawn between cause and effect. Such morphological changes in pituitary cells have recently been re-examined by Weiss and Lansing (1953) and by Shanklin (1953), but without any new findings on the rate of cellular replacement. In some glandular organs, such as rat salivary glands, mitosis becomes both rare and abnormal in pattern after the end of active body growth, while in senile rats numerous imperfect mitoses occur (Andrew, 1953). For a review of adult cell turnover see Leblond and Walker (1956), Abercrombie (1957).

6·1·3 SOMATIC MUTATION

Somatic mutation as a cause of ageing appears to owe its popularity to three considerations—the fact that mutative change in cell lines would probably lead to eventual ageing if no other cause did so first; the prevalence of theories based upon it in cancer and radiation research; and the readiness with which it lends itself to speculative exercises in higher mathematics (Maynard Smith, 1962).

The Mechanisms of Senescence

The irruption of physicists into age studies—largely because of their current involvement with radiation biology—has produced a whole series of stochastic or 'shooting' theories of ageing, which attempt to view it for purposes of description or explanation, in terms of a combination of random events.

The prototype of these theories is the idea that the predominant process in ageing is somatic mutation, leading to changes in the properties of clonally dividing cells and loss of capacity in fixed postmitotics. Its cause would be the sum of mutagenic influences on the body, and if radiation accelerated ageing, it would do so, in part at least, by increasing the mutation rate. The first suggestion of this in the literature seems to be that of Kunze (1933), who put it down to cosmic rays. In putting it forward again Failla (1960) points out that the large discrepancy between the observed and calculated 'background equivalent' dose in irradiated mice can be removed if we allow for exposure to 'background' in prenatal life, when radiation sensitivity is substantially higher. Failla is the originator of the term 'hit' to describe a hypothetical lesion—point mutation, chromosome loss, or other—occurring in a cell and inactivating it. The term has been taken further in the elaborate stochastic model devised by Szilard (1959a, b).

Szilard assumes that the elementary step in ageing is a 'hit' (not necessarily by a radiant particle) which renders inactive all the genes on one chromosome of a somatic cell. 'Hits' are random events; the probability of any one chromosome being hit remains constant throughout life, and the over-all rate of occurrence of hits is characteristic of the species. As a result of hits, the proportion of adequately functioning somatic cells declines with time until it reaches f^*, at which point the probability of death within unit time (in man, one year) is unity.

At the same time, each individual is assumed to carry a load of genetic 'faults'.

A 'fault' is a mutation in one of the genes essential to the proper working of a somatic cell. Szilard assumes that the number of these genes in man is 3000 out of a probable total of 15,000. A cell becomes inoperative when both of the pair of any such genes are put out of action. Accordingly, when a chromosome receives a hit, the cell will cease to function (*a*) if the

223

homologous chromosome has already also received a hit, or (*b*) if the homologous chromosome carries a 'fault' at any point. By assuming probable values for several quantities which no one accurately knows, Szilard proceeds from this model to draw plausible approximations to quantities which are known, such as the concordance between twin ages at death. He also proposes not an experimental proof, but at least one critical experiment—the reduction of life-span of the progeny of irradiated mice could support or negate the model.

The model itself has other interesting implications. One is that if m, the number of chromosome pairs, differs between species, the specific life shortening per rem will be greater for that in which m is the smaller, and vary inversely as $\sqrt{m}$. Szilard also works out, on the assumption of an average on $n = 2.5$ inherited faults per head for the human female, the modal longevity of a genetically perfect female with no such faults; it comes to 92 as against the present 80 years. If $n > 2.5$, it would be more.

Szilard's model is deeply ingenious, but for the biologist, as for the late Ernie Pyle, 'the first word which comes to mind is But'. Such simplified mathematical models can bring light to a subject—as did Morgan's assumption of the simple linearity of the genes—or merely darken it further. For the model to be relevant at all it seems essential that ageing should be timed by a fault in replication following the loss of one allele in the cell. This raises two grave objections, pointed out at once by Maynard Smith (1959b) and met by Szilard only at the expense of new variables (1959). The first is that, if the fault-hit hypothesis is right, the life of homozygous and inbred animals should be longer than that of heterozygous and hybrid animals, whereas the reverse is almost universally true. The second is that the only reason for Szilard's assumption that a hit inactivates a whole chromosome appears to be the need to find a hittable object yielding the right order of magnitude to account, for example, for the difference between male and female longevity, there being too many genes and too few cells to do so. It is also difficult to relate the whole model to the dynamics of cell division in a system which contains fixed and multiplying cells, where faults acquired by stem cells as the result of 'hits' will be

224

communicated to a varying cellular progeny. If the critical fraction f^* represents simply surviving cell number in general, it is difficult to credit either Failla's or Szilard's version of the cell-loss hypothesis, even if the effect of a 'hit' is not necessarily the physical removal of the cell. Failla (1960), for example, assumes that 'vitality' (the reciprocal of mortality) is ∞f, the proportion of effective cells remaining, so that

$$\frac{f^t}{f^o} = e^{-at} = \text{spontaneous mutation rate, } a \text{ being the slope}$$

factor of the Gompertz equation; and he points out that in this case the hitting process must damage rather than destroy the cell, as otherwise only 5·8 per cent of the cells alive in man at the age of 35 would survive in him at the age of 65.[1] Szilard's theory seems to give an almost equally high rate of cell loss, whereas both completely ignore the question of replacement. If, on the other hand, f^* represents a fraction, not of cell number but only of an unspecified stuff 'vitality', the further equations do no more than restate actuarial observation in new terms. To make them experimentally useful it would seem that ageing must be timed by the loss of key postmitotics (possibly in a single organ) or by a process with the same mathematical shape.

The third stochastic theory, by contrast with the Szilard-Failla model, places the emphasis specifically on the dividing cell, but on one particular clonal system. Antibodies are now thought to be produced by lymphocytes, and the acquired power of making a particular antibody appears to be transmitted by a lymphocyte to its progeny. A mechanism, not fully understood, determines that lymphocytes shall not normally respond to their proprietor's body constituents by forming antibodies against them.

Campbell and Work (1953) have recently drawn attention to the significance of the fact that animals cannot in general be immunized against their own proteins; and they suggest that the action of the genotype in determining specificity may be

---

[1] This is an arbitrary assumption, and Failla moreover undermines our confidence, in this paper, by devising a 'constant' which is discovered by ceremoniously taking away the number he first thought of.

chiefly a negative one, in the prevention rather than the creation of a specific configuration. Burnet (1959) has suggested that if mutation in lymphocytes followed by selection determines the various reactive capacities which they show, and if one possible mutation is the loss of this negative specificity to homologous antigens, then the organism might be expected to face a steady increase in autoimmune reactions with the passage of time—reactions which might well be of precisely the polymorphic, diffuse, and variable type which characterizes the infirmities of ageing, whereas the statistical constancy of the mutation rate and/or the rate of occurrence of Szilardian 'hits' would remain to provide the stability of the survival curve on which life assurance depends.

The revival of immunological age theories is an unexpected return to Metchnikoff (1899), who always predicted that the same cellular mechanism would prove to be morphogenetic in the embryo, defensive in the adult, and destructive in the end. Burnet's suggestion is open to experiment, and may possibly be confirmed or refuted reasonably quickly. Moreover, if true, it would mean that ageing was likely to be much more accessible to medical interference than it is now prudent to expect. It is not incompatible with some aspects of the Szilard-Failla model —the effect of a hit in this case is not that it removes a cell from useful activity, but that it puts a cell and its progeny into harmful activity. Burnet's general theory of 'clonal selection' (1959) seems to imply that mutational instability in the lymphocyte system is used adaptively by the body, and moreover that the harmful mutation with loss of negative specificity also confers protection on the mutant against being 'selected out' by normal body mechanisms, f^* being now no longer a cell balance below which we are bankrupt, but the fraction remaining after a lethal percentage of cells has become corrupted in this way. Burnet's theoretical argument persuasively urges that something of the sort ought to happen. What is now required is experimental evidence that it does so: Cole (1962) has lately shown that the lymphocytes of old mice are less active in proliferating after isogenic transplantation, but not the reason for this behaviour.

The gerontological interest of these suggestions lies in the fact that they come at a time when, in reviewing likely mechanisms of ageing, both somatic mutation and autoimmunity are being re-examined. The grounds for this re-examination are so far hypothetical, not experimental. In general the re-examiners argue on the following lines:

(1) Somatic mutation causes divergence in tissue cells, albeit at an unmeasured rate. It would eventually impair tissue vigour if nothing else did.

(2) Among its likely consequences is the production of new cells which are to some degree 'not-self', as a result of the mutation of structural genes. If these cells are viable they will excite autoimmune reactions of varying degree. The incidence of autoimmune disease increases with age in a Gompertzian manner (as do many other things—logarithms are great levellers).

(3) The syndrome of chronic incompatibility ('runt disease') bears, to the eye of faith, certain resemblances both to senescence and to progeria (Tyler, 1960); more specifically, the splenic index and the incidence of hepatomegaly increase in ageing, progeria and runt disease (Krumbhaar and Lippincott, 1939; Manschot, 1940; Simonsen *et al.*, 1958).

(4) There is a suggestive three-cornered relationship between age processes, neoplastic processes, and autoimmune or supposedly autoimmune phenomena such as scleroderma.

(5) Autoimmune phenomena are at present a 'growth stock' and they should be re-examined in connection with every unsolved biological problem. This unspoken, but none the less defensible, argument applies equally to mutation, radiation-induced or otherwise.

All these arguments save the last have been intelligently amplified by Walford (1962). There are experimental instances of immunological diversity in leukaemias (Anderson, Walford and Doyle, 1961) and tumours generally (Tyler, 1960), but not very many in normal ageing—chiefly, perhaps, because they have not yet been extensively sought by the sophisticated methods now available for histocompatibility analysis. Mariani (Mariani *et al.*, 1960) grafting from male to female 'A' strain mice of different ages found signs of 'a gradual immunologic maturation coupled with constantly changing skin properties': of the old—old grafts, none took.

By locating the mutation in the antibody-producing cell rather than in the target tissue cell, Burnet's hypothesis steps over one prime difficulty of other somatic mutation hypotheses, that the likely mutation rate in tissue cells can hardly be high enough to account for ageing if cells are to be lost one by one, as they mutate—particularly if the mutant gene is recessive, or more than one mutation is involved. The gap we have to bridge to resolve this 'bifurcation of Nature' is in finding some way in which somatic mutation of one cell could induce these mutation-like consequences in its unmutated neighbours of similar cell type. If it is the antibody-producing cell which is affected, this difficulty does not arise; it needs only one mutation, followed by rapid clonal multiplication, to do extensive damage to the correspondingly antigenic target tissue. The mutation need not, indeed, affect specificity—if, as Burnet suggests, 'self' reacting clones are inhibited by overstimulation, it need only affect sensitivity, and the setting of the stimulation-inhibition mechanism.

Burch's hypothesis of malignant change (1963a, b) involves the assumption that there are epigenetic regulators (of cell differentiation and, indirectly, of cell number) within the cell, which are accessible to immunological interference by antibody at the cell surface. Mutation in a structural gene leads to production of a sterically incorrect messenger-substance, hence to an immunological incompatibility. This change, once it occurs, leads to disorganization of the endoplasmic reticulum and an irreversible loss of a control-substance normally present in the cell, probably a lipo-protein. There is a schematic likeness between Burch's hypothesis of malignancy and Szilard's 'hits' and 'faults', in that it is assumed to depend on four events of mutation in each of two genes, probably in each member of two gene-pairs, one structural and the other regulator, of which one or two are commonly prezygotic, and correspond to 'faults'. The balance between prezygotic and postzygotic mutations is further affected, however, because this is an autoimmune process, and the homozygote mutant will accordingly be tolerated.

For this mechanism to be fitted into general epigenetics we can consider the reaction at the cell surface, which precedes or initiates disturbance in hypothetical 'differentiation-mitosis metabolites' of the cytoplasm, as an 'echo' or negative feedback from the body's total immunological self-awareness evoked by a wrong identification-signal. The mutated cell misidentifies itself to its cellular neighbours, thereby evoking immunological reprisals—which, in this case, instead of destroying the mutant cell, put it 'out of control' by normal epigenetic mechanisms.

Burch has elaborated his whole model to account for one special case of what can happen when a cell, through mutation, mis-identifies itself to a control mechanism—namely escape into malignancy. This is an easy consequence to detect, because a tumour is a visible object. If Burch is right, however, one might envisage a wide spectrum of other consequences of structural gene mutation depending on the kind of cell involved, the other genes or mutations present, the number and character of the structural mutations which had already appeared during the period of prenatal tolerance, and, most important, the nature of the feedback mechanisms normally present. One likely consequence would be cell deletion, but this, unlike tumour production, would not be detectable, if it involved only the mutated cell. For an immunological mechanism to produce progressive cell loss, a 'negative' malignancy, we should have to postulate either a loss of specificity in the immunological response of the body as a whole, or a response damaging to the mutated cell's neighbours. Burnet's suggestion gets over the difficulty by postulating a mutation in the antibody-producing not the antigen-producing side.

The answer to the impasse could also conceivably lie in the nature of the body's reply to a cell which misidentifies itself. In Burch's theory this is straightforwardly immunological. But there may be more than one reply. It is an old idea that a mutated cell might multiply anaplastically if through non-recognition it fails to evoke some hypothetical humoral feedback mechanism. The assumptions made about humoral influences in maintaining tissue structure and organ size have been criticized by Abercrombie (1957), and Burch's hypothesis is in accord with modern epigenetics in attributing malignancy to consequences of antibody reaction with the cell, not to its failure to evoke an extracellular negative feedback. We should mention this type of humoral hypothesis only because if it were true, and if mutation in a tissue cell were able to produce over-correction, the difficulty over mutation rate and 'negative' malignancy would be elegantly solved: mutation in one cell would then produce feedback effects not only on the mutated cell, but on all its normal neighbours of similar type.

It would now be tempting to bring Metchnikoff up-to-date on the lines along which Weiss (1950) and Burnet (1959a, b) are apparently thinking, by identifying the epigenetic 'net' or mould which maintains somatic differentiation with two factors —cell surface effects and immunological factors which influence them, in response to the appearance not of 'non-self' structural materials, but of cellular constituents which were absent, or occurred in subcritical amounts, at earlier stages of development. If this were so, it might mean that the 'self' reacting lymphocyte clones postulated by Burnet are not abolished or held in a suppressed condition, so much as otherwise occupied as parts of a functioning epigenetic mechanism.

So far so good—with a little ingenuity and in the absence of experimental fact we could very easily wrap up somatic mutation, Szilardian faults, autoimmunity and senescence into a single package: loss of cells and loss of function are a polymorphic form of runt disease, due to growing diversity of body constituents and lymphocyte clones with age, and all reflecting the consequences of mutation. Unfortunately, the suggestions of Burch (1963c) also point to an important snag in Burnet's hypothesis, in so far as it is applied to explain ageing. Autoimmune phenomena increase regularly in incidence as a power of age, but are notoriously more prevalent in females: for inflammatory polyarthritis, the extrapolated age of 50 per cent incidence is 230 years in males and 115 in females. On these and other grounds Burch has suggested that the site of autoimmunity should be a mutation on one or both X chromosomes. Following this line of argument, the mutation rate of lymphocytes should, in women, be double that in men: they should produce prohibited clones with a double frequency, but they should also have double the repertoire of competent antibody-producing clones in general, and, Burch argues, a correspondingly lower incidence of infectious disease—as, indeed, they have. On these assumptions they should, if Burnet's mechanism is responsible for ageing, age twice as fast as men, instead of somewhat more slowly, as they in fact do. Arguments about the X chromosome apart, the observed incidence of autoimmune disease between the sexes runs counter to the idea that autoimmunity, at least of the kind under discussion, is the chief timer of human ageing. As to the X chromosome, the findings of Jacobs and Court Brown (1963) suggest that there is a good deal still to be learned about the behaviour of this structure in the two sexes with increasing age.

The activities of other mathematicians in speculating about the form of the mortality curve are reviewed by Mildvan and Strehler (1960). One fatal objection to any simple theory of ageing as a result of somatic mutation seems to have been removed by the finding that some, though not all, radiomimetic drugs can produce life-shortening (p. 265); but other, equally grave, objections remain. Maynard Smith (1962) has drawn attention to two of these. One is the huge somatic mutation-rate which would be required to account for the observed rate of ageing: if we assume a rate in man of the same order as that assignable to germ cells, the likelihood that a given locus will have mutated in a man of 35 is 10^{-5}, and if the mutant is recessive the likelihood of its double occurrence is therefore 10^{-10}.[1] If there are 20,000 such cell-killing loci, the proportion of cells inactivated by mutation could not be much more than 2 per million at the age of 30, and perhaps 4 per million by the age of 60. This is not enough.

A second objection is that if ageing is due solely to point mutation the life of a haploid should be vastly inferior to that of a diploid. In haploid amphibia it is, but they are poor things, while in *Habrobracon* haploid and diploid males have about equal life-spans, though the haploids are much more sensitive to radiation (Clarke, 1957; Clark and Rubin, 1961). Another if weaker objection is that dietary restriction slows ageing, but

[1] It is conceivable, of course, that there is a class of somatic mutations which are epigenetically dominant (due to 'masking' of the other allele in certain body cells): such mutations would be tissue-selective in their expression.

231

cannot slow mutation (Bjorksten, 1962)—it might presumably influence the expression of mutations which had already occurred, without preventing their occurrence, and certainly affects the number of cell-generations in which mutations could be expressed.

It is necessary, however, to distinguish between somatic mutation of genes and other chromosomal damage, leading, e.g., to aneuploidy. There may also be special effects whereby particular mutations produce peculiarly catastrophic results.

It is clear that if mammalian tissues exhibit either 'distribution' or increasingly imperfect mitosis with increasing age, resulting in the accumulation of aneuploid or effectively aneuploid cells, this would lead to steady deterioration of equilibrium. Any difference in liability to senescence between mammals and lower vertebrates would be explicable, in terms of this theory, on the ground that mutation rate would be higher, in all probability, with higher temperatures and chromosome numbers.

This is another highly ingenious but unproven suggestion. Mammalian somatic cells are known to display some aneuploidy (Hsu and Pomerat, 1953; de Carli, 1961; a large and even more contentious body of data is reviewed by Sorokina, 1950).

If the copying-mechanisms of somatic cells could be shown to deteriorate, like those of the *Paramecium* macronucleus, the further they travel from the germ line, senescence might result from the fact of cell turnover, not from its cessation. A possible mechanism for this has been suggested to me by Dr. Helen Spurway. She suggests that as a result of somatic mutation the constituent cells of some mammalian tissues may lose their autarky and become a 'community', in which both function and the capacity for replacement have undergone distribution. Such a community would contain both irreplaceable and indispensable members, and would therefore ultimately undergo senescence. Apart from actual aneuploidy, moreover, it appears from nuclear transplantation experiments that with differentiation there is a steady decline either in the completeness or in the availability of genetic information—in frogs, for example, the percentage of nuclei containing full genetic complements and able to generate a whole viable animal falls from 30 per cent or more in the blastula to 3 per cent in swimming tadpole gut epithelium (Gurdon, 1962)—whether parts of the complement are lost or only masked is not yet known.

Variation in chromosome number has been reported in human (Andres and Jiv, 1936; Timonen and Therman, 1950; Therman and Timonen, 1951) and pig embryos (Sorokina, 1950). In adult rat liver, Tanaka (1961, 1953) recently described wide variation in chromosome number. He found that cells with 42 chromosomes (diploids) contribute primarily to the growth of embryonic liver and to regeneration after hepatectomy in adults, and that growth and restoration were apparently confined to diploids and subdiploids. Walker and Boothroyd (1953) have shown that such 'aneuploidy' is easily simulated by faulty technique. But clearly any evidence that the copying of somatic cells deteriorates is of gerontological importance, and might restore the relevance to metazoan ageing of much which was formerly written concerning the senescence of clones: the most striking observation of this kind so far is the finding of Court Brown that aneuploidy in human leucocytes increases from about 4 per cent at 10 years to 13–15 per cent at 80 years (Jacobs, Court Brown and Doll, 1961). This is an unequivocal demonstration that either chromosomal abnormality in the body, or the liability to it in culture, increase sharply with age in some cells at least. According to more recent work, it looks as if only the sex chromosomes, not the autosomes, are affected by the presumed error of division (Brunton, Jacobs and Court Brown, 1962). It now looks doubtful whether any normal, untransformed human tissue cells can really be propagated in tissue culture (Hayflick and Moorhead, 1961).

The character of the proteins produced by the animal may also change in successive cellular generations. Apart from the theory of clonal selection in lymphocytes (Burnet, 1959; see p. 265) it has occasionally been suggested that senescence is a manifestation of an 'immune' response to endogenous hormones (e.g. Picado and Rotter, 1936; Freud and Uyldert, 1947; Walford, 1962). A more subtle change in specificity of cell response, or of the properties of cellular products, whether it be interpreted immunologically, or, more probably, morphogenetically, cannot be ruled out. If cells in general or certain cells could be shown to acquire adaptive resistance to physiological regulators, as do bacteria to unfamiliar metabolites, from generation to generation, interesting possibilities would certainly be opened. Compensatory hypertrophy declines with age: Gregerman (1959), however, found no decline in the adaptive enzyme production of old rats, as judged by their ability to form tryptophan peroxidase and tyrosine transaminase. (See also Bertolini, 1962.)

Gaillard (1942) has carried out a long series of studies relating the degree of differentiation which can be produced and maintained in tissue explants to the age-status of the press juice in which they are grown. According to these results, functional differentiation in endocrine and other explants can be obtained if they are grown successively in press juices from embryos of increasing age, while some degree of regression of structure occurs if the series is reversed, and explants are grown in juices of decreasing age-order. This process has not so far been followed into senescence. No doubt if explants could be cultivated in media exactly simulating the chemical and physical environment and its changes through all the stages of development, they would pass through all the normal phases of *in vivo* histology. The point of interest to the gerontologist is to know how far it is possible to maintain a *status quo* at any point. Analysis of the power of tissues to mark time developmentally while retaining function requires more elaborate methods of organ and tissue culture than are so far available, but the lead given by Carrel in applying these techniques to age-processes has hardly been pursued with the vigour it merits. Gey (1952) has recently referred to the *in vitro* culture of 'thyroid, parathyroid, adrenal cells, and the germinal epithelium of the ovary', even to the production of follicles, but these findings remain contentious.

6·1·4 'CROSS LINKING' OF MACROMOLECULES

The thermal contractility of collagen in man, rat, mouse, chinchilla and rabbit undergoes a progressive age change at a rate consistent for the species (Verzár, 1955, 1956, 1957, 1959a; Banfield, 1956; Banga, 1957; Brown and Consden, 1958; Kohn and Rollerson, 1960; Lupien and McCay, 1960; Chvapil and Hrůza, 1959; Hrůza, Chvapil and Kobrle, 1961). In scar tissue the collagen present has the age-status, thus judged, of the scar, not of the animal (Verzár, in press) while in dietarily retarded animals it remains apparently young (Chvapil and Hrůza, 1959). Pregnancy apparently hastens its ageing (Árvay, Takács and Verzár, 1963).

This process is a model for a revived form of the old hypothesis of colloidal ageing, which attributes age-processes to slow physical change in body colloids of low turnover—based, now, not on progressive dehydration, as originally proposed by Růžícká (1924) and Marinesco (1934), but on the cross-linking of macromolecules, with consequent inactivation (Harman, 1955, 1956; Bjorksten, 1962, review; Miescher, 1955; Gross, 1962). According to this view, both radiation and chemical mutagens act on the age-process by the liberation of free radicals and the promotion of cross-linking in cell constituents generally —not necessarily nor only in the genetic information store. The appearances in ageing collagen are consistent with cross-linking, but other changes occur, particularly in the associated polysulphates (Gross, 1962, review). The influence of dietary retardation and the fact that collagen is not significantly aged by X-ray exposure at levels which reduce the life-span (Sinex, 1957; Verzàr, 1959) both have to be fitted into the theory. The thermal denaturation of bovine thymus DNA also changes significantly with age (von Hahn and Verzár, 1963). That from old cows has a higher thermal stability to 0.0025M $NaNO_3$ than DNA from calf thymus. According to Parhon, excision of the thyroid and gonad in rats appears to accelerate the age change in collagen (Parhon, Pitis, Stan and Petresco, 1962). In general, as has already been remarked (p. 46) the idea of 'colloidal' senescence now looks more plausible than it did a few years ago, and the turnover even of active body constituents seems to be more uneven than some of us expected (Comfort, 1956; Lansing, 1952).

6·2 *Endocrine Senescence*

6·2·1 GENERAL

The early discoverers of hormones were fully convinced that they had in their hands the key to the prevention of senescence in man. The fact that little of their enthusiasm persists today is due very largely to the manner in which the confluence of two deeply emotive subjects—ageing and the gonad—affected scientific judgement in the early years of the century. The hypotheses of the rejuvenators were in many respects reasonable, if their published claims were not. In any discussion of endocrine senescence it is probably worth restating (1) that organ and tissue grafting are appropriate and fully respectable techniques for the investigation of senile change, and that they have given misleading answers chiefly because the wrong questions were asked, (2) that the use of hormones in the palliation of senile changes in man, although it is largely ineffective, was a reasonable experiment which has not yet been exhausted, and (3) although gonadal 'senescence' does not 'cause' somatic senescence (this was self-evident in antiquity, from the life-histories of eunuchs, long before testosterone was found to be unavailing in reversing general senile decay), it is a highly important model process, and a relatively accessible one for further study.

Characteristic variations in hormone output occur throughout the mammalian life-cycle; they are of two types—cyclical and secular. These changes are the biochemical equivalent of the sudden movements of embryonic tissue which are seen in speeded-up films of developing organisms—they are part cause, part effect, and they represent only the outward and visible manifestation of changes in the quality and quantity of cell response. The hormones most likely to be linked directly with the senile process, such as the growth hormone of the pituitary, cannot be estimated in the intact animal. Of those which can be so estimated, the group of 17-ketosteroids show a decline which continues with the rise of the force of mortality (McGavack, 1951; Kirk, 1949; Hamburger, 1948; Robinson, 1948; Hamilton and Hamilton, 1948; Hamilton, Hamilton and Mestler, 1954 (Fig. 66)). The concept of an 'adrenopause' analogous to the menopause seems to have little to support it at present. Apart from this, there is no single hormonal change which correlates with senescence, no single endocrine organ, of those which can be removed without fatal results, whose extirpation produces the syndrome of senility in mammals; and no hormone or combination of hormones which is known to produce more than a

236

limited, and apparently secondary, reversal of senile changes. Ablation of a gland is not the same thing as its senescence *in situ*, and in surgical castration for prostatic and mammary cancer there is evidence that interconversion may take place between adrenal and gonadal steroids, but no simple hypothesis that senescence is a 'withdrawal' effect is substantiated by the existing experimental evidence. It appears that the sequence of developmental changes in endocrine activity which ends in

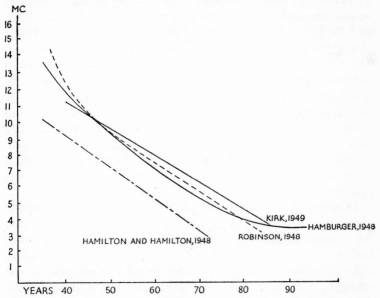

Fig. 66.—Neutral 17-ketosteroids, 24-hour urinary excretion (Kirk, 1949).

senescence cannot so far be made to run backwards by hormone supplements, except in a very minor degree.

In a long series of studies, Korenchevsky (e.g. Korenchevsky and Jones, 1947, 1948; Korenchevsky, Paris and Benjamin, 1950, 1953; Korenchevsky, 1961) has tried to show how far hormone supplements can reverse the senile process, judged by the restoration of the relative hypoplasia of organs. A great many of the senile structural changes described in endocrines are closely paralleled, though at a lesser level of severity, by the changes in structure which follow gonadectomy, and many of them are reversible by gonadal hormones. (Korenchevsky *et al.*, 1950; McGavack, 1951). The peripheral effects of sex hormones in senility, such as the recornification of the vagina by oestrogen (Loeb, 1944), are familiar enough. The decrease of mitotic rate and degree of vacuolation in the adrenal (Townsend, 1946; Blumenthal, 1945) and the increase of collagen and reticulum in the capsule and in the parenchyma (Dribben and Wolfe, 1947) which occur with advancing age are partially reversible by oestrogen, and more fully reversible by a combination of oestrogen, androgen and progesterone (Korenchevsky, Paris and Benjamin, 1950). In the pituitary of the senile rat, Wolfe (1943) found a decrease in eosinophils, but no increase in basophils; vacuolation, like that which follows castration, occurred in the basophils with increasing age. These changes, particularly the decrease in eosinophils, are at least partially reversed by testosterone propionate (Wolfe, 1941). The senescent changes in fowl pituitary described by Payne (1949, 1952) were greatly hastened by gonadectomy. In other words, gonadal failure may contribute to senescence, but probably does so only when it occurs at a certain point in the endocrine developmental programme.

In some instances, direct estimations of the capacity of senile endocrines to respond to physiological stimuli have been made. The thyroid of aged males shows no loss of capacity to respond to thyrotropic hormone (Baker, Gaffney, Shock and Lansdowne, 1959). Solomon and Shock (1950) tested the response of the adrenal cortex in 27 young and 26 old men to a dose of adrenocorticotropic hormone (ACTH) and in 15 young and 13 old men to a dose of 0·4 mg. adrenaline. No difference in eosinopenia was observed after ACTH, but adrenaline produced a significantly greater eosinophil depression in the young group. From this it was inferred that the senile cortex can still secrete 11-17 oxysteroids without gross impairment, but that the response of the pituitary to acute adrenaline stimulation is lower in old than young subjects. Pincus (1950) likewise found no impairment of response to ACTH in old men compared with young controls. But with chromatographic techniques, Rubin, Dorfman and Pincus (1955) have examined the range of α-17 ketosteroids produced at different ages. There is here little

238

difference between men and women: in both, the greatest decline with age is in androsterone and aetiocholan-3α-ol-17-one, and the second greatest in the 5α-11-oxygenated steroids. Such studies offer considerable promise.

The hypophysis is clearly the site of election for 'fundamental' and all-explaining endocrine changes leading to senescence—the part which it has played in the provision of such emotionally-satisfying theories follows naturally from the fact that it is known or credibly suspected to be involved in the regulation of almost all mammalian processes of homoeostasis. Its proximity to the hypothalamus enables it to be linked with theories which locate senescence in the central nervous system. Hypophysial factors in senescence have also a special importance because of the relation of the hypophysis to the control of growth. In its simplest form, starting from cellular exhaustion, the idea of a primary pituitary senescence drew plausible anatomical arguments from the histological studies of Parsons (1936) and Simmonds (1914) on long series of glands from subjects of various ages, or from more recent work such as that of Payne (1949, 1952) on the ageing fowl.

If there has been a tendency for the existence of the pituitary gland to serve as a pretext for vagueness of thought concerning the nature of senescence in mammals—the function formerly discharged by the pineal in the search for the seat of the soul —there are also solid arguments for its direct involvement, certainly as mediator, but possibly also as originator, of senile processes. Because the pituitary is profoundly concerned with several processes of homoeostasis, and is involved with morphogenetic timing mechanisms like that which initiates puberty, it is easy to develop by hypotheses of pituitary senescence which do not depend upon an unbiological argument in terms of single hormones.

The function of trophic hormones appears to be the provision of one limb of a system of negative feedback, by which the level of effector-organ secretion is maintained and kept constant. If senescence be regarded as a continuously self-aggravating disequilibrium (a positive feedback process), then such a process can be induced in a model control system, normally dependent upon negative feedback, by several types of change.

Consider a system in which a device A produces a signal which increases the activity of a second device B, and in which, at the same time, the activity of B produces a signal which reduces the activity of device A. The properties of most self-regulating biological systems can be reproduced in this model by varying the characteristic of the stimulus A → B or the negative feedback B → A, and the number of stable states of A or B. If there is no time-lag in either of these processes, the level of output B will tend to be constant and self-restoring. If there is an appreciable time-constant in one limb of the circuit, the system will tend to function as a relaxation oscillator. In this case, A stimulates B, which does not immediately respond. Stimulus A → B continues to increase, reaching a level which corresponds to an ultimate response in B sufficient to inhibit A completely. The output of B then declines, permitting A to recover, and this represents one whole cycle. It is a requisite for the functioning of such a system that the unmodified output of A shall tend to increase in the absence of output B, i.e. that the state of A is inherently unstable. If output A be assumed to be the pituitary gonadotrophin and output B the gonadal hormone, then the immediate response of the pituitary to castration, or senile decline in gonadal response, is of the unstable type, though other mechanisms operate later to restore regulation. Where, as may be the case in the male, the pituitary-gonad balance operates as a level-control, gradual failure of B's response would be expected to cause a gradual increase in output A. In a similar system containing a time-constant, and therefore behaving cyclically, blocking would be expected to occur at one point in one particular cycle, with a proportionately greater rise in output A.

The importance of this homoeostatic concept is that in the simplified model self-regulating equilibrium can be turned to progressive disequilibrium by several types of change. Decline in the capacity of either A or B to respond to B → A or A → B will result in a permanently unstable state of A. If the response of A fails, B will also be driven into maximum output. Decline in the capacity of B to produce B → A will induce the unstable state of A. Decline in the capacity of A to produce A → B will lead to the relapse of B into its stable state of zero output. This, however, where B's output effects other systems, will cause disequilibrium in a complex physiology. In addition to these purely quantitative changes, biological cybernetic mechanisms are also capable of exhibiting, and in development, characteristically do exhibit, qualitative change in the specificity both of signal and response, which further complicates the picture.

Although analogies from circuits oversimplifying the reality of mammalian homoeostasis, they indicate the number of variables to be considered in studying the senescence of homoeostatic systems; and they indicate some of the ways in which such senescence can be analysed. Evidence suggests that in the case of the gonad it is the function of B which declines. With the pituitary trophic hormones, other than the gonadotrophins and ACTH, *in vivo* estimation of levels, corresponding to the measurement of output A, cannot as a rule be carried out. The action of these homoeostatic systems, moreover, is not expressed through static components but through a developing organism in which long-term trends in cell specificity are themselves controlled by the signals involved in the homoeostatic process—as if the system $A \rightleftharpoons B$ were fitted in a vehicle whose movement it controlled, but which travelled into a hotter and hotter environment, thereby upsetting the characteristics of A and B.

These highly complex hormonal homoeostatic systems are of the greatest importance in higher vertebrates, although the problem of 'three-dimensional' homoeostasis, or homoeostasis superimposed on morphogenesis, is general in all developmental physiology. The views of Minot (1908) upon 'cytomorphosis' (differentiation and maturation) as a cause of senescence carry the very important, and at first sight very probable, inference that no complex organism, and certainly no vertebrate, can remain in an indefinitely stable equilibrium. Where growth processes and differentiation are superimposed on homoeostasis they are analogous to 'drift' in a control system—on this basis any system of differential growth must tend to increasing disequilibrium, unless the developmental 'drift' itself modifies the homoeostatic system to keep them appropriate to the altered situation.

6·2·2 GONAD-PITUITARY SYSTEM

Senescence of the *gonad* regularly precedes or accompanies senescence of the owner in a number of phyla—so much so that declining reproductive capacity is a token of senescence almost as valuable as the direct measurement of increased force of mortality. The relation of gonadal senescence to somatic senescence has clearly much evolutionary interest, since once the first is complete, in an organism, to the point at which that organism's contribution to posterity is no longer statistically significant, any further adverse change in viability is generally speaking inaccessible to the influence of natural selection, except in a very roundabout way.

In almost all litter-bearing mammals, a decline in litter size is characteristic of senescence. The long post-reproductive period found in women is exceptional in mammals. It probably represents a genuine biological difference, quite apart from the far greater perfection of the techniques for keeping human beings alive (Bloch and Flury, 1959). Compared with the more gradual disappearance of ova in other mammals, the human menopause is unusually complete and sudden. The range of this phenomenon among primates is not at present known. Nobody has seen a postmenopausal monkey (Krohn 1955).

There is some cause for regarding gonadal senescence and the group of effects which follow senile gonadal withdrawal as a separate 'senescence' from that of the animal as a whole, since gonadal supplements can reverse a whole series of subsidiary senile changes without materially reversing the progress of somatic senescence judged by survival. In the castrated male mammal, gonadal hormone supplements may perhaps actually shorten life. There is no demonstrable androgen deficiency in normal senile male rats (Korenchevsky, Paris and Benjamin, 1953), nor, probably, in most old men.

Although sex hormones do not rejuvenate the organism in the manner envisaged by writers such as Voronoff, they produce a closer approach to 'rejuvenation', covering more structures and body processes than do any other hormones which have been investigated. In addition to their effects upon the secondary sexual characters, such as beard growth (Chieffi, 1949) or structure of vaginal epithelium (Loeb, 1944; Allen and Masters, 1948) and upon the genitalia themselves, androgens (Kenyon, 1942; Kochakian and Murlin, 1931; Kochakian, 1937) and probably also oestrogens (Kenyon, 1942) exert an important 'anabolic' effect with nitrogen retention and increased protein synthesis, and produce a number of unexpected peripheral changes, generally in the direction of a restoration of 'young' structure (Korenchevsky, Paris and Benjamin, 1953). Thus oestrogens have been stated to produce a striking reversal of the atrophy of the senile nasal mucosa (Kountz, 1950) and certainly produce extensive changes in senile skin, with dermal regeneration (Goldzieher and Goldzieher, 1950; Chieffi, 1950a) and restoration of elasticity (Chieffi, 1951). That the possibility of 'rejuvenation by replacement' is limited, even where the reproductive organs are concerned, is shown by Kirk's failure (1948, 1949) to restore the phosphatase activity of senile prostatic secretion with androgens, although this activity is so restored in young hypogonadal males.

The relation of these changes and their reversal to the general picture of senescence in mammals remains extremely obscure. Of the more general processes in which gonadal hormone withdrawal plays a part, few have been identified with certainty. It has been suggested, for instance, that the osteoporosis of old age is a result of the withdrawal of gonadal anabolic hormones (Allbright, 1947). All theories of gonadal action in senescence have, however, to accommodate the probability that *in mammals senile change in the force of mortality of apparently typical form, and at approximately the typical specific age, occurs in both sexes in the absence of both gonads*, regardless of the age at which these are removed.

The mechanisms which fix the timing of puberty, and of the human menopause, are the most obvious of all mammalian age processes, and quite the most promising experimentally. The key problem is to determine whether the timing-factors reside primarily in the gonadal cells or elsewhere. The application of transplantation techniques to this question has been reviewed by Krohn (1955). Unfortunately, it already appears likely that there are considerable interspecific differences. The ability of the gonadal cells *in situ* to respond to gonadotrophin has sometimes been regarded as controlling the onset of puberty.

Pituitary gonadotrophin is detectable in the hypophysis of the 17 cm. pig foetus (Smith and Dortzbach, 1929) and the implantation of glands from 3-month-old rabbits is as effective in inducing puberty as implantation of adult glands (Saxton and Greene, 1939). The ovaries of immature rabbits do not respond to injected gonadotrophin (Hertz and Hisaw, 1943; Parkes, 1942–44; Adams, 1953). On the other hand, it has long been known that when ovaries are transplanted reciprocally between young and old animals, it is the age of the recipient before or after puberty, not that of the ovary, which determines function or non-function (Foà, 1900, 1901; Long and Evans, 1922) and in some species gonadotrophin readily induces precocious ovarian and testicular development. Domm (1934) was able to induce crowing at 9 days of age and treading at 13 days in cockerel chicks by injections of pituitary gonadotrophins. The timing-mechanism is stable within a species or a genetic strain. Human puberty very exceptionally occurs during childhood without any obvious pathological cause ('constitutionalprecocious puberty'—Novak, 1944) and pregnancy has actually been reported in a child of five (Escomel, 1939). In albino rats, according to Mandl and Zuckerman (1952), genetic factors seem to play the major part in determining the age of puberty. Lorenz and Lerner (1946) likewise found clear evidence that age of sexual maturation in turkeys is heritable. 'The reactivity of the gonads may be the most important factor in determining the time at which sexual maturity actually occurs, but the factors which affect this reactivity are largely unknown' (Robson, 1947). Change also takes place at puberty in the specificity of pituitary response—while oestradiol induces pituitary and adrenal hypertrophy in rats castrated after puberty, it reduces pituitary and adrenal weight in animals castrated while still immature (Selye and Albert, 1942).

The end of the reproductive period, as well as the beginning, is marked by changes in gonadal reactivity. These have led some writers to regard the human menopause as a form of depletion-senescence (Swyer, 1954): Hertig (1944) describes the exhaustion of a 'capital' of ova, which is not increased during post-natal life, but his findings suggest that the actual menopause precedes the end of all follicular activity. In man and many other mammals (the only admitted exceptions occur in

Lemuroidea, the galago and the loris), the occurrence of oogenesis during post-puberal life has been doubted—the case against it has been persuasively put by Zuckerman (1951): this 'perennial controversy' has been continued by Parkes and Smith (1953), who found evidence of oocyte regeneration in rat ovaries grafted after freezing.

One of the most characteristic features of mammalian ageing is the steady loss of oocytes from the ovary through follicular atresia. It apparently also occurs in birds (Dominic, 1962). Jones and Krohn (1961) have investigated this process in mice—it is significantly retarded by hypophysectomy, but not arrested altogether. Explanation itself causes a massive loss of oocytes in the explanted ovary, but this appears to be due to anoxia when the blood supply is interrupted (Jones and Krohn, 1960b). There is some evidence that the menopause occurs in women because the supply of ova is exhausted. In mice, unilateral ovariectomy halves the total number of offspring and shortens reproductive life (Jones and Krohn, 1960a; Thung, 1962; Biggers, Finn and McLaren, 1962). Engle (1944) mentions the finding of apparently normal corpora lutea in women of 50: at the menopause most if not all ova and follicles have normally disappeared. Kurzrok and Smith (1938) found that in the human ovary, in contrast to the senile ovary of some other mammals, ova cease to be found, and that this change occurs at or soon after the menopause. They consider that the postmenopausal ovary can no longer respond to pituitary gonadotrophin. Gardner (1952) transplanted ovaries between old and young rats, and apparently found a greater tendency to malignant change in old ovaries carried by young hosts. The ovary of the mouse, transplanted into an animal of a different age, behaves selfwise —passage in young mice does not prolong its life (Jones and Krohn, 1960b); the ovary of the hypophysectomized mouse does not deteriorate with age, but remains able to function on explantation (Jones and Krohn, 1959). An interesting possibility arises that the suppression of ovulation as a contraceptive measure may actually postpone the menopause. This seems unlikely, for it only re-instates the *status quo* in man under 'wild' conditions, where for the greater part of adult life ovulation is inhibited by pregnancy.

In rats semicastrated during old age Wiesner (1932) found a marked reduction in compensatory hypertrophy of the remaining ovary. One major feature of senescence is probably progressive reduction of the ovarian reserve in terms of hormone production. Failure of the ovary to respond to pituitary stimulation may be one precipitant of the human menopause. (See also Klebanow and Hegnauer, 1949.)

By far the most interesting fact from the standpoint of senescence is the striking increase in pituitary gonadotrophin level at the human menopause, and the comparable but more gradual increase in senile men (Henderson and Rowlands, 1938) and rats (Lauson, Golden and Severinghaus, 1939). This not only indicates a change in gonadal tissue reactivity with age, but it also shows how limited senile processes may provoke compensatory reactions and further disturb homoeostasis. Ovariectomy in certain strains of mice predisposes them to carcinoma of the adrenal cortex, which can be prevented by oestrogens (Woolley and Little, 1946). The senile increase in gonadotrophin closely resembles that which follows castration, though it develops more gradually (in female rats—Lauson, Golden and Severinghaus, 1939). Witschi (1952) found that in women the castrate level of FSH by pituitary gland assay is established very rapidly after the menopause, and persists for the rest of life, while in men the rise is far more gradual, the castrate level being reached only at 70 years and only by a few individuals. In a majority of cases the hypophyseal FSH content either remains at the normal adult level or falls, occasionally even below childhood levels. But in male eunuchs castrated in childhood, pituitary gonadotrophin output may remain, from the time of normal puberty into middle age, at about ten times the normal level (Hamilton, Catchpole and Hawke, 1944, 1945). There is no evidence that this staggering increase, maintained over 40–50 years, has any observable effect on the rate of ageing.

Procain, which has lately been recommended on the basis of some papers which appear humane and optimistic rather than critical (Aslan, 1956, 1957–58; Aslan and David, 1957) as a 'remedy' for age changes, is perhaps—if it has any action at all —a 'mild activator of the pituitary-adrenal system' (Greene,

1959; anon., 1959). Ungar (1944) found that in the presence of an intact adrenal it caused the release of a histamine antagonist. There is so far no satisfactory evidence that it affects any basic ageing process, and it does not increase the life-span of mice (Verzár, 1959b). Aslan (in press) has found that it does so in rats.

6·2·3 HORMONAL REGULATION OF GROWTH IN VERTEBRATES

In mammals, where growth and differentiation are difficult to dissociate experimentally, we have abundant evidence of senescence even in the longest-lived forms. In amphibia, where there is a clear-cut metamorphosis, and where growth and differentiation can be manipulated with relative ease, we have so far no direct evidence of senescence. We cannot readily find out whether the life of intact amphibia, the neoteny of the axolotl, or the gigantism of athyroid tadpoles, ends in senescence, for the practical reason that axolotls may well be capable of living for 50, and normal frogs for 12, 15 or 20 years. This conspiracy of circumstances perpetually recurs in the study of ageing. The large literature of lower vertebrate endocrinology and morphogenesis cannot be brought to bear on the problem, for lack of actuarial data.

Both homoeotherms and poikilotherms, whether they metamorphose or not, tend to pass through an earlier phase of active growth and a later phase of active reproduction, each characterized by a separate type of endocrine control, and the second by a relative loss of regenerative in favour of reproductive capacity. These phases are separated by the operation of a timing-mechanism which is linked to processes in the juvenile phase. In mammals, these phases are apparently controlled by the pituitary growth and gonad-regulating mechanisms successively. In lower vertebrates the differentiation-process and the transition to adult function appears to depend on a pituitary-thyroid balance. Pituitary growth hormone of mammalian origin is able to promote the growth of fish (Swift, 1954).

The relation between morphogenesis under the influence of gonadal hormones and loss of regenerative power has special interest in gerontology. Grobstein (1947) found that when the gonopodium of poecilid fish differentiates, under the influence of androgens, regenerative power is lost: he stresses the analogy between this process and the loss of regenerative capacity in the developing anuran limb. Such a change need not depend upon irreversible loss of cellular capacity to grow—this does not appear to be the case in amphibian limbs (Borssuk, 1935; Poležaiev and Ginsburg, 1939) but the physiological loss of repair-power may be as complete, so far as the intact animal is concerned, as is the loss of moulting-power in *Rhodnius* once the evocator is lost. There is clearly here, as Minot recognized, a possible mechanism for the induction of senile change.

A certain amount of evidence is available concerning the hormonal influences which affect protein anabolism, and regulate growth in mammals, especially in man. Where these factors have been studied, they give little support to the idea of a simple relation between senescence and growth-cessation, and even less to the conception of a single, 'master', endocrine inhibitor which can be detached from the general pattern of progressing developmental change. The pattern which exists in man has all the complication of a dynamic system where homoeostasis co-exists with change. Much of the existing information is provisional, and there are as yet no studies extending into the period of senescence. It is plain, however, that in man, and probably in some but not all other mammals, the 'anabolic' stimulus to form new protein is not the same throughout life. In adult life it is closely linked to the gonadal cycle. The extent of the differences in endocrine control of growth between determinate growers such as man and continual growers such as the rat has not yet been mapped, and very little is known of the hormonal control of growth in lower vertebrates. The existing evidence is quite enough, however, to render any static conception of growth-cessation in terms of single-hormone deficiencies untenable. A more accurate picture would perhaps be obtained by treating prepuberal and puberal life as separate instars separated by what amounts to a biochemical metamorphosis.

The growth of human beings, like that of *Daphnia* (p. 129), occurs in two overlapping cycles—one prepuberal, the other coinciding with puberty. (See Figs. 67, 68.) The prepuberal cycle has its most active phase during the first six months of life. This cycle, according to Kinsell (1953), is almost wholly controlled by the pituitary growth hormone. The puberal cycle appears to be evoked directly by anabolic steroid hormones derived from the gonad and adrenal cortex. During both cycles a minimum output of thyroid hormone is required to maintain

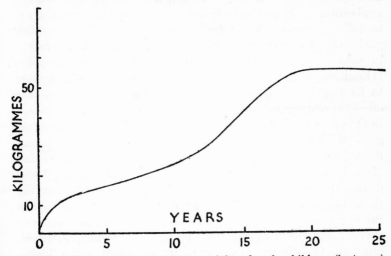

FIG. 67.—The postnatal growth in weight of male children (kg/years) (from the data of Quetelet).

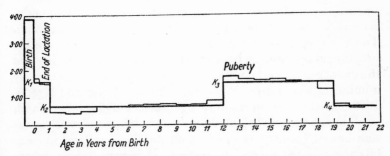

FIG. 68.—Annual growth increment in boys, from the data of Quetelet k_1–k_4 = growth constants at each period (from Schmalhausen, 1928).

growth and development. At puberty, in response to the pituitary gonadotrophins, the gonads produce steroid hormones which directly stimulate the growth of bone and of soft tissues. The process of bone growth in man is, however, self-limited, since the same hormones produce skeletal maturation and fusion of the epiphyses. There is reason to suspect that they also inhibit the production of pituitary growth hormone—probably through a negative feedback system from the level of protein anabolism. It is particularly interesting to notice that acromegalic symptoms (McCullagh and Renshaw, 1934) or frank gigantism (Joedicke, 1919) are occasional sequels to castration in males—so, however, are polyuria and diabetes insipidus (Hamilton, 1948). The puberal growth phase in girls appears to be largely of adrenal origin, since the growth-promoting effects of oestrogens and of progesterone are less marked, except in the promotion of Ca and PO_4 retention, than those of androgens (Kinsell, 1953). It is generally held that thyroxin potentiates the action of pituitary growth hormone in mammals (Evans, Simpson and Pencharz, 1939; Scow and Marx, 1945) during the prepuberal phase, as well as hastening differentiation. This does not appear to be the case in anurans, where thiouracil produces pseudogigantism, and a balance between thyroid and pituitary has been postulated (Steinmetz, 1954), one evoking differentiation and the other growth and a 'juvenile' condition.

This picture, which requires considerable amplification, accords reasonably well with the known effects of various endocrine deficiencies in producing dwarfism or gigantism in man. To some extent the appearance of the puberal cycle curtails the prepuberal by inducing bone maturation. Epiphyseal union and the change-over to the puberal phase of growth are delayed by administration of growth hormone (Freud, Levie and Kroon, 1939), as they are in natural gigantism. On the other hand, abolition of the whole gonadal influence by prepuberal castration has, at least, no gross effect on the life-span, and in cases of constitutional precocious puberty of genetic origin, where puberal changes are complete by the age of six, and the lag-phase of the growth curve is suppressed, the expectation of life is apparently normal (Jolly, 1955).

Various workers have suggested that mammalian senescence 'is' (or involves) the decline of growth hormone production, and that it 'is' (or involves) the long-term effect of the pituitary gonadotrophin on non-gonadal tissues. In so far as senescence results from differentiation, this is doubtless true, but the experimental question is rather this—to what extent can the administration of one or more 'anabolic' hormones affect the power of continued homoeostasis in adult animals? It is possible that the growth hormone itself may be the 'juvenile hormone' of the mammalian pre-imaginal period. It is a primary stimulator of protein anabolism and somatic growth. (Oddly enough, the insect juvenile hormone also occurs in mammalian organs— Williams, Moorhead and Pulis, 1959). What, if anything, it does there is quite unknown.) The change from a protein-building and nitrogen-retaining economy, and the negative specific acceleration of growth, are two of the most evident correlates of senescence (Mayer, 1949). The administration of growth hormone 'confers strangely youthful proportions on the nitrogen, fat and water components of the body, even in old animals' (Asling *et al.*, 1952), but does not prolong life (Everitt, 1959). Change in specificity of tissue response to growth hormone certainly *appears* to occur in some mammals, and this change coincides with the attainment of maturity and the appearance of a fresh anabolism-maintaining mechanism. The experimental work of Young in England and Li in America suggests that before a critical time, injected growth hormone induces only protein anabolism—after that time, it also induces diabetes. This is the pattern in man, the kitten (Cotes, Reid and Young, 1949) and the dog (Campbell *et al.*, 1950) but not in the rat (Bennett, Li and Evans, 1948) or, apparently, the mouse (Moon *et al.*, 1952) which respond by continued growth. That the change in specificity involves endogenous as well as exogenous hormone is evident from the occurrence of diabetes in association with spontaneous acromegaly. Evidence for the existence of a separate diabetogenic principle is not very impressive (Raben and Westermeyer, 1952; Young, 1953). Todorov (1959) has found chemical evidence of an age change in response to somatotrophin, even in the rat, in that the latent period of the response of rat liver RNA and DNA to its administration increases steadily with age. Complete ablation of the anterior lobe in adults leads to failure of growth but not, in general, to other acceptable evidences of senility (in rats) though this cannot be shown from the life-table.

In experimental studies, even highly purified growth hormone administered to rats produces decreasing effects upon nitrogen retention and upon growth after repeated administration (Whitney *et al.*, 1948). These experiments, however, have invariably been carried out with heterologous (usually ox) hormones, and, as in the case of antigonadotrophic effects, no physiological importance can be attached to the apparent increase in tissue resistance.

Of the other hormones concerned in growth and differentiation, the pituitary thyreotropic hormone appears in most mammals which have been studied (rats—Turner and Cupps, 1938; rabbits—Bergman and Turner, 1941; mice—Adams and Mothes, 1945; cattle—Reece and Turner, 1937) to reach a peak at or about puberty, with a subsequent decline which has never been followed by assay into old age. The decline of general metabolism with increasing age, which has been frequently linked with the decline of growth-capacity as an index of 'physiological ageing', appears to involve both a fall in thyroid activity and perhaps a decline in cell response, since thyroidectomized rats show no senile decline in heart-rate and O_2 uptake, and old normal rats are decreasingly responsive to thyroxin administration (Grad, 1953). The declining heat-production of ageing human subjects may well be a reflection as much of muscle atrophy as of thyroid involution: the power of the thyroid to respond to thyrotrophin is apparently unimpaired (Banks, Gaffney, Shock and Lansdowne, 1959).

The results obtained by McCay, using dietary restriction, could be regarded as the consequences of dietary hypophysectomy. Such a state of affairs interferes with the production of both growth hormone and gonadotrophin, and its effect is a general slowing of the 'integrating system' of growth + development. The separation of these systems in mammals is a problem of great interest and considerable practical difficulty. Dietary retardation greatly postpones, but cannot be kept at such a level as to prevent, the onset of oestrus (Asdell and Crowell, 1935). McCay, Sperling and Barnes (1943) found that the capacity of retarded rats to resume growth was ultimately lost if retardation was prolonged. Apparently if growth is delayed without differentiation, it may ultimately encounter a block at the cellular level.

252

A beginning has been made on the problem of selective interference with mammalian differentiation by the school of Li and Evans (Walker *et al.*, 1952; Asling *et al.*, 1952a, b). Hypophysectomy in 6-day-old rats does not arrest the eruption of teeth or the opening of the eyes, but later sexual and pre-sexual development is suppressed. Untreated animals ultimately die from paralysis due to cerebral compression, the brain outgrowing the cranium. Rats which survive the postoperative period have been maintained in good health by growth hormone supplements. In these supplemented rats, the rate of growth was only slightly less than that of unoperated controls. Skeletal development was normal, but adult organ-differentiation and sexual maturation did not take place. Three such 'metathetelic' individuals were kept for 200–300 days in an attempt to produce gigantism. It would be interesting to know how long such animals are capable of living, and what senile changes they ultimately exhibit.

Selective suppression of gonadotrophin production is not yet feasible, though recent studies with *Lithospermum* extracts suggest that the chemical 'dissection' of pituitary effects with chemical antagonists is not, perhaps, an unreasonable hope (Wiesner and Yudkin, 1952). The effect upon life-span of inducing precocious puberty in mammals other than man, where it sometimes occurs spontaneously, does not appear to have been studied: mice, which mature very early, are not ideal subjects, and an experiment on longer-lived mammals encounters the familiar practical difficulties.

7

AGEING AND THE EFFECTS OF IONIZING RADIATION

IONIZING radiation is harmful to living cells; the mischief it does depends on the kind and amount of radiation, the identity of the subject, and the dose-time relationship. One expression of the sum of this mischief is a reduction in the average life-span of animals acutely or chronically exposed. Part of this is due to specific and identifiable effects, such as radiation sickness and the induction of malignant tumours. Part is due to damage of a less easily identifiable kind.

Chiefly from a consideration of this second type of life-shortening, the view has been put forward that radiation increases the rate of ageing (Alexander, 1957). Since the cause and mechanism of natural ageing in man and animals are quite unknown, this assertion, if true, is of great interest to gerontologists. For the same reason, however, it cannot be tested in the most satisfactory manner by comparing natural ageing with the effects of radiation at a fundamental level. There is also a measure of ambiguity in the meaning which different workers attach to the statement. For most purposes, indeed, it is preferable to follow Mole (1957) in referring to the chronic toxicity of radiation.

If radiation increases the rate at which the force of mortality rises with age, and if, as is usually the case, increase in the force of mortality is an acceptable index of ageing, there is a sense in which the statement is true by definition. The same could be said of some but not all noxious influences which shorten life, particularly if, as has been maintained by Harden Jones (1955), physiological mischief is self-aggravating. The question is not whether radiation is a noxious influence of this kind, however,

254

but whether its effect on general vigour is 'something special'—whether in particular it acts by accelerating, augmenting, or simulating some of the processes that cause intact animals to age. The idea has even been put forward (Kunze, 1933) that natural ageing itself is a toxic effect of background radiation; quantitative experiment does not seem to bear this out. The causes of natural ageing being unknown, however, radiation studies might possibly throw light on them. Evidence from the experiments which have so far been carried out, both by scientists on animals and by psychopaths on the human species, suggests that it is in any case important to understand the nature of the effect of radiation upon vigour.

Inspection of non-radiation effects suggests four main ways in which adverse factors can modify the survival curve:

Case 1. By producing an added standing mortality, as in zoo animals. The curve is intermediate between the 'physiological' and the logarithmic—its exact form will depend on how much of the added component is itself age-dependent, and whether a resistant subgroup is selected. Age-dependence decreases as the total mortality increases. When the curve is a straight line there is no commonest age of adult death; when it is logarithmic, mortality is independent of age.

Case 2. By producing a general decrement of vigour which is roughly equal for all the affected animals. This appears to be the case in some but not all examples of inbreeding depression. Senile changes appear precociously but progress at the usual rate.

Case 3. By producing an acceleration of the whole process of mortality increase; i.e. the shape of the survival curve is virtually unaltered, but it is redrawn to a different time scale. The survival of *Daphnia* responds to moderate temperature increase in this way: McCay's rat curves are in much the same relationship, though the fit is considerably less good.

Case 4. By producing 'all or none' damage. Certain animals die, at once or later; those that survive have undergone no loss of life-expectation.

Of these hypothetical 'pure' instances, cases 2 and 3 come nearest to representing a speed-up of age processes; in case 2 ageing is precocious, in case 3 it is precocious and itself accelerated. Specific increase in the rate of a hypothetical clock for natural ageing could presumably have either of these results, depending on the competence of the clock. But combinations of all four cases could produce curves of any shape, especially if some have latent periods and others show substantial recovery, and the most that can properly be said of a curve is that it is compatible or incompatible with a supposed process.

A factor could be said to cause 'precocious ageing', beyond reasonable cavil over definitions, if (1) it caused the force of mortality to rise more rapidly in affected than in control animals, (2) it brought forward the age of onset of diseases which affect the controls, but did not greatly alter the sequence or the incidence of causes of death, (3) it made any characteristic features of the ageing syndrome in that species—e.g. greying, loss of skin elasticity—appear at a proportionately lower age. In this case its effects could not be distinguished from those of an accelerated natural ageing, at least until more of the processes involved in natural ageing are known. It might act by accelerating the whole developmental programme; in this case presenile landmarks in development, such as the age of puberty or bony union, would also be affected, but if its contribution were wholly to the deteriorative effects of development it need not do so.

We can translate this into more concrete terms. If radiation accelerates ageing, it should move the histogram of pedestrian road deaths (Fig. 7) to the left—it need not alter its proportions. An irradiated population should retire earlier, though it might well leave school later, than an unirradiated.

7·1 Long-term Effects of Irradiation on Survival Curves

7·1·1 CHRONIC EXPOSURE

All the experimental studies which have appeared indicate that ionizing radiations, at least above a certain threshold of exposure, shorten life. The observations are difficult to compare because of their heterogeneity in type, relative efficiency, and dose of radiation, choice of animal and strain, method of analysis, and method of expressing result. They have been reviewed by Mole (1957); reference here will be confined to those giving enough of the survival curves of control and irradiated animals for their shapes to be compared. Much of the work on chronic irradiation has been concerned to establish a dose-response curve. The consistency of the published findings for mice, at least for doses of 10 r/week or more (fast neutrons = 1 rad/week) is remarkable in view of the diversity of strain and experimental conditions (Blair, 1954).

Many of the results raise important questions of method. Survival is a most sensitive biological index, and the curves obtained in such experiments can be profoundly affected by minor environmental factors such as handling, temperature gradients, and population density in cages. Neary *et al.* (1957) found that if, instead of four mice being kept in one cage, two were kept in a cage half the size, growth was almost completely arrested. The estrous cycle and tumour incidence of mice can be altered by the presence or absence of other individuals (Andervont, 1943–44). Even in Neary's experiments, which were planned with great care to avoid such effects, there was a significant difference of 5 per cent in the survival curves of randomly chosen control groups caged 20 ft. apart. Mole (1957) has pointed out that a low-dose group of irradiated mice in the experiments of Lorenz *et al.* (1954), which had an apparently increased life-span compared with controls, were kept in a different room, without air conditioning. Factors of this order are probably more serious hindrances to work on the effects of very low-level radiation than to assessments of the significance of larger life-span changes, but they cannot be ignored.

Some of the curves obtained by various investigators working on chronic irradiation are reproduced in Figs. 69 to 71. Neary *et al.* (1957) compared the effects of γ-irradiation and neutron irradiation of mice and analysed the data to determine whether the shapes of the survival curves were in better accord with the hypothesis of excess mortality (case 1), precocious ageing (case 2) or accelerated ageing (case 3). The fit to case 1, by a probit transformation, was not convincing. Case 3 requires a general contraction of the time scale of the whole curve; the standard deviations of the mean survival times decreased with increasing dosage, but not greatly, and there was no evidence to suggest

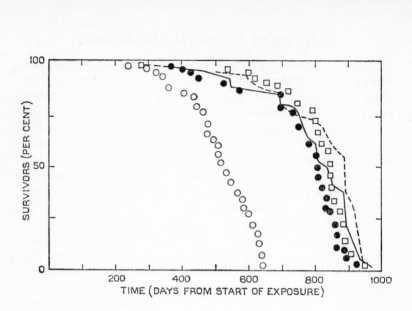

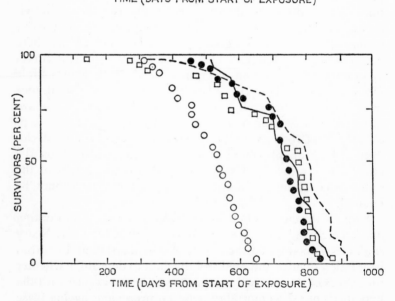

Fig. 69.—Survival curves of CBA male mice (lower graph) and female mice (upper graph) and duration of irradiation by fast neutrons (days): ○ fast neutrons, 6·4 rads/week; ● fast neutrons, 0·54 rad/week; □ fast neutrons, 0·19 rad/week. Hard line: mice exposed to residual γ-ray component only. Dashed line: controls (adapted from Neary *et al.*, 1957).

a more rapid advance of senile change once the decline had begun. Neary *et al.* conclude that 'the simple hypothesis of premature ageing represents our data reasonably well, particularly if early deaths are excluded'.

In the earlier experiment of Lorenz *et al.* (1954) the curves obtained by γ-irradiation of mice show some evidence of whole-scale contraction if control and maximally irradiated groups are

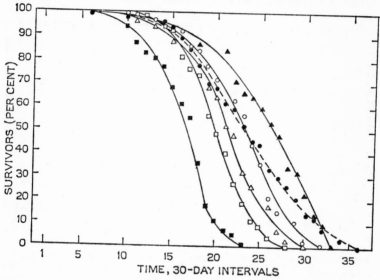

Fig. 70.—Survival curves of LAF$_1$ mice, showing percentage survivors at 30-day intervals: ○ controls; ▲ 0·11 r/8-hr day; ○ 1·1 r/8-hr day; △ 2·2 r/8-hr day; □ 4·4 r/8-hr day; ■ 8·8 r/8-hr day (from Lorenz *et al.*, 1954).

compared, but mice at the lowest level of irradiation (0·11γ/day) outlived the controls, as already mentioned: if this, and not the control curve, is taken as the base line, the decline in standard deviation at high doses is less evident, though still greater than in Neary's study (Figs. 70 and 71). According to Mole and Thomas (1961) when mice receive 3–200 rem daily, it is the initial dose-time which produces most of the observed life-shortening, i.e. the mechanism appears to saturate. The curve for guinea pigs is similarly intermediate between case 2 and case 3; their control curve is, incidentally, the first full survival curve to be published for these animals, apart from the brief account of their longevity given by Rogers and Rogers (1957). 'Precocious' ageing would again seem the description of these results which begs fewest questions. In preparing most of the curves the sexes were combined, although there was separate analysis of the performance of each. Gowen (1961) recently found a significant increase in life-expectancy of female mice

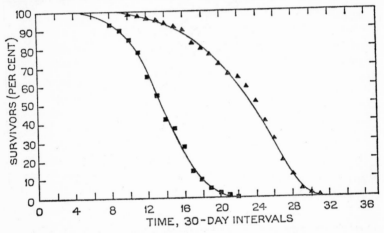

Fig. 71.—Survival curves of C_3Hb mice, showing percentage survivors at 30-day intervals: ▲ virgin control; ■ exposed to 8·8 r/8-hr day (from Lorenz *et al.*, 1954).

after single X-ray doses, due wholly to the suppression of litter-bearing. Very low doses may also lengthen the life of animals whose health is suboptimal—possibly by doing more damage to the pathogens than to the mice, or through a 'stress' effect (Sacher and Trucco, 1962).

Tumours apart, the long-term histological results of irradiation cannot usually be distinguished from those of natural ageing, though they can be induced locally (Casarett, 1956; Henshaw, 1944; Upton, 1957). The 'characteristic pathological change' of mammalian ageing is probably an increase in the number of pathological changes. In animals short-lived as a result of irradiation the balance of these is in general preserved.

7·1·2 SINGLE EXPOSURES

Excluding acute and subacute mortality experiments, there is a shortage of completed survival curves for animals after one moderate or small dose of irradiation. In the original pile experiments of Henshaw *et al.* (1947), the tails of the low-dosage curves were not completed: so far as they go, they suggest an increase in standing mortality as well as, or rather than, displacement of the adult mode. Furth *et al.* (1954) studied the longevity and pathology of several thousand LAF₁ mice exposed to radiation from a nuclear bomb (chiefly gamma-rays with an admixture of fast and slow neutrons). The tails of the curves are again not completed; for both males and females the scatter decreased slightly with increasing dose.

The decline in survivorship with age might be expected to begin unusually early after one dose and proceed unusually fast during continued exposure. This it apparently does (Sacher, 1959), but in chronic experiments most of the harm may well be done early (Neary *et al.*, 1957) though sensitivity has been reported to increase in animals already old (Sacher, 1957). The exact form of the survival curve depends on the strain of mouse used (Grahn and Hamilton, 1958). It is probable that the variance in control life-spans will fall steadily with better attention to biological conditions. In this context, however, *constant* conditions are not invariably optimal for longevity or for unanimity in dying.

To resolve some of these questions Lindop and Rotblat (1959a, b; 1961a, b, c) have carried out a very large-scale study of the effects of a single exposure to X-rays on the longevity of mice. Survival curves are being drawn for 3500 SAS/4 mice exposed at 30 days of age to 15-Mev X-rays, in fourteen dose groups ranging from 50 to 850 r, and for 1200 sham-irradiated controls, with special attention to the age distribution and incidence of causes of death. A detailed post-mortem was done on every animal, and physiological tests were carried out on random samples as subsidiary measurements of ageing. In a second experiment, on a further 5000 mice, the sensitivity to radiation, judged both by LD_{50} and by life-shortening, were determined at a series of ages from 30 days onward. Breeding experiments were also undertaken, in which the longevity, leukaemia incidence, and cause of death are compared in successive generations bred from irradiated and non-irradiated males. Special measures were taken in all this work to secure accurate dosimetry and to keep control and test series under biologically identical conditions.

The results indicate that the life-shortening produced by radiation is not due to a single disease, but to the bringing forward in time of all causes of death. The order and frequency of these causes is altered compared with controls—the result is not, therefore, identical with the effects of natural ageing, though it resembles them (Lindop and Rotblatt, 1960).

7·1·3 EFFECTS IN MAN

Neither studies of occupational exposure nor military experiments, deliberate and accidental, on human populations have yet yielded satisfactory evidence about the long-term effects of radiation on human ageing. Warren (1956) compared the obituaries of radiologists with those of other physicians; he found not only a significant increase in leukaemia but earlier death from each of a number of major diseases, the mean loss of life-expectation from all causes being 5·2 years. This is more than double Hursh's estimate (1957), since the average dose received would probably lie between 100 and 200 mr/week (Osborn, 1955). Warren's computation has been cogently attacked (Seltser and Sartwell 1958) because of his method of treating the age distributions involved. Court-Brown and Doll (1958) have now analysed the records of longevity in English radiologists from 1897 to the present day. They find no tendency to shorter life, even in the pioneer years when protection was minimal, apart from a small excess mortality from skin tumours. In their study, the performance of radiologists is if anything slightly better than that of comparable professional groups.

Data from atomic bomb and fallout casualties, though they have covered many types of ill-health and injury, have not so far proved more acceptable practically than ethically in assisting age studies. Some knowledge may in time be gained from them, but the two most heavily exposed populations are probably undergoing large social changes in age mortality.

Accurate matching of human controls is not easy, and objective as well as subjective age changes can be modified in man by psychological as well as physical stress, even by the knowledge of having been exposed to radiation. 'Early ageing' is occasionally mentioned in the victims of comparable maltreatment which did not include irradiation—in survivors of prison camps, for example. Effects on the human rate of ageing may be found to occur, but it seems there is now no information from which their size can be estimated (Izumi, 1956; Hollingsworth, 1960).

7·2 *Summary*

It is difficult to draw a brief description of the effects of radiation on life-span from these data. One such description is that it seems to reduce vigour, in the same sense that heterosis increases it. The resemblance between the effects of irradiation and of inbreeding, like that between the effects of radiation and age changes, may be fortuitous, but is suggestive. The radiation resistance of hybrids is greater than that of inbreds (Rugh and Wolff, 1958). Radiation, inbreeding, and ageing all diminish the resourcefulness of the organism in maintaining homoeostasis against random environmental attack. In inbred animals, this instability is expressed as a high variability in characters such as drug resistance (Maclaren and Michie, 1954); it would be interesting to compare the variability of irradiated animals by similar tests. Since inbreeding has acted throughout development, inbred animals are likely to be more variable in any case than those irradiated postnatally, but mice have been reared under constant irradiation from conception (Neary, Munson and Mole, 1957) and were found to be very vulnerable.

Apart from the induction of tumours, radiation does not greatly alter the distribution of causes of death—the tendency is for irradiated animals to die earlier from all of them. Nor does it accelerate 'development'; like inbreeding, it more commonly slows it.

Further experiment might show whether there is any real identity of process behind this resemblance There are several hypotheses of ageing which are relevant to it, and to the possible mechanism of life-shortening by radiation (Strehler, 1959). Ageing has often been treated as the sum of inconstant changes due to external injury and to side effects of metabolism (Furth *et al.*, 1954; Jones, 1955; Sacher, 1955). Failure of repair with increasing age would then be due to differentiation, or to self-aggravation of changes when several happen to coincide (Hinshelwood, 1957; Sacher, 1956), the consistency of the survival curve being statistical rather than developmental. This dynamic version of the old theory of 'wear' (*Abnutzungstheorie*) is more plausible when it is made more specific, and the changes are supposed to affect one or more groups of postmitotic cells which cannot be renewed by division. Ionizing radiation can increase the reactivity of structures normally stable and might hasten this type of deterioration as grit increases the rate of wear in bearings, by making the same changes occur for a smaller molecule tumour (Harman, 1957). There is here the possibility of a direct estimation, both of the molecule life of cells and of radiation effects on it, in animals of fixed cell number. The equally venerable theories of deterioration in the cellular or noncellular microstructure (Marinesco, 1934; Rúzička, 1924) as manifestations of ageing, if not causes, have some support from recent work on collagen (Banga, 1947; Hall and Tunbridge, 1957; Verzár, 1957), but in this case the changes are not accelerated by local irradiation (Sinex, 1957). The identity of process between ageing and radiation damage may, indeed, be in the processes of repair rather than in the nature of the damage or changes induced (Stover, 1959).

Most attention has naturally focused on the ability of radiation to disorganize chromatin. The similarity between mortality curves and entropy functions was noticed by Gompertz (1825). Perks (1932) remarked some time ago that loss of vigour, measured as 'inability to withstand destruction', was of the same nature as 'diminution of energy' in entropy theory, and the generation of a random element. It now seems likely that the information content of cell systems is the 'biological energy' which was postulated in the last century, and thought to be dissipated with age. Inbreeding may reduce the fund of information by limiting the variety of genetic material present (Castle, 1926; Crow, 1948; Gowen, Stadler and Johnson, 1946;

Maynard Smith and Maynard Smith, 1954). Radiation might do so by its specific effects (point mutation, chromosome breakage) or merely by raising the noise level of the system; ageing might reflect a similar rise in noise level from metabolic 'wear' of the molecules concerned, and from random injury. Mathematical consideration of such ideas (Sacher, 1955, 1956, 1961; Yockey, 1956) has so far out-stripped experiment. They cannot yet be related, for example, to normal interspecific differences in life-span. Some, if not most, radiation damage to cells is extragenic, at least in ciliates (Power and Ehret, 1955); point mutation alone is probably not enough to account statistically for the observed rates of animal ageing (Failla, 1961). Russell (1957) has shown, however, that the shortening of life in male mice exposed to radiation from a nuclear bomb is transmitted to their progeny. Particularly interesting is Harman's finding (1957) that radiation-protective chemicals prolonged the life of unirradiated mice.

Hypothermia, like underfeeding, also gives some protection (Hornsey, 1959); underfed rats exposed to radiation fail, however, to resume growth when fed (Carroll and Brauer, 1961). All these results, however, depend chiefly on maintaining a rigid technique for survival experiments, and the difficulties of doing so are only now becoming evident. It is already clear, however, that polyploids are highly radioresistant (Sparrow and Shaiver, 1958) and that haploids (*Habrobracon*, Clark, 1960, 1961; Clark and Rubin, 1961) are more vulnerable than diploids to radiation-induced life-shortening. Curtis and Gebhard (1958) found that non-specific toxicity and nitrogen mustards did not accelerate ageing, but more recently chemical mutagens have been reported to produce life-shortening (Alexander, Connell, Brohult and Brohult, 1959; Upton, McDonald, Christenberry and Gude, 1961; Conklin, Upton, Christenberry and McDonald, 1963), a finding which removes one grave objection to mutational theories of ageing.

Radiation biology can probably offer fundamental information about natural ageing processes. The most obvious field for this contribution, and one which need involve no assumptions about the identity of radiation damage with age changes, is in our understanding of the nature of vigour. Other possible applications may become evident as its cellular and physiological consequences are understood. There is at least no other immediately obvious line of attack on age problems which seems to hold out better prospects of a fundamental advance. The relative contributions of gerontology and radiation biology to the understanding of long-term radiation hazards would appear to be roughly equal, and any modern programme of health protection should promote research in both. Sufficient time has now been devoted to experiments in which radiations have been administered to animals and shown to do them no good. This point having been established, it should be possible to fix the requirements for more instructive comparisons.

It would be profitable to compare the action of small doses of radiation on animals of determinate and indeterminate cell number. It would also be profitable to extend the work, done with other objectives, on partial-body and single-organ irradiation, with or without the use of modern orthotopic grafting methods. There is also full scope for relatively simple comparisons between the responses of hybrid and inbred lines and their individual cells. The most important requirement for our understanding of tissue ageing may be the development of techniques to analyse epigenetic change in tissue cells throughout life, their turnover, and the effects of differentiation and use on their cytoplasmic and nuclear complement. No really detailed understanding of irradiation effects on the vigour of whole mammals, and on their survival curves, is likely without some progress in this field.

'The most rational single explanation of the functional impairment of the ageing tissue is that it reflects an absolute loss in the cell population with replacement of these cells by extracellular fluid or connective tissue—the cell-deletion hypothesis' (Handler, 1961). But it is extremely difficult to relate this process to simple 'genetic death' of fixed postmitotics resulting from mutation, for the reasons given—and still more difficult to relate it to a mutational theory of radiation life-shortening. Evidence suggests that at doses below 200r cell damage in mammals is chromosomal, with an average chromosome breakage dose of 19 rads, and the sensitivity of mammalian cells growing in tissue culture has been confirmed, to a large extent, in vivo, the mean lethal dose for the interphase human cell being put at about 86 rads. All the evidence tells against equal sensitivity in fixed postmitotics, however (Hewitt and Wilson, 1959; Puck, 1961; Till and McCullouch, 1961): in animals without cell division, such as *Habrobracon*, radiation does indeed shorten life, and more in haploid than in diploid individuals, but only at doses one or two orders of magnitude greater than those which shorten the life of rodents (Clark, 1960, 1961; Clark and Rubin, 1961). Moreover there are indications of change in the response of clonally-dividing mammalian cells, both to age and to low-dose irradiation; thus Pratt found that irradiated mice showed the same qualitative and quantitative lag in liver volume restoration after partial hepatectomy which is seen in old mice (Puck, 1961). Even if we substitute chromosomal damage for point mutation as the commoner mechanism of age and radiation damage (assuming they are the same, which they may well not be) it looks as if survival of damaged but clonally viable cells may be more important than cell loss as a factor in reducing vigour and upsetting homoeostasis (Puck, 1961). Loss of fixed postmitotics could be secondary—but if it is primary, we cannot say which of the two mechanisms is the overriding 'clock' in fixing life-spans.

8

CONCLUSION

WE have now briefly examined some of the evidence which requires to be considered, and some of the questions which require to be answered, in attempting to understand animal senescence. We have seen, in particular, that many organisms appear to have been provided by evolutionary selection with a 'programme' of development and function which is directional and finite, and that progressive loss of the power to remain in stable function occurs towards the end of that programme. Weismann suggested that senescence is itself a functionally-determined item in the programme: it seems more probable that as the contribution of successive age groups to the next generation of progeny is reduced by natural causes, so the selection-pressure declines, and the efficiency of the homoeostatic mechanisms with it. The organism ultimately dies of old age because it is now an unstable system which is provided with no further sequence of operational instructions, and in which divergent processes are no longer co-ordinated to maintain function.

In some cases the system fails suddenly, at a fixed point, after the pattern of the senescence of rotifers or red blood corpuscles. Some such cases apparently depend on the existence of cell constituents renewable only by division. In mammals the decline of resistance and the rise of the force of mortality are gradual and smooth, and agree well with the probable shape of a curve representing the declining efficiency of the evolutionary pressure towards survival at different ages.

In so far as any general theory of senescence is justified, this seems at present the most plausible. It is probably as unprofitable to discuss the 'cause' of ageing as to discuss the 'cause' of development. Senescence is a change in the behaviour of the organism with age, which leads to a decreased power of survival and adjustment. It is not a single overall process, except in the evolutionary sense which we have outlined. Various factors in varying proportions contribute to the senile change in different species. Among these are the deterioration of irreplaceable structures; the sum of previous injuries which are imperfectly repaired; and progressive morphogenetic changes in the nature and specificity of cell response and organ function. Any or all of these factors may contribute to senescence in a given species. Experimental removal of the factor which operates earliest in the life-span may reveal another subsequent to it, and so on. There is no conclusive evidence to incriminate cessation of growth as a 'cause' of senescence, except in cases where cell division ceases altogether. Senescence is not an 'inherent' property of the metazoa, but one which they have on several occasions acquired as a potentiality, probably through the operation of evolutionary forces directed to other biological ends. In this respect the senescence of insects and of man is probably a comparable process only to the same extent that the eyes of these organisms are comparable structures. It is obvious that such a conception, while it does not prevent us from ascertaining what factors produce the age-deterioration in a given species, excludes general physiopathological theories of the 'causation' of ageing as a whole.

Unlike the functional evolution of the eye, senescence is typically an undirected process—not a part of the programme but a weakening of the directive force of the programme, escape from co-ordination, combined with the arrears of processes which once contributed to fitness but are now running free. Attempts to invest the programme of morphogenesis with metaphysical or supra-natural properties (Driesch, 1941; Bürger, 1954) have already been adequately answered by J. Needham (1942), and need not be dealt with here. The idea of senescence as the 'fated' or 'destined' end of the organism, i.e. a positively-subsistent and ordered process of life-curtailment, though it is not always the fruit of an avowed vitalism, has much in common with it. Such treatment of senescence as an evolved entity, and the idea that it must have developed as a positive character, has almost certainly gained plausibility, like so much else in the biological literature of old age, from human preoccupations. The gerontologist, with the prolongation of human life in mind, is interested in something which is not, as such, of interest to the evolutionary 'demon', and whose evolution is in no sense comparable with the evolution of sight. Senescence has no function—it is the subversion of function. On the other hand, as Huxley (1942) suggests, the evolutionary process in man has been transferred in the process of cephalization from the 'demon' to the operation of conscious intellect. It should now be possible in our thinking to separate human goals from the effects of selection, and to renounce the animistic confusion between them which has influenced the past theoreticians of old age. The whole conception of 'senescence', in fact, belongs to the field of applied science. It embraces a group of deteriorative effects which we have isolated because they are deteriorative—in other words, because human beings dislike them. Some biological thinkers have reduced themselves to impotence in this field by the cultivation of philosophic doubt whether senescence is an 'entity' at all. Viewed abstractly it is not, any more than disease is an 'entity', but the same biologists will certainly encounter, as they approach their seventieth year, a sequence of changes which will kill them within a limited time.

In so far as biology is more than a branch of idle curiosity, its assignment in the study of old age is to devise if possible means of keeping human beings alive in active health for a longer time than would normally be the case—in other words, to prolong individual life. People now rightly look to 'science' to provide the practical realization of perennial human wishes which our ancestors have failed to realize by magic—or at least to investigate the prospect of realizing them. Under the influence of the study which is necessary to fulfil such wishes, the character of the wish itself generally changes in the direction of realism, so that most people today would incline to prefer the prospect of longevity, which may be realizable, to a physical immortality which is not, and, *pari passu*, 'potentielle Unsterblichkeit' is already disappearing from the biological literature. An analogous process can be seen in the psychology of individual growing-up.

The objective of prolonging human life is one which can bear aggressive restatement from gerontologists, particularly at a time when there are scientists who seek ethical reasons why human life ought not to be prolonged, at least in communities of which they are not themselves members. Although it has much fundamental interest, we have seen that senescence is not biologically speaking a very satisfactory entity. It appears in most animals only under artificial conditions, and it would probably seem to most of us pointless to devote great effort to so arbitrary a part of development if it were not involved with a primary human desire. As it is, medicine has always accepted the prolongation of active and healthy human life in time as one of its self-evident objects, and this object has only been seriously challenged in the past two decades by the growth of pathological forms of anti-liberalism. Gerontology differs from other fields of medical biology only in the fact that while most medical research is directed to making the curve of human survival as nearly as possible rectangular, gerontology is directed to prolonging the rectangle, and shifting the point of decline further in time from the origin. The applied character of such work, and the object it has in mind, would not require emphasis or defence at a period of culture when they ran no risk of provoking a neo-Malthusian uproar. The beggarly opinions of such writers as W. Vogt (1949) merit the rebuke of James Parkinson (1755–1824), that 'if the population exceeded the means of support, the fault lay not in Nature, but in the ability of Politicians to discover some latent defect in the laws respecting the division and appropriation of property'. Postponement of old age, like all the other advances in human control of environment, must involve corresponding social adjustments: in the prevention of presenile mortality, as the graphs in Fig. 72 abundantly indicate, social, economic and political factors clearly predominate already. But whatever problems might be raised by future increases in the human specific age, in this and other fields medicine can afford to treat protests based upon an interested misreading of the biology of human societies with the contempt they deserve, as a compound of illiberal opinions and bad science. The emotional preoccupation of former workers with magical rejuvenation did no good to the progress of science, but it was at least a humane preoccupation.

The social correlates of longevity, which are probably its most

271

important practical aspects, have been omitted altogether from consideration in this book. It is clear throughout phylogeny that there is a relation between survival into the senile period and the existence of a social mode of life. In some cases longevity has

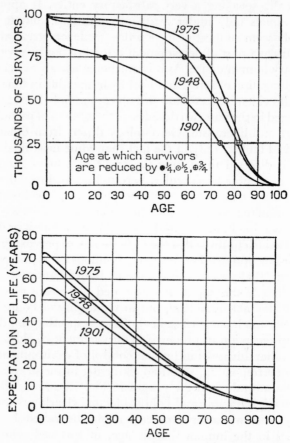

Fig. 72.—Comparison of survivorship and expectation of life: life-tables for the United States, 1901 to 1948, and forecast for 1975.

evolved as a prerequisite of social organization, in others social organization itself increases the possibility of survival into old age, while the social group very probably draws adaptive benefits from the existence of old individuals. Both these trends

272

appear to be at work in social primates. The potential life-span
in palaeolithic man probably resembled our own: its realization
has been possible through the development of a complex social
and rational behaviour. While therefore it is legitimate to
abstract the idea of an evolutionary programme in morphogenetic or physiological terms when we discuss the development
and senescence of an individual man or of a worker bee, in
neither case is this 'programme' really detachable from the
social programme which coexists with it, and which plays an
equally important part in the determination of selection or
survival. The irrelevance of discussing the biology of *individual*
animals, even of non-social species, divorced from their ecology,
has long been evident. Prolongation of the social activity and
significance of the individual human being almost certainly
leads to a change in the shape of the life-table, other things
being equal. Continuance of active work, retention of interests,
of the respect of our fellows, and of a sense of significance in the
common life of the species, apparently make us live longer—
loss of these things makes us die young. This is a result we might
have expected, but which we still largely ignore in practice.
How much of senile 'involution' is the effect of the compulsory
psychological and social 'winding-up' imposed on the human
individual by our form of society and our norms for the behaviour of old people we do not yet know, but it is certainly a
very considerable part, and the most important measures for
the prolonging of useful individual life which come within the
range of the immediately practicable are all concerned with
social adjustment. In point of fact, any increase in the life-span
produced by slowing down the process of ageing would be an
increase in the working life-span of already productive persons
—the training of a doctor or a farmer now occupies nearly one-
third of his total life-span and a half his expected working life.
The exact demographic effects of an increase cannot be known
until the pattern of the increase is known (whether childhood,
old age or both are prolonged in step with adult vigour, or not;
and the relative proportions of the new survival curve) but any
gain in period of maximum vigour and in working life is a free
gift to the productivity of the world, and a decrease in the
relative proportion of life spent in apprenticeship of various

kinds. The contrast between the place of the (relatively few) aged in primitive societies (Simmonds, 1945, 1946) and the relatively many in our own (Sheldon, 1949; Sanderson, 1949) is particularly striking. In primitive cultures 'important means of security for old people are their active association with others and assistance in their interests and enterprises. They are regarded as repositories of knowledge, imparters of valuable information, and mediators between their fellows and the fearful supernatural powers . . . The proportion of the old who remain active, productive, and essential in primitive societies is much higher than in advanced civilization, for they succeed to an amazing degree in providing cultural conditions which utilize the services of their few old people' (Simmonds, 1946). How little this applies to our own culture is evident from the studies of Sheldon (1949); other evidence suggests that although in certain groups (Lehman, 1943), such as amateur naturalists —or among those who retain, perhaps, some of the magico-social functions of the primitive elder (politicians, judges and clergy) the element of social support based upon continued activity leads to an apparently superior retention of the capacity for public life, the society of compulsory retirement, individual privacy and the small family has little to offer to old people. This is a topic which cannot be pursued here, but its importance in the social medicine of age is paramount at present.

'Civilized races', said Metchnikoff, 'do not act like the Fuegians or other savages: they neither kill nor eat the aged, but none the less life in old age often becomes very sad' (1907). It was once believed that with the removal of 'pathological' causes of death the specific age would rise very rapidly in man and approach the recorded maximum, about 120 years. We know much less about the diseases of later life than about life-saving by means of surgery and epidemiology in early life, but it seems possible that even with increased control over malignant tumours and blood-vessel disease the age at death might only come to be more and more normally distributed about seventy-five or eighty years. The characteristic pathological change of age is an increase in the number of pathological changes, and most people who die *late in life* from one of these causes also exhibit several other pathological processes which would probably have killed them very soon, had they survived the actual cause of their deaths.

The most important single change in our world, where life-span is concerned, is that in privileged countries our children grow up and reach old age and our wives no longer die in childbirth. We now know more accurately than ever before when we are likely to die. The most important future change, if it proves possible to control human ageing, may be that we no longer 'look to our end', certainly as that end will come. The likelihood of such a change depends on the progress of our understanding of fundamental age processes. If the present trend of medicine continues without such progress, all that will happen is that the commonest age of dying will shift from being nearer 75 to being nearer 85, and the commonest causes may change so that we die of conditions which are not now so common, today's most frequent killers having been removed to uncover the next layer of the onion. If this is all, not many more than the present 1 in 100 born will reach 90, and not many more than the present 1 in 1000 will reach 100. Those who do will still be the progeny of long-lived stocks, and owe more to their parents' genes than to medical science.

If, on the other hand, fundamental interference does become possible, so that we can modify not the diseases of age but the rate of ageing itself, the picture will be different. In what way and to what extent it will differ from the life-table today we do not know. There are several possibilities. It might prove possible, first of all, to lengthen the period of adult vigour without increasing the final life-span. This would produce a nearly square survival curve with its limit short of the century, and a situation like that in Huxley's *Brave New World*, where people remained apparently young until high ages and then died suddenly at approximately the usual time. This seems biologically the least likely pattern for us to achieve. More probably we might find means of prolonging the period of adult vigour, either alone, or with proportional prolongation of the pre-adult and the senile stages—a scalar expansion of our present survival pattern. Finally, and perhaps least profitably, it might be possible to prolong the total duration of life only by prolonging the stages prior to maturity. This seems to be the nature of the

McCay effect observed in rats. Its utility in man would depend entirely how late in the process of development it could be made to operate. There would be little point in interpolating 5 or 10 years at a physical and mental age of 12, except perhaps to make a longer period of pre-adult training possible. If there were any way of stopping or slowing the clock at a later age, that would represent a more significant achievement—a marking-time for, say, 5 years at the apparent age of 20 or 30, after which bonus we should complete a normal life-cycle. Of all the possible modifications which the system childhood-adulthood-senescence could undergo, this comes nearest to the aims of von Boerhaave's alchemist, leaving aside the reversal of established senility, and it seems the most socially desirable.

The problem of medical gerontology at the biological level, then, is to prolong the human life-cycle in time, either by deformation and stretching or by addition, and in particular to prolong that part of it which contains the period of 'adult vigour'. Such a problem could theoretically be solved in any of three ways, bearing in mind the evidence regarding the existence of a developmental 'programme'—that programme could be prolonged by the provision of new developmental operations; or its movement, throughout or in part, could be slowed down; or active life could be maintained after the expiry of the programme by piecemeal adjustment of homoeostatic mechanisms with supplements, medicaments and prostheses of various kinds.

The first of these possibilities, though it is biologically the most interesting, does not merit discussion at present, at any rate in relation to man. We do not know enough about morphogenesis to interfere with it clinically, except in a few simple deficiency states, let alone devise and apply a sequence of self-regulating operations in growth or development subsequent to normal adulthood. The third possibility is already receiving the greater share of the energy devoted to clinical studies upon human ageing, as opposed to fundamental research into its biology. We might in theory expect that the removal of successive causes of death would increase the expectation of life of the old as well as the young. It is interesting to notice that there is so far very little evidence of such an effect from the general advance of medicine in the last century (Fig. 72). It may be that the time scale of the adult period, after somatic growth has ceased, is not susceptible to any major interference without at the same time destroying normal function. To assess the possibilities of such interference we require to know how far 'marking time' at each stage of the mammalian developmental programme is possible, and, if possible, is compatible with functional health. It is also a matter of practical import whether the rate of child growth influences the length of the period of adult vigour in man (Sinclair, 1955). The degree of linkage between growth, development, and metabolism may vary considerably at different periods of the life-cycle, and the bulk of the work upon their separation has been carried out only in non-mammalian embryos and larvae. We have to reckon with the possibility that the post-puberal mammal behaves like an imago—that its life-span is closely linked to metabolism, which, in homoeotherms, is virtually invariable by the methods which can affect it in invertebrates, and that the fundamental change which leads to eventual senescence has already taken place at puberty. In this case, interference with the length of the adult phase could only be prosthetic.

Some biologists would share the pessimism recently expressed by Strehler (1962) about the practicality of a fundamental intervention in human age processes: suggesting that the only unity in age effects may be a 'loss of programme', due to the failure of natural selection to secure homoeostasis at high ages, Strehler goes on: 'The evolutionary dereliction is probably so manifold and so deeply ingrained in the physiology and biochemistry of existing forms, including man, that the abolition of the process is a practical impossibility.' At the same time, such pessimism, while it may eventually prove correct, is less in evidence than it was ten, or even five years ago. The operational attempt to interfere in age processes is now, at least, being taken seriously by people other than quacks and the obsessed: the number of teams clocking in daily to work on the project, in the United States alone, was over 800 last year, and is going up in the same country by about 200 a year.

The longevity of human tissues in storage is not, perhaps, likely to have a great influence on our longevity as individuals. There is the same fallacy in the conception of spare parts as a fundamental remedy for senescence as in the idea that better medical services will push up the limit of the life-span; some of us certainly age more rapidly in one system than in another, but ageing is characteristically an increase in the number and variety of homoeostatic faults. For this reason alone the interest of grafting and storage techniques for age studies is still much more for their contribution to theory than for the chance of using them as a prosthetic remedy for ageing. Krohn's work in making age chimaeras by grafting mouse ovaries from old to young and from young to old is an elegant example of this kind (Jones and Krohn, 1960; Krohn, 1962), where the investigators used orthotopic grafting to discover whether the ageing of mouse ovary was a somatic or a tissue-sited process, and found that the transplanted ovary did not gain in longevity from being in a young environment.

Both organ culture and organ storage might throw some light on the role of somatic ageing in mutation, and on the related problem of the general stability of somatic cell-clones.

If somatic mutation, or any similar process based on copying faults, really does operate to time the rate of ageing, then we should find signs of it in stored and in cultured organs, unless (1) isolation leads to selective proliferation of unmutated cells, or (2) there are very big differences in the rate or the expression of the process between different organs. This line of attack on ageing should, perhaps, be encouraged, because we may find that in pursuing it we end by having to unravel the whole of tissue epigenetics.

There remains the possibility that a substantial change in the specific age, and in the duration of healthy life, might result from *one particular* adjustment. This was the hope which led to the use of sex hormones for purposes of 'rejuvenation', and which was largely disappointed. If such an adjustment is poss-ible, it is most likely, perhaps, to concern one or more of the anabolism-promoting substances which maintain growth in the young animal (or, more fundamentally, substances able to pro-tect cells or tissues as dietary retardation may possibly protect them).

One difficulty is that we do not know what makes fixed post-mitotic cells die, or how far their enzyme systems can be damaged by events analogous to mutation. Certainly animals such as insect imagines, which have little or no cell division, are inordinately resistant to life-shortening by radiation. It may be that the McCay rat experiments in which life was prolonged, effectively, by lengthening childhood through calorie restriction, are in a sense irrelevant to the problem of prolonging human adult vigour, for in all probability this type of manœuvre acts by delaying development, and perhaps merely by postponing the age at which certain timekeeping cells reach their fixed postmitotic state; and it may be that the real problem will prove to be one of conserving these cells as we conserve irreplaceable teeth—not so much of postponing the age at which the permanent set erupt, as of preventing decay and filling biochemical cavities as they develop. It would be tempting to look on loss of neurones *per se* as a possible timekeeping mechanism, for both between species and between breeds within a species it is the index of cephalization—the excess of brain over the expected amount—which correlates most closely with longevity (Sacher, 1958; Comfort, 1960). Certainly degree of mental vigour is a prognostic for physical longevity in the old (Jarvik and Falek, 1963). Next to the biochemical information store in cell nuclei the central nervous system is our main and overriding homoeostatic system. Since this is so, if the deterioration of fixed postmitotics were the timing mechanism for mammalian senescence, the prospect of slowing it seems by no means hopeless, for the very diversity in the rate of ageing between similar mammalian species suggests that the rate of spoilage might be accessible. When typical ageing can be produced by experimental damage to the brain, one might be prepared to take this particular speculation further. It is in fact one of the most venerable of gerontological theories. At the moment, though some would locate the cause of Simmonds' disease, which has some characters of a reversible senescence, in the pituitary-hypothalamic system, nobody has apparently ever produced ageing effects by giving a nerve cell poison or by experimental injury to the brain. It may be that the effects of these are too local or too widespread. And there for the moment the matter must rest.

To the question 'Can the effective human life-span be prolonged artificially?' the most probable answer, based on all these possibilities, would appear to be 'Yes'. To the further question 'By what factor?' no meaningful answer can be given until we know more of the nature of the predominant processes which determine human senescence. Supplementary questions dealing with the degree of reversibility in established senile change cannot at present be answered at all, beyond the conjecture that the morphogenetic programme in man is hardly likely to be simply reversible in any fundamental sense, but that the irreversibility of local changes in ageing is at present probably over- rather than under-estimated.

The only excuse for such speculation is, in any case, the possibility that it will drive us into the laboratory to ascertain the facts and to answer the questions it raises, thereby removing gerontology from the field of 'entelechies' and 'inherent principles' into that of intelligible evidence.

With the growth of international gerontology we no longer find ourselves waiting for the main problems of understanding age processes to be solved *incidentally*, in the course of general biological research upon other topics, but even so much of the information which is missing on other specific points is likely to be derived eventually from studies in endocrinology or morphogenetics which are not undertaken *ad hoc*; this type of background research cannot be hurried on, ahead of the general progress of knowledge, except by the cultivation of interest in ageing among biologists of all kinds.

Three main types of research have so far been involved in the investigation of ageing study of the phylogeny of senescence in vertebrates, study of the correlations and the experimental modification of growth and development in populations where the life-span can be concurrently measured, and study of tissue-environment relationships through the creation of age chimaeras. To these we can now add radiation biology, cell chemistry, and direct attempts to distinguish between age effects due to changes in cell number and in cell quality. Yet another new field has been opened by the recognition of chromosomal variation in man.

The problems of phylogenetic studies have already been mentioned. A reliable test of 'senescence' which correlates with the decline of resistance, does not kill the individual animal, and can be related to actuarial senescence by an intelligible process of reasoning, might offer some solution. The development of such a test would probably depend, however, upon the establishment of the part which declining growth-energy plays in the process of ageing. The time-lag in explant growth might still conceivably give a basis for some such attempt. Any method of marking tissue cells *in situ*, to enable their life-span to be determined like that of red blood corpuscles, would be a highly desirable advance, and a key to many doors. The study of growth and development relations, and the whole group of studies which require to be undertaken in determining the factors which predominate in mammalian ageing, or which can modify it, encounter a rather different obstacle. The choice of experimental animals for such work obviously presents great difficulty, since it is necessary either to work on forms whose life-span is short compared with that of the investigator, or to use elderly individuals whose early history has not been followed. The complication which this time-factor introduces is of great importance for the planning of research. Man is by far the most numerous senile animal, and his life-cycle is extremely well known—even to the point at which we can estimate his physiological age by inspection; some research on senile men can be justified ethically, but the gerontological aspects of laboratory animal-breeding cannot much longer be neglected, since in many problems no further progress is possible until mammals of known life-cycle, heredity and physiology are available in quantity. At present the choice lies between experiment on patients, the basing of general conclusions upon the behaviour of invertebrates and small rodents, and postponing investigation for several years while a chosen population of larger mammals completes its life-cycle, though lifetime studies of dogs are being initiated for radiation research nevertheless (A. E. C. Projects nos. 4 and 6, Univ. of California). Failure to deal with the logistics of this problem now will hinder research in ten or twenty years' time, and that hindrance could be avoided by forethought.

Apart from specialized investigations, serious progress now depends on the cultivation of general awareness among biologists of the importance of prolonging their study of every animal into the senile period, of collecting and publishing life-tables, especially for cold-blooded vertebrates under good laboratory conditions, and of seeking confirmatory evidence of the distribution of senescence in phylogeny. A few years of propaganda to biologists and administrators has already brought in a rich factual harvest. Much modern research into ageing tends still to be desultory, although the single subjects with which it deals are important in themselves. We ought to try to devise critical experiments, and if we destroy more hypotheses than we demonstrate, this is a subject which can well stand such treatment in contrast to the speculation which has gone before. The most desirable condition for progress in gerontology at the moment is still that the exact nature and scope of the problems raised by senescence should be understood, and the possibility of new experimental evidence borne in mind, during the planning and assessment of all biological research, even when it is primarily directed to other objects. Senescence, like Mount Everest, challenges our ingenuity by the fact that it is there, and the focusing of our attention on it is unlikely to be fruitless.

BIBLIOGRAPHY

ABDEL-MALEK, E. T. (1950). 'Susceptibility of the snail *Biomphalaria boissyi* to infection with certain strains of *Schistosoma mansoni*.' *Amer. J. trop. Med.*, **30,** 887–94.

ABE, N. (1932). 'The age and growth of the limpet (*Acmaea dorsuosa* Gould).' *Sci. Rep. Tôhoku Univ.*, **7,** 347–63.

ABELOOS, M. (1942). 'Sur la régénération de la tête des mollusques gastéropodes.' *C.R. Acad. Sci.*, **214,** 883–4.

ABERCROMBIE, M. (1957). 'Localized formation of new tissue in an adult animal.' *Sympos. Soc. exp. Biol.*, XI, 235–54.

ACHAN, D. N. (1961). 'On prolonging the longevity of the dog tick *Rhipicephalus sanguineus latr.* after oviposition.' *Current Sci.*, **30,** 265–6.

ADAMS, A. E., and MOTHES, A. M. (1945). 'The thyrotrophic potency o. the pituitaries of albino mice with respect to age and sex.' *Anat. Rec.*, **91,** 21.

ADAMS, C. E. (1953) in Ciba Foundation Symposium—*Mammalian Germ Cells*, p. 198. London: Churchill.

AGDUHR, E. (1939). 'Internal secretion and resistance to injurious factors.' *Acta medica scand.*, **99,** 387.

AGDUHR, E., and BARRON, D. H. (1938). 'Further observations on the increased resistance of mated animals to toxic agents: Medinal.' *Arch. int. Pharmacodyn.*, **58,** 351.

AHRENS, K. (1938). 'Lokaler Nachweis von Kalzium in den Membranen des *Elodea*-blattes mittels Natriumoleat.' *Protoplasma*, **31,** 508.

ALEXANDER, P. (1957). 'Accelerated ageing—a long term effect of exposure to ionizing radiations.' *Gerontologia*, **1,** 174–92.

ALEXANDER, P., CONNELL, D. I., BROHULT, A., and BROHULT, S. (1959). 'Relation of radiation induced shortening of the life-span by a diet augmented by Alkoxyl glycerol esters and essential fatty acids.' *Gerontology*, **3,** 147–52.

ALLBRIGHT, F. (1947). 'Osteoporosis.' *Ann. int. Med.*, **27,** 861.

ALLEE, W. C., EMERSON, A. E., PARK, O., PARK, T., and SCHMIDT, K. P. (1949). *Principles of animal ecology*. Philadelphia: W. B. Saunders Co.

ALLEN, J. A. (1952–3). 'Observations on *Nucula turgida* Marshall and *N. moorei* Winckworth.' *J. mar. Biol. Ass. U.K.*, **31,** 515–27.

—— (1958). 'Observations on *Cochlodesma praetenue* (Pult.).' *J. mar. biol. Res. Assn.*, **37,** 97–112.

—— (1960). 'Manganese deposition on the shells of living molluscs.' *Nature, Lond.*, **185,** 337.

Bibliography

ALLEN, W. M., and MASTERS, W. H. (1948). 'Investigation of sexual rejuvenation in elderly women.' *Tenth Conference on Problems of Aging*. Josiah Macey, Jr. Foundation, 1948.

ALPATOV, V. V., and GORDEENKO, N. A. (1932). Алпатов, В.В. и Гордеенко, Н.А. 'Влияние спаривания на продолжителность жизни шелкопрядов.' (Influence of mating on the longevity of silk-moths.) *Zool. Zh.*, **11**, (2), 60.

ALPATOV, W. W. (1930). 'Experimental studies on the duration of life. XIII. The influence of different feeding during the larval and imaginal stages on the duration of life in the imago of *Drosophila melanogaster*.' *Amer. Nat.*, **64**, 37.

ALPATOV, W. W., and PEARL, R. (1929). 'Experimental studies on the duration of life. XII. Influence of temperature during the larval period and adult life on the duration of life in the imago of *Drosophila melanogaster*.' *Amer. Nat.*, **63**, 37.

ALTNÖDER, K. (1926). 'Beobachtungen über die Biologie von *Margaritana margaritifera* und über die Oleologie ihres Wohnorts.' *Arch. Hydrobiol.*, **17**, 423–51.

ANDERSON, B. G., and JENKINS, J. C. (1942). 'A time study of events in the life-span of *Daphnia magna*.' *Biol. Bull. Wood's Hole*, **83**, 260.

ANDERSON, R. E., WALFORD, R. L., and DOYLE, P. C. (1961). 'Leucocyte antibodies in acute leukaemia of the monocytic and monocytoid forms.' *Amer. J. clin. Path.*, **36**, 25–30.

ANDRES, A., and JIV, B. V. (1936). 'Somatic chromosome complex of human embryos.' *Cytologia*, **7**, 371.

ANDREW, W. (1953). 'Phenomena of abnormal nuclear division in relation to the ageing process.' *J. Gerontol.*, **8**, 372.
    (1955). 'Amitotic division in senile tissues as a probable means of self-preservation in cells.' *J. Gerontol.*, **10**, 1.

ANDUSEN, A. C. (1961). *Tenth Annual Progress Report of A.E.C. Project No. 4.* University of California Veterinary School, Davis, California.

ANNANDALE, N., and SEWELL, R. B. S. (1921). 'The banded pond-snail of India—*Vivipara bengalensis*.' *Rec. Indian Mus.*, **22**, 215–48 and 279–86.

ANON. (1959). 'A remedy for ageing?' *Lancet*, **i**, 562–3.

ANSELL, A. D. (1961). 'Reproduction, growth and mortality of *Verus Striatula* (Da Costa) in Kames Bay, Millport.' *J. marine Biol. Ass. U.K.*, **41**, 191–215.

ARNDT, W. (1928). 'Lebensdauer, Altern und Tod der Schwämme.' *S.B. Ges. naturf. Fr., Berl.*, **23**, 44.
    (1941). 'Lebendbeobachtungen an Kiesel- und Horn-Schwämmen des Berliner Aquarium.' *Zool. Gärt., Lpz.*, **13**, 140.

ÁRVAY, A., TAKÁCS, J., and VERZÁR, F. (1963). 'Der Einfluss von Graviditäten auf das Altern des Kollagens.' *Gerontologia*, **7**, 77–84.

Bibliography

ASDELL, S. A., and CROWELL, M. F. (1935). 'The effect of retarded growth upon the sexual development of rats.' *J. Nutrit.*, **10**, 13–24.

ASHWORTH, J. H., and ANNANDALE, N. (1904). 'Observations on some aged specimens of *Sagartia troglodytes* and on the duration of life in Coelenterates.' *Proc. Roy. Soc. Edinb.*, **25**, 295.

ASLAN, A. (1956). 'Eine neue Methode zur Prophylaxe und Behandlung des Alterns mit Novocain.' *Therapiewoche*, **7**, 14–22.

(1957–8). 'Neue Erfahrungen über der verjüngende Wirkung des Novocains.' *Ibid.*, **8**, 3–12.

ASLAN, A., and DAVID, C. (1957). 'Ergebnisse der Novocain—behandlung—Stoff H₃—bei dysmetabolischen Arthropathien.' *Ibid.*, **8**, 1–5.

ASLING, C. W., MOON, H. D., BENNETT, L. L., and EVANS, H. M. (1952a). 'Relation of the anterior hypophysis to problems of ageing.' *J. Gerontol.*, **7**, 292.

ASLING, C. W., WALKER, D. G., SIMPSON, M. E., LI, C. H., and EVANS, H. M. (1952b). 'Deaths in rats submitted to hypophysectomy at an extremely early age and the survival effected by growth hormone.' *Anat. Rec.*, **114**, 49.

BAB, H. (1948). 'The process of ageing.' *Brit. med. J.*, **i**, 1000.

BACELAR, A., and FRADE, F. (1933). 'Sur la longévité chez les araignées.' *C.R. Soc. Biol.*, **113**, 523.

BACKMAN, G. (1938). 'Wachtumszyklen und phylogenetische Entwicklung.' *Lunds Univ. Årskrift*, N.F. Avd., 2, **34**, Nr. 5.

(1944). 'Der Lebenslauf der Organismen nebst kritischen Betrachtungen zu meiner Wachtumstheorie.' *Z. Altersforsch.*, **4**, 237.

(1945). *Altern und Lebensdauer der Organismen*. (Uppsala and Stockholm).

BACON, F. (1645). *Historia Vitae et Mortis*. Dillingen.

BAER, K. (1864). *Reden*. St. Petersburg.

BAERG, W. J. (1945). 'The black widow and the tarantula.' *Trans. Conn. Acad. Arts Sci.*, **36**, 99.

BAFFONI, G. M. (1954). 'La citomorfosi degli elementi di Purkinje del cervelletto.' *Ricerc. scient.*, Rome, **24**, 1641.

BAILY, J. L. (1931). 'Some data on growth, longevity and fecundity in *Limnaea columella* Say.' *Biol. Generalis*, **7**, 407–28.

BAKER, F. (1934). 'A conchological Rip van Winkle.' *Nautilus, Phil.*, **48**, 5.

BAKER, L. E., and CARREL, A. (1926). 'Au sujet du pouvoir inhibiteur du sérum pendant la vieillesse.' *C.R. Soc. Biol.*, Paris, **95**, 958.

BAKER, S., GAFFNEY, G., SHOCK, N., and LANSDOWNE, M. (1959). 'Physiological responses of five middle-aged and elderly men to repeated administration of thyrotropin.' *J. Gerontol.*, **14**, 37–47.

Bibliography

BALÁSZ, A. (1960). 'Die Korrelation der praeimaginalen Lebensdauer und gerontologische Prozesse bei holometabolen Insekten.' In *The Ontogeny of Insects*. Prague, Nakladelství Ceskoslovenské Akademie.

BALÁSZ, A., and BURG, M. (1962). 'Span of life and senescence of *Dugesia lugubris*.' *Gerontologia*, Basel, **6**, 227–36.

BALL, J. P., and SQUIRE, J. R. (1949). 'A study of mortality in a burns unit.' *Ann. Surg.*, **130**, 160.

BALL, Z. B., BAINES, R. H., and VISSCHER, M. B. (1947). 'The effects of dietary caloric restriction on maturity and senescence, with particular reference to fertility and longevity.' *Amer. J. Physiol.*, 1947, **150**, 511–19.

BANFIELD, A. W. F. (1960). 'The use of caribou antler pedicels for age determination.' *J. wildl. Manag.*, **24**, 99–102.

BANFIELD, W. G. (1952). 'The solubility and swelling of collagen in dilute acid with age variations in man.' *Anat. Rec.*, **114**, 157.
　(1956). 'Age changes in the swelling capacity of the human Achilles tendon.' *J. Gerontol.*, **11**, 372.

BANGA, I. (1957). 'Der Effect der schwachen organischen Saüren auf die Rattenschwanz-Kollagenfasern von jungen und altern Tieren.' *Gerontologia*, **1**, 325–46.

BANTA, A. M. (1914). 'One hundred parthenogenetic generations of *Daphnia* without sexual forms.' *Proc. Soc. exp. Biol.*, *N.Y.*, **11**, 7.

BANTA, A. M., and WOOD, T. R. (1937). 'The accumulation of recessive physiological mutations during long-continued parthenogenesis.' *Genetics*, **22**, 183.

BARDACH, J. E. (1955). 'The opercular bone of the yellow perch. *Perca flavescens*, as a tool for age and growth studies.' *Copeia*, 1955, 107–9.

BARLOW, C. H., and MUENCH, H. (1951). 'Life span and monthly mortality rate of *Bulinus truncatus* and *Planorbis boissyi*, the intermediate hosts of Schistosomiasis in Egypt.' *J. Parasitol.*, **37**, 165–73.

BARNES, D. W. H., LOUTIT, J. F., and WESTGARTH, D. R. (1959). 'Longevity of radiation chimaeras.' *Gerontologia*, **3**, 137–46.

BARNES, H. F., and STOKES, B. M. (1951). 'Marking and breeding *Testacella* slugs.' *Ann. appl. Biol.*, **38**, 540–5.

BARNES, L. L. (1942). 'The deposition of calcium in the hearts and kidneys of rats in relation to age, source of calcium, exercise and diet.' *Am. J. Path.*, **18**, 41.

BARRETT-HAMILTON, G. E. H. (1911). *History of British Mammals*. London.

BAUER, E. (1924). 'Beitrage zum Studium der Protoplasmahysteresis, etc.' II. *Arch. mikr. Anat.*, **101**, 483. VIII. *Arch. mikr. Anat.*, **101**, 521.

BAZILEVITCH, I. V. (1938a). Базилевич, И.В.: 'Синдром нормалной старости.' (The syndrome of normal old age.) *Proc. Conf. Probl. Old Age*, *Kiev*, 255.

Bibliography

BAZILEVITCH, I. W. (1938b). 'Sur l'âge des vieillards centenaires d'Ab-khasya.' *Medits. Zh.*, **8,** 7.

BAZYKALOVA, A. (1934). Базыкалова, А.: 'Возраст и темп роста *Pecten jessoensis* Jay.' (Age and growth-rate of *P. j.*) *Bull. Acad. Sci. U.R.S.S.,* 2–3, 389.

BEERS, C. D. (1929). 'On the possibility of indefinite reproduction in the ciliate *Didinium* without conjugation or endomixis.' *Amer. Nat.,* **63,** 125.

BEETON, M., and PEARSON, K. (1901). 'On the inheritance of the duration of life, and on the intensity of natural selection in man.' *Biometrika,* **1,** 50.

BÉLÁR, K. (1924). 'Untersuchungen an *Actinophrys sol* Ehrenburg. II. Beitrage zur Physiologie des Formwechsels.' *Arch. Protistenk.,* **48,** 371.

BELLAMY, A. W. (1934). 'Life span of *Platypoecilus, Xiphophorus* and their hybrids in the laboratory.' *Science,* **80,** 191.

BENDER, A. E. (1953). 'Recent advances in protein synthesis.' *Lancet,* **265,** 1142.

BENEDICT, F. G. (1935). 'Old age and basal metabolism.' *New Engl. J. med.,* **212,** 1111.

BENEDICT, F. G., and ROOT, H. F. (1934). 'The potentialities of extreme old age.' *Proc. nat. Acad. Sci.,* **20,** 389.

BENEDICT, F. G., and SHERMAN, H. C. (1937). 'Basal metabolism of rats in relation to old age and exercise during old age.' *J. Nutrit.,* **14,** 179.

BERDISHEV, G. D., and STARIKOV, N. M. (1960). Бердышев Г.Д., Стариков Н. М. Проблема долголетия в Сибире и на Дальнем Востоке. ('Longevity in Siberia and Far Eastern Russia.' *Second Conf. on Gerontology and Geriatrics,* Moscow Natural Society, pp. 25–6.)

BERG, B. N. (1960). 'Nutrition and longevity in the rat. I: Food intake relative to size, health and fertility.' *J. Nutrit.,* **71,** 242–54.

BERG, B. N., and SIMMS, H. S. (1960). 'Nutrition and longevity in the rat. II: Longevity and onset of disease with different levels of food intake.' *J. Nutrit.,* **71,** 255–63.

(1962). 'Relation of nutrition to longevity and onset of disease in rats.' *Biological Aspects of Aging,* New York and London, 35–7.

BERG, K. (1948). 'Biological studies on the River Susaa.' *Folia Limnol. Scand.,* **4,** 1–318.

BERGAUER, V. (1924). 'Beitrage zum Studium der Protoplasmahysteresis, etc.' III. *Arch. mikr. Anat.,* **101,** 489. VI. *Arch. mikr. Anat.,* **101,** 508. VII. *Arch. mikr. Anat.,* **101,** 512.

BERGMAN, A. J., and TURNER, C. W. (1941). 'Thyrotropic hormone content of rabbit pituitary during growth.' *Endocrinology,* **29,** 313.

BERNINGER, J. (1910). 'Über Einwirkung des Hungers auf Hydra.' *Zool. Anz.,* **36,** 271.

BERRILL, N. J. (1931). 'The natural history of *Bulla hydatis* Linn.' *J. mar. biol. Ass. U.K.,* **17,** 567–71.

Bibliography

BERTALANNFY, L. von. (1933). *Modern theories of development*. London: Humphrey Milford.

—— (1941). 'Stoffwechseltypen und Wachtumstypen.' *Biol. Zbl.*, **61**, 510.

BERTIN, L. (1956). *Eels, a biological study*. London: Cleaver-Hume Press.

BERTOLINI, A. M. (1962). 'Modifications of cellular enzyme systems during ageing.' *Gerontologia*, **6**, 175–87.

BEVERTON, R. J. H., and HOLT, S. J. (1959). 'A review of the life-spans and mortality rates of fish in nature.' *CIBA Foundation Colloquia on Ageing*, **5**, 142–77.

BIDDER, G. P. (1925). 'The mortality of plaice.' *Nature, Lond.*, **115**, 495.

—— (1932). 'Senescence.' *Brit. med. J.*, **ii**, 5831.

BIGGERS, J. D., FINN, C. A., and McLAREN, A. (1962). 'Long term reproductive performance of female mice. 1: Effects of removing one ovary.' *J. Repr. Fertil.*, **3**, 303–12.

BILEWICZ, S. (1953). 'Doświadczenia nad wpływem czynności rozrodczych na długość życia u muchy owocowej *Drosophila melanogaster*.' (Influence of mating on the longevity of *D. m.*) *Folia Biol. Warsaw*, **1**, 175.

BILLINGHAM, R. E., BRENT, L., and MEDAWAR, P. B. (1953). 'Actively acquired tolerance of foreign cells.' *Nature, Lond.*, **172**, 603.

BILLINGHAM, R. E., and RUSSELL, P. S. (1956). 'Studies on wound healing with special reference to the phenomenon of contracture in experimental wounds in rabbits' skin.' *Ann. Surg.*, **144**, 961–81.

BIRREN, J. E. (1961). *Handbook of aging and the individual*. Univ. Chicago Press.

BISHOPP, F. C., and SMITH, C. N. (1938). 'The American dog tick, eastern carrier of Rocky Mountain spotted fever.' *Circ. U.S. Dep. Agric.*, No. 478, 1.

BITTNER, J. J. (1937). 'Mammary tumours in mice in relation to nursing.' *Amer. J. Cancer*, **30**, 530.

BJORKSTEN, J. A. (1962). 'Aging: present status of our chemical knowledge.' *J. Amer. Geriat. Soc.*, **10**, 125–39.

BLAIR, H. A. (1955). 'A formula of the relation between radiation dose and shortening of life span.' *Peaceful Uses of Atomic Energy*, Geneva, **XI**.

BLEST, A. D. (1960). 'A study of the biology of saturniid moths in the Canal Zone biological area.' *Smithsonian Rep.*, 1959, 447–64.

BLOCH, S., and FLURY, E. (1959). 'Untersuchungen über Klimakterium und Menopause an Albino-Ratten, 11.' *Gynaecologia*, Basel, **147**, 414–38.

BLUMENTHAL, H. (1945). 'The ageing process in the endocrine glands of the guinea pig. I. The influence of age, sex and pregnancy on the mitotic activity and the histological structure of the thyroid, parathyroid and adrenal glands.' *Arch. Path.*, **40**, 284.

Bibliography

BLUNCK, H. (1924). 'Lebensdauer, Fortpflanzungsvermögen und Alterserscheinungen beim Gelbrand (*Dytiscus marginalis* L.).' *Zool. Anz.*, **58**, 163.

BODENHEIMER, F. S. (1938). *Problems of animal ecology*. Oxford University Press.

BODENSTEIN, D. (1943a). 'Factors influencing growth and metamorphosis of the salivary gland in *Drosophila*.' *Biol. Bull. Wood's Hole*, **84**, 13.

(1943b). 'Hormones and tissue competence in the development of *Drosophila*.' *Biol. Bull. Wood's Hole*, **84**, 35.

(1953). 'Endocrine control of metamorphosis.' *Proc. IX Int. Cong. Entom. Amsterdam*, 1951.

BOECKER, E. (1914). 'Depression und Missbildungen bei *Hydra*.' *Zool. Anz.*, **44**, 75.

BOETTGER, C. R. (1953). 'Riesenwuchs der Landschnecke *Zebrina* (*Z.*) *detrita* (Müller) als Folge parasitären Kastrations.' *Arch. Molluskenk.*, **82**, 151–2.

(1953). 'Grössenwachstum und Geschlechtsreife bei Schnecken und pathologische Riesenwuchs folge einer gestörten Wechselwirkung beider Faktoren.' *Zool. Anz.*, **17**, Suppl-Bd., 468–87.

BOGOMOLETS, A. A. (1947). *The prolongation of life*. Duell Sloan and Pearce, New York, 1946.

BONNET, P. (1935). 'La longévité chez les araignées.' *Bull. Soc. ent. Fr.*, **40**, 272.

BONNOT, P. (1940). 'California abalones.' *Calif. Fish. Game.*, **26**, 200–11.

BOOTHBY, W. M., BERKSON, J., and DUNN, H. L. (1936). 'Studies of the energy metabolism of normal individuals.' *Amer. J. Physiol.*, **116**, 468.

BORISENKO, E. Ya. (1939). Борисенко, Е.Я.: 'Блияние условий развития на последствия инбридинга.' (Influence of conditions of development on the effects of inbreeding). *Yarovizatsiya*, **5–6**, 162.

(1941). 'К вопросу об инбридинге в животноводстве.' (On inbreeding in animal husbandry.) *Trud. sel.-Khoz. Acad. Timiryazeva*, **5**, 5.

BORSSUK, R. A. (1935). 'Untersuchung des Verlustes der Regenerationsfähigkeit der hinteren Extremität von *Rana temporaria*.' *Arch. EntwMeck. Org.*, **133**, 349.

BOUNHIOL, J. (1938). 'Recherches expérimentales sur la déterminisme de la métamorphose chez les Lepidoptères.' *Biol. Bull. Suppl.*, **24**, 1.

BOURLIÈRE, F. (1946). 'Longévité moyenne et longévité maximum chez les vertébrés.' *Année Biol.*, *Paris*, **22**, 10.

(1947). 'Quelques remarques sur la longévité des petits mammifères sauvages.' *Mammalia*, **11**, 111.

(1950). 'Sénescence et vitesse de cicatrisation chez le rat.' *Rev. med. Liège*, **5**, 669.

(1951). *Vie et mœurs des mammifères*. Payot, Paris.

(1959). 'Life-spans of mammalian and bird populations in nature.' *CIBA Foundation Symposium on Ageing*, **5**, 90–103.

Bibliography

BOWERMAN, W. G. (1939). 'Centenarians.' *Trans. Actuarial Soc. Amer.*, **40,** 360.

BOYCOTT, A. E. (1934). 'The habits of land mollusca in Great Britain.' *J. Ecol.*, **22,** 1–38.

—— (1936). 'The habits of freshwater mollusca in Britain.' *J. anim. Ecol.*, **5,** 116–86.

BOYKO, E. G. (1946). 'Age determination in fishes based on examination of fin ray sections.' *C.R. Acad. Sci. U.R.S.S.*, **53,** 483–4.

BRAADBART, S. (1961). No title. See *Lancet*, 1961, **ii,** 764.

BRANDER, T. (1956). 'Über Dimensionen, Gewicht, Volumen und Alter grosswüchsiger europaischer Unionazeën.' *Arch. Molluskenk.*, **85,** 65–8.

BRESSLAU, E. (1928–33). *Turbellaria*: in Kükenthal, W., and Krumbach, T. *Handbuch der Zoologie*, II.

BRIEN, P. (1953). 'La pérennité somatique.' *Biol. Rev.*, **28,** 308.

BROCAS, J., and VERZÁR, F. (1961a). 'Measurement of isometric tension during thermic contraction as criterion of the biological age of collagen fibres.' *Gerontologia*, **5,** 223–7.

—— (1961b). 'The ageing of *Xenopus laevis*, a South African frog.' *Gerontologia*, **5,** 228–40.

BROCKMEIER, H. (1888). 'Zur Fortpflanzung von *Helix nemoralis* und *H. hortensis* in der Gefangenschaft.' *Nachrbl. deutsch. malak. Ges.*, **20.**

—— (1896). 'Beiträge zur Biologie unsere Süsswassermollusken.' *Nachrbl. deutsch. malak. Ges.*, **57.**

BRODY, S. (1924). 'The kinetics of senescence.' *J. gen. Physiol.*, **6,** 245.

—— (1945). *Bioenergetics and Growth*. Baltimore.

BRODY, S., RAGSDALE, A. C., and TURNER, C. W. (1923). 'The rate of growth of the dairy cow. IV. Growth and senescence as measured by the size and fall of milk secretion with age.' *J. gen. Physiol.*, **6,** 31.

BROUN, H. H. (1934). 'A study of the Tectibranch Gasteropod Mollusc, *Philine aperta* (L). *Trans. Roy. Soc. Edinb.*, **58,** 179–210.

BROWN, G. W., and FLOOD, M. M. (1947). 'Tumbler mortality.' *J. Amer. Statist. Ass.*, **42,** 562.

BROWN, M., SINCLAIR, R. G., CRONK, L. B., and CLARK, G. C. (1948). 'Some remarks on premature aging in the Eskimos.' *Rév. Canad. Biol.*, **7,** 178.

BROWN, P. C., and CONSDEN, R. (1958). 'Variation with age of shrinkage temperature of human collagen.' *Nature, Lond.*, **181,** 349–50.

BRUCE, H. M., and HINDLE, E. (1934). 'The golden hamster, *Cricetus* (*Mesocricetus*) *auratus* Waterhouse. Notes on its breeding and growth.' *Proc. zool. Soc. Lond.*, p. 364.

BRUCH, H. (1941). 'Obesity in relation to puberty.' *J. Pediat.*, **19,** 365.

BRUNTON, M., JACOBS, P. A., and COURT BROWN, W. M. (1962). 'Aneuploid cells and age.' *Human Chromosome Newsletter* (in press).

Bibliography

BRUUN, A. F. (1943). 'The biology of *Spirula spirula* (L).' *Dana Rep.*, **4**, 1–44.

BRYUZGIN, V. L. (1939). 'A procedure for investigating age and growth in reptilia.' *C.R. Acad. Sci. U.R.S.S.*, **3**, 403.

BUCHANAN, J. W. (1938). 'Developmental acceleration following inhibition.' *J. exp. Zool.*, **79**, 109.

BUCHER, N. L. R., and GLINOS, A. D. (1950). 'The effect of age on the regeneration of rat liver.' *Cancer Res.*, **10**, 324.

BUCHER, N. L. R., SCOTT, J. F., and AUB, J. C. (1950). 'Regeneration of liver in parabiotic rats.' *Cancer Res.*, **10**, 207.

BULL, H. O. (1934). 'Aquarium observations on the rate of growth and enemies of the common starfish (*Asterias rubens* L.).' *Rep. Dove Marine Lab.*, 3rd series, **2**, 60.

—— (1938). 'The growth of *Psammechinus miliaris* (Gml) under aquarium conditions.' *Rep. Dove Marine Lab.*, **6**, 39.

BULLOUGH, W. S. (1949). 'Age and mitotic activity in the male mouse, *Mus musculus* L.' *J. exp. Biol.*, **26**, 261.

BURCH, P. J. R. (1963a). 'Carcinogenesis and cancer prevention.' *Nature, Lond.*, **197**, 1145–51.

BURCH, P. R. J. (1963b). 'Human cancer: Mendelian inheritance or vertical transmission?' *Nature, Lond.*, **197**, 1042–6.

BURCH, P. R. J. (1963c). 'Autoimmunity: some aetiological aspects.' *Lancet*, **i**, 1253–7.

BURGER, M. (1954). *Altern und Krankheit*. 2. Aufl. Leipzig: Georg Thiene.

BURNET, F. M. (1959). 'Clonal selection.' *Croonian Lecture*. Roy. Coll. of Physicians of London, 1959.

—— (1961). 'The new approach to immunology.' *New England J. Med.*, **264**, 24–34.

BURT, W. H. (1940). 'Territorial behaviour and populations of some small mammals in southern Michigan.' *Misc. Publ. Mus. Zool. Univ. Mich.*, **45**, 1–58.

BUTSCHLI, O. (1882). 'Gedanke über Leben und Tod.' *Zool. Anz.*, **5**, 64.

BUXTON, J. (1950). *The redstart*. London: Collins.

CAGLE, F. R. (1946). 'Growth of the slider turtle, *Pseudemys scripta elegans*.' *Amer. Midl. Nat.*, **39**, 685.

CAIREY, C. F. (1954). 'Simplified comparison of man-dog age.' *J. Am. Vet. M. A.*, **125**, 56.

CALKINS, G. N. (1919). '*Uroleptus mobilis* Eng. II. Renewal of vitality through conjugation.'

CAMBOUÉ, P. (1926). 'Prolongation de la vie chez les papillons décapités.' *C.R. Soc. Biol., Paris*, **183**, 372.

291

Bibliography

CAMPBELL, J., DAVIDSON, I. W. F., SNAIR, W. D., and LEI, H. P. (1950). 'Diabetogenic effect of purified growth hormone.' *Endocrinology*, **46,** 273.

CAMPBELL, P. N., and WORK, T. S. (1953). 'Biosynthesis of proteins.' *Nature, Lond.*, **171,** 997.

CARLSON, A. J., and HOELZEL, F. (1946). 'Apparent prolongation of the life-span of rats by intermittent fasting.' *J. Nutrit.*, **31,** 363–75.
  — (1947). 'Growth and longevity of rats fed omnivorous and vegetarian diets.' *J. Nutrit.*, **34,** 81–96.
  — (1948). 'Prolongation of the life-span of rats by bulk formers in the diet.' *J. Nutrit.*, **36,** 27.

CARR, C. J., KING, J. T., and VISSCHER, M. B. (1949). 'Delay of senescence infertility by dietary restriction.' *Feder. Proc.*, **8,** 22.

CARREL, A. (1912). 'On the permanent life of tissues outside the organism.' *J. exp. Med.*, **15,** 516.

CARREL, A., and EBERLING, A. H. (1912). 'Antagonistic growth principles of serum and their relation to old age.' *J. exp. Med.*, **38,** 419.

CARROLL, H. W., and BRAUER, R. W. (1961). 'Residual radiation injury: impaired regrowth of realimented hypocalorically reared rats.' *Am. J. Physiol.*, **201,** 1078–82.

CARTER, T. O. (1955). 'Remarkable age attained by a bobcat.' *J. Mammal.*, **36,** 290.

CASTLE, W. E. (1929). 'A further study of size inheritance in rabbits, with special reference to the existence of genes for size characters.' *J. exp. Zool.*, **53,** 421.

CHAI, C. K. (1959). 'Life-span in inbred and hybrid mice.' *J. Hered.*, **50,** 203–8.

CHAMBERLAIN, T. K. (1931). 'Annual growth of freshwater mussels.' *Bull. U.S. Bur. Fish*, **46,** 713–39.
  — (1933). 'Ages and shell measurements of two large specimens of *Megalonaias gigantea* Barnes.' *Nautilus*, **47,** 29.

CHANG, H. S. (1951). 'Age and growth of *Callionymus lyra* L.' *J. mar. Biol. Ass. U.K.*, **30,** 281.

CHEYMOL, J., and PELOU, A. (1944). 'La réspiration du muscle du lapin suivant l'âge.' *C.R. Soc. Biol., Paris*, **138,** 91.

CHIEFFI, M. (1949). 'Effect of testosterone administration on the beard growth of elderly males.' *J. Gerontol.*, **4,** 200.
  — (1950). 'An investigation of the effects of parenteral and topical administration of steroids on the elastic properties of senile skin.' *J. Gerontol.*, **5,** 17.
  — (1951). 'The effect of topical oestrogen application on the elastic properties of the skin of elderly men.' *J. Gerontol.*, **5,** 387.

Bibliography

CHILD, C. M. (1911). 'A study of senescence and rejuvenation based on experiments with planarians.' *Arch. EntwMeck. Org.*, **31**, 537.

— (1913). 'The asexual cycle in *Planaria velata* in relation to senescence and rejuvenescence.' *Biol. Bull. Wood's Hole*, **25**, 181.

— (1914). 'Asexual breeding and prevention of senescence in *Planaria velata*.' *Biol. Bull. Wood's Hole*, **26**, 286.

— (1915). *Senescence and rejuvenescence.* Chicago: University of Chicago Press.

— (1918). 'Physiological senescence in hydromedusae.' *Biol. Bull. Wood's Hole*, **34**, 49.

CHITTLEBOROUGH, R. G. (1959). 'Determination of age in the humpbacked whale *Megaptera nodosa* (Bonaterre).' *Aust. J. mar. freshw. Res.*, **10**, 125–41.

CHOLODKOWSKY, N. (1882). 'Tod und Unsterblichkeit in der Tierwelt.' *Zool. Anz.*, **5**, 264.

CHRISTOPHERSON, J. B. (1924). 'Longevity of parasitic worms: the term of living existence of *Schistosoma haematobium* in the human body.' *Lancet*, p. 742.

CHU, J. (1934). 'Reproduction, life-span, growth and senescence of *Brachionus*.' *Sci. Rep. Univ. Chekiang*, No. 1.

CHUGUNOV, N. I. (1925). 'On the methods of age determination in sturgeons.' *Bull. fish. Econ. U.R.S.S.*, **11**, 33.

— (1949). Чугупов Н. И. Лромысловые рыбы СССР. (*Economic Fishes of the U.S.S.R.*) Moscow.

CHVAPIL, M., and HRŮZA, Z. (1959). 'The influence of aging and undernutrition on chemical contractility and relaxation of collagen fibres in rats.' *Gerontologia*, **3**, 241–52.

CLARK, A. M. (1957). 'The relation of genome number to radio sensitivity in *Habrobracon*.' *Amer. Nat.*, **91**, 111–19.

— (1960). 'Modification of life span by X rays for haploids and diploids of the wasp *Habrobracon* sp.' *Biol. Bull.*, **119**, 292.

CLARK, A. M., and RUBIN, M. A. (1961) 'The modification by X-irradiation of the life span of haploids and diploids of the wasp *Habrobracon* sp.' *Radiation Res.*, **15**, 244–53.

CLARK, T. B. (1940). 'The relation of production and egg weight to age in White Leghorn fowls.' *Poultry Sci.*, **14**, 54.

CLARKE, J. M., and MAYNARD SMITH, J. (1955). 'The genetics and cytology of *Drosophila subobscura*. XI. Hybrid vigour and longevity.' *J. Genet.*, **53**, 172.

— (1961a). 'Two phases of ageing in the *Drosophila subobscura*.' *J. exp. Biol.*, **38**, 679–84.

— (1961b). 'Independence of temperature of the rate of ageing in *Drosophila subobscura*.' *Nature, Lond.*, **190**, 1027–8.

CLARKE, M. F., and SMITH, A. (1938). 'Recovery following suppression of growth in the rat.' *J. Nutrit.*, **15**, 245.

293

Bibliography

CLELAND, D. M. (1954). 'A study of the habits of *Valvata piscinalis* (Müller) and the structure and function of the alimentary canal and reproductive system.' *Proc. malac. Soc. Lond.*, **30**, 167–202.

CLEMENTE, C. D., and WINDLE, W. F. (1955). 'Regeneration of severed nerve fibres in the spinal cord of the adult cat.' *J. compar. Neurol.*, **101**, 691.

CLEVELAND, L. R. (1938). 'Longitudinal and transverse division in two closely-related flagellates.' *Biol. Bull. Wood's Hole*, **74**, 1.

COCKRUM, E. L. (1956). 'Homing, movements and longevity in bats.' *J. Mammal.*, **37**, 48–57.

COE, W. N. (1947). 'Nutrition, growth and sexuality of the Pismo clam (*Tivela stultorum*).' *J. exp. Zool.*, **104**, 1–24.

COE, W. R. (1948). 'Nutrition, environmental conditions, and growth of marine bivalve mollusks.' *J. mar. Res.*, *New Haven*, **7**(3), 586–601.

COE, W. R., and FOX, D. L. (1942). 'Biology of the California mussel (*Mytilus californiensis*). 1. Influence of temperature, food supply, sex and age on the rate of growth.' *J. exp. Zool.*, **90**, 1–30.

COHAUSEN, J. H. (1742). *Hermippus Redivivus, sive exercitatio physico-medica curiosa de methodo raro ad CXV annos prorogandae senectutis per anhelitum puellarum, ex veteri monumento Romano deprompta, etc.* Frankfurt.

COHN, A. E., and MURRAY, H. A. (1925). 'The negative acceleration of growth with age, as demonstrated by tissue culture.' *J. exp. Med.*, **42**, 275.

COKER, R. E., SHIRA, A. F., CLARK, H. W., and HOWARD, A. D. (1919–20). 'Natural history and propagation of the freshwater mussels.' *Bull. U.S. Bur. Fish.*, **37**, 75.

COLE, H. A. (1956). 'A preliminary study of growth rate in cockles (*Cardium edule* L.), in relation to commercial exploitation.' *J. Cons. int. Exp. Mer.*, **22**, 77–90.

COLE, L. J. (1962). 'Ageing at the cellular level. Differential effect of transplanted isogenic lymphoid cells from old versus young mice.' *Gerontologia*, **6**, 36–40.

COLLINGE, W. E. (1944). 'Notes on the terrestrial Isopoda (Woodlice).' *Northw. Nat.*, **19**, 112.

COMFORT, A. (1953). 'Absence of a Lansing effect in *Drosophila subobscura*.' *Nature, Lond.*, **172**, 83.

(1954). 'Biological aspects of senescence.' *Biol. Rev.*, **29**, 284–329.

(1956a). *The Biology of Senescence*. Routledge and Kegan Paul. London, 257.

(1956b). 'The longevity and mortality of Irish wolfhounds.' *Proc. zool. Soc. Lond.*, **127**, 27–34.

(1956c). 'Maximum ages reached by domestic cats.' *J. Mammal.*, **37**, 118–19.

COMFORT, A. (1957a). 'The duration of life in molluscs.' *Proc. malac. Soc. Lond.*, **32**, 219–49.

(1957b). 'Survival curves of mammals in captivity'. *Proc. zool. Soc. Lond.*, **128**, 349–64.

(1957c). 'The biological approach in the comparative study of ageing.' *CIBA Foundation Colloquia on Ageing*, **3**, 2–19.

(1958a). 'The longevity and mortality of Thoroughbred mares.' *J. Geront.*, **13**, 342–50.

(1958b). 'Coat colour and longevity in Thoroughbred mares.' *Nature, Lond.*, **182**, 1531–2.

(1958c). 'Mortality and the nature of age processes.' Alfred Watson Memorial lecture, *J. Inst. Actu.*, **84**, 263–80.

(1959a). 'Natural ageing and the effects of radiation.' *Radiation Res. (Suppl.)*, **1**, 226–34.

(1959b). 'Studies on the longevity and mortality of English Thoroughbred horses.' *CIBA Foundation Colloquia on Ageing*, **5**, 35–54.

(1959c). 'The longevity and mortality of Thoroughbred stallions.' *J. Gerontol.*, **14**, 9–10.

(1960a). 'Longevity and mortality in dogs of four breeds.' *J. Gerontol.*, **15**, 126–9.

(1960b). 'The effect of age on growth-resumption in fish (*Lebistes*) checked by food restriction.' *Gerontologia*, **4**, 177–86.

(1960c). 'Darwin and Freud.' *Lancet*, **ii**, 107–11.

(1961a). 'A life table for Arabian mares.' *J. Gerontol.*, **17**, 14.

(1961b). 'The expected rate of senescence and age-dependent mortality in fish.' *Nature, Lond.*, **191**, 822–3.

(1961c). 'The longevity and mortality of a fish (*Lebistes reticulatus* Peters) in captivity.' *Gerontologia*, **5**, 209–22.

(1962). 'Survival curves of some birds in the London Zoo.' *Ibis*, **104**, 115–17.

COMFORT, A., and DOLJANSKI, F. (1959). 'The relation of size and age to rate of tail regeneration in *Lebistes reticulatus*.' *Gerontologia*, Basel, **2**, 266–83.

CONANT, R., and HUDSON, R. G. (1949). 'Longevity records for reptiles and amphibia in the Philadelphia Zoological Garden.' *Herpetologia*, San Diego, **5**, 1–8.

CONKLIN, J. W., UPTON, A. C., CHRISTENBERRY, K. W., and McDONALD, T. P. (1963). 'Comparative late effects of some radio-mimetic agents and of X-rays.' *Radiation Res.*, **19**, 156–68.

CONWAY, W. G. (1961). 'Humming birds with wrinkles.' *Animal Kingdom*, New York, **64**, 146–50.

COOPER, J. E. (1931). 'Life history of *Myxas glutinosa* (Müller)'. *J. Conchol.*, **19**, 180.

CORI, C. I. (1925). 'Morphologie und Biologie von *Apsilus vorax*.' *Z. wiss. Zool.*, **125**, 557.

Bibliography

COTES, P. M., REID, E., and YOUNG, F. G. (1949). 'Diabetogenic action of pure anterior pituitary growth hormone.' *Nature, Lond.*, **164**, 209.

COURT BROWN, W. M. (1962). 'Role of genetic change in neoplasia.' *Brit. med. J.*, (i), 961–3.

COURT BROWN, W. M., and DOLL, R. (1958). 'Expectation of life and mortality from cancer among British radiologists.' *Brit. med. J.*, 1958 (ii), 181–9.

COUTELEN, F. (1935). 'La longévité de la filaire *Loa loa* (Guyet 1778) et des embryons de filaires.' *Bull. Soc. Path. exot.*, **28**, 126.

COUTELEN, F., RAZEMON, P., and BIGUET, J. (1950). 'La longévité des échinocoques—étude critique.' *Ann. Parasitol.*, **25**, 267.

COWDRY, E. V. (1952). In Lansing, A. I., *Problems of Ageing*. Baltimore: Williams and Wilkins Co.

CRABB, E. D. (1929). 'Growth of a pond-snail, *Limnaea stagnalis appressa*, as indicated by increase in shell size.' *Biol. Bull.*, **56**, 41–63.

CROCKER, W. (1939). 'Ageing in plants.' In Cowdry, E. V., *Problems of Ageing*, 1st edn.

CROWELL, S. (1953). 'The regression-replacement cycle of hydranths of *Obelia* and *Campanularia*.' *Physiol. Zool.*, **26**, 319.

CROZIER, W. J. (1914). 'The growth of the shell in the lamellibranch *Dosinia discus*.' *Zool. Jb. (Anat.)*, **38**, 577–83.

—— (1918a). 'Growth and duration of life in *Chiton tuberculatus*.' *Proc. nat. Acad. Sci.*, **4**, 322–5.

—— (1918b). 'Growth of *Chiton tuberculatus* in different environments.' *Proc. nat. Acad. Sci.*, **4**, 325–8.

CUÉNOT, L. (1911). *La genèse des espèces animales*. Paris.

CURTIS, H. J., and GEBHARD, L. (1958). 'Comparison of life shortening effects of toxic and radiation stresses.' *Radiation Res.*, **9**, 104.

DAIBER, F. C. (1960). 'A technique for age determination in the skate, *Raja eglanteria*.' *Copeia* (1962), 258–60.

DALL, W. H. (1907). *Nautilus*, **21**, 90. (No title.)

DALYELL, J. G. (1848). *Rare and remarkable animals of Scotland*, **ii**, ch. 10. London.

DANCE, S. P. (1958). 'Drought resistance in an African freshwater bivalve.' *J. Conchol.*, **24**, 281–3.

DÁRÁNYI, G. (1930). 'Fejlödés, fajfenntartás és öregedés a természetben.' *Term. Tud. Közl.*, **62**, 305.

DARBISHIRE, R. D. (1889). *J. Conchol.*, **6**, 101. (No title.)

DARLINGTON, C. D. (1948). 'The plasmagene theory of the origin of cancer.' *Brit. J. Cancer*, **2**, 118.

DARLINGTON, C. D., and MATHER, K. (1949). *The elements of genetics*. London: Allen and Unwin.

Bibliography

DARWIN, C. (1874). *The descent of man.* London: John Murray.

DATHE, H. (1935). *Zool. Gärten., Lpz.*, **7**, 303.

DAVAINE, C. (1887). *Traité des Entozoaires et des maladies vermineuses de l'homme et des animaux domestiques.* 2nd edn., Paris: Baillière.

DAVID, K. (1925). 'Zur Frage der potentiellen Unsterblichkeit der Metazoen.' *Zool. Anz.*, **64**, 126.

DAW, R. H. (1961). 'The comparison of male and female mortality rates.' *J. roy. statist. Soc.*, **124**(A), 20–43.

DAWIDOFF, C. (1924). 'Sur le retour d'une Némerte, *Lineus lacteus*, en inanition, à un état embryonnaire.' *C.R. Acad. Sci., Paris*, **179**, 1222.

DEANSLEY, R. (1938). 'The reproductive cycle of the golden hamster (*Cricetus auratus*).' *Proc. zool. Soc. Lond.*, p. 31.

DE CARLI, L. (1961). 'I cromosomi nella vecchiaia.' *Giorn. Geront.*, **9**, 849–57.

DECK, R. S. (1936). 'Longevity of *Terrapene carolina* Linn.' *Copeia*, **160**, 179.

DEEVEY, E. S. (1947). 'Life tables for natural populations of animals.' *Quart. Rev. Biol.*, **22**, 283.

DEEVEY, G. B., and DEEVEY, E. S., Jr. (1945). 'A life table for the black widow.' *Trans. Conn. Acad. Arts Sci.*, **36**, 115.

DELAGE, Y. (1903). *L'hérédité et les grandes problèmes de la biologie.* Paris.

DE LEERSNYDER, M., and HOESTLANDT, H. (1958). 'Extension du gastropode méditerranéen *Cochlicella acuta* (Mull), dans le sud-est de l'Angleterre.' *J. Conchol.*, **24**, 253–64.

DEMANGE, E. (1886). *Études clinques et anatomopathologiques de la vieillesse.* Paris: Baillière.

DENFFER, D. V. (1948). 'Über einen Wachstumshemmstoff in alternden Diatomeenkulturen.' *Biol. Zbl.*, **67**, 7–13.

DE SILVA, H. R. (1938). 'Age and highway accidents.' *Sci. Mon.*, **47**, 536–45.

DE WITT, R. M. (1954). 'Reproductive capacity in a pulmonate snail, *Physagyrina* Say.' *Amer. Nat.*, **88**, 159–64.

DHAR, N. H. (1932). 'Senescence, an inherent property of animal cells.' *Quart. Rev. Biol.*, **7**, 70.

DIDLAKE, M. L. (1937). In Needham, J. G. (Ed.). *Culture methods for invertebrate animals.* New York: Comstock. p. 244.

DIMON, A. C. (1905). 'The mud snail (*Nassa obsoleta*).' *Cold Spr. Harb. Monogr.*, **2**, 1–48.

DITMARS, R. L. (1934). 'A review of the box turtles.' *Zoologica, N.Y.*, **17**, 1.

DOBERS, E. (1915). 'Biologie der Bdelloidea.' *Int. Rev. Ges. Hydrobiol.*, Ser. 6, suppl. 7.

Bibliography

DOLJANSKI, F. (1960). 'The growth of the liver with special reference to mammals.' *Int. Rev. Cytol.*, **10**, 217–41.

DOMINIC, C. J. (1962). 'The ovary of the domestic pigeon, *Columba livia*, with special reference to follicular atresia.' *Proc. ind. Sci. Congr.*, **49**, 405.

DOMM, L. V. (1934). 'The precocious development of sexual characters in the male chick by daily injections of thebin.' *Anat. Rec.*, **58**, 6.

DONALDSON, H. H. (1924). 'The Rat.' *Mem. Wistar Inst. Philadelphia*, No. 6.

DONISTHORPE, H. (1936). 'The oldest insect on record.' *Ent. Rec.*, **48**, 1.

DORST, J. (1954). 'La longévité des Chiroptères.' *Mammalia*, **18**, 231–6.

DOWDESWELL, W. H., FISHER, R. A., and FORD, E. B. (1940). 'The quantitative study of populations in the Lepidoptera. I. *Polyommatus icarus* Rott.' *Ann. Eugen., Camb.*, **10**, 123.

DRAPER, C. C., and DAVIDSON, G. (1935). 'A new method of estimating the survival rate of anopheline mosquitoes in nature.' *Nature, Lond.*, **172**, 503.

DRIBBEN, I. S., and WOLFE, J. M. (1947). 'Structural changes in the connective tissue of the adrenal glands of female rats associated with advancing age.' *Anat. Rec.*, **98**, 557.

DRIESCH, H. (1941). 'Zur Problematik des Alterns.' *Z. Altersforsch.*, **3**, 26.

DUBLIN, L. I., LOTKA, A. J., and SPIEGELMAN, M. (1949). *Length of Life: a study of the life table*. New York: Ronald Press Co.

DUETZ, G. H. (1938). 'Comments on longevity and average exhibition ages during the year 1937.' *Lab. Rep. zöol. Soc. Philadelphia*, **66**, 31.

(1939). 'Revised tables of maximum exhibition periods for animals in the Philadelphia Collection.' *Ibid.*, **67**, 22.

(1940). *Ibid.*, **68**, 26.

(1942). *Ibid.*, **70**, 23.

DUNHAM, H. H. (1938). 'Abundant feeding followed by restricted feeding and longevity in *Daphnia*.' *Physiol. Zoöl.*, **11**, 399.

DUNN, C. W. (1946). 'Endocrines in senescence.' *Clinics, Phil.*, **5**, 847.

DURAN- REYNALS, F. (1940). 'Neutralisation of tumour viruses by the blood of normal fowls of different ages.' *Yale J. Biol. Med.*, **13**, 61.

DURHAM, L., and BENNETT, G. W. (1963). 'Age, growth and homing in the bullfrog.' *J. wildl. Manag.*, **27**, 104–23.

ECKE, D. H., and KINNEY, A. R. (1956). 'Aging meadow mice (*Microtus californicus*) by observation of moult progression.' *J. Mammal.*, **37**, 249–54.

EDLÉN, A. (1937). 'Experimentelle Wachstumstudien an *Daphnia magna*.' *Lunds Univ. Arsberätt* (Avd. 2), **34**, 1.

(1938). 'Geburt, Geschlechtsreife und Vermehrung in Beziehung zum Wachstumsverlauf bei *Daphnia magna*.' *Arch. EntwMeck.*, **137**, 804.

Bibliography

EDMONDS, T. R. (1832). 'Life tables founded upon the discovery of a numerical law, etc.' London: J. Duncan.

EDMONDSON, W. T. (1945a). 'Ecological studies of sessile Rotatoria.' *Ecol. Monogr.*, **14,** 15.

(1945b). 'Ecological studies of sessile Rotatoria. II.' *Ecol. Monogr.*, **15,** 141.

EDNEY, J. M., and ALLEN, W. R. (1951). 'Age of the box turtle, *Terrapene carolina carolina* L.' *Copeia*, **312,** 644.

EGLIS, A. (1960). 'Hardy rayed tortoise from Brooklyn.' *Herpetologica*, **16,** 28.

EJIRI, J. (1936). 'Studien über die Histologie der menschlichen Haut. II. Über die Alters und Geschlechtsverschiedenheiten der elastischen Fäsern.' *Jap. I. Derm. Urol.*, **40,** 173.

ELMAN, R. (1953). 'Surgical problems in the aged.' In Cowdry, E. V. *Problems of Ageing*, 2nd edn., 1953.

ELTON, C. (1942). *Voles, mice and lemmings. Problems in population dynamics.* Oxford: Clarendon Press.

ENGLE, E. T. (1944). 'The menopause, an introduction.' *J. clin. Endocrin.*, **4,** 567.

ERNEST, M. (n.d.). *The longer life.* London: Adam and Co.

ESCOMEL, E. (1939). 'La plus jeune mère du monde.' *Pr. méd.*, **47,** 875.

EVANS, H. M., SIMPSON, M. E., and LI, C. H. (1948). 'The gigantism produced in normal rats by injection of the pituitary growth hormone. I. Body growth and organ changes.' *Growth*, **12,** 15.

EVANS, H. M., SIMPSON, M. E., and PENCHARZ, R. I. (1939). 'Relation between the growth-producing effects of the pituitary and the thyroid hormone.' *Endocrinology*, **25,** 175.

EVANS, R., COWDRY, E. V., and NIELSON, P. E. (1943). 'Ageing of human skin.' *Anat. Rec.*, **86,** 545.

EVERITT, A. V. (1959). 'The effect of pituitary growth hormone on the ageing male rat.' *J. Gerontol.*, **14,** 415–24.

FAILLA, G. (1960). 'The aging process and somatic mutations.' *AIBS Symposium*, 'The Biology of Aging'. *AIBS publ.*, **6,** 170–5. Washington D.C.

FAIRBRIDGE, W. S. (1952). 'A population study of the Tasmanian "commercial" scallop, *Notovola meridionalis* (Tate).' *Aust. J. marine freshw. Res.*, **4,** 1–40.

FALZONE, J. A., BARROWS, C. H., and SHOCK, N. W. (1959). 'Age and polyploidy of rat liver as measured by volume and D.N.A. content.' *J. Gerontol.*, **14,** 2–8.

FARNER, D. S. (1945). 'Age groups and longevity in the American robin.' *Wilson Bull.*, **57,** 56.

Bibliography

FAURÉ-FRÉMIET, E. (1953). 'L'hypothèse de la senescence et les cycles de réorganisation nucleaire chez les Ciliés.' *Rev. suisse Zool.*, **60**, 426.

FEDERLEY, H. (1929). 'Über subletale und disharmonische Chromosomen-kombinationen.' *Hereditas*, **12**, 271.

FELIKSIAK, S. (1947). 'Essai sur la régénération de la tête chez *Physa acuta* Dp.' *Ann. Mus. zool. polon.*, **14**, 7–11.

FELIN, F. E. (1951). 'Growth characteristics of the poeciliid fish, *Platypoecilus maculatus.*' *Copeia*, p. 15.

FERRARA, B. (1951). *La determinazione dell' età negli animali domestici.* Ed. Scientifiche Italiane, Naples.

FERRIS, J. C. (1932). 'Comparison of the life histories of mictic and amictic females in the rotifer, *Hydatina senta.*' *Biol. Bull. Wood's Hole*, **63**, 442.

FICINO, M. (1498). *De triplici vita libri tres.* Venice.

FINDLEY, T. (1949). 'Role of neurohypophysis in the pathogenesis of hypertension and some allied disorders associated with ageing.' *Amer. J. Med.*, **7**, 70.

FISCHER, P. H. (1931). 'Recherches sur la vie ralentie de l'Escargot. (*H. pomatia* Linn.).' *J. Conchyl.*, **75**, 5–100, 111–200.

FISCHER-PIETTE, E. (1939). 'Sur la croissance et la longévité de *Patella vulgata* L. en fonction du milieu.' *J. Conchyl.*, **83**, 303.

FISCUS, C. H. (1961). 'Growth in the Steller sea lion.' *J. Mammal.*, **42**, 218–23.

FISHER, I. (1923). *Report on national vitality, its wastes and conservation.* Washington.

FITCH, H. S. (1956). 'Early sexual maturity and longevity under natural conditions in the Great Plains narrow-mouthed frog.' *Herpetologica*, **12**, 281–2.

FITZINGER, L. J. F. J. (1853). *Versuch einer Geschichte der Menagerien des Österreichisch-Kaiserlichen Hofes.* Vienna.

FLOWER, S. S. (1922). 'Longevity of molluscs.' *Cairo Sci. J.*, **10**, 115.
    (1925). 'Contributions to our knowledge of the duration of life in vertebrate animals.'
        'I. Fishes.' *Ibid.*, 247.
        'II. Batrachians.' *Ibid.*, 269.
        'III. Reptiles.' *Ibid.*, 911.
        'IV. Birds.' *Ibid.*, 1365.
    (1931). 'V. Mammals.' *Ibid.*, 145.
    (1935). 'Further notes on the duration of life in animals.'
        'I. Fishes.' *Ibid.*, 265.
    (1936). 'II. Amphibians.' *Ibid.*, 369.
    (1937). 'III. Reptiles.' *Ibid.*, 1.
    (1938). 'IV. Birds.' *Proc. zool. Soc. Lond.*, A, 195.
    (1945). 'Persistent growth in the tortoise, *Testudo graeca*, for 39 years, with other notes concerning the species.' *Proc. zool. Soc. Lond.*, **114**, 451.

Bibliography

FLYGER, V. F. (1958). 'Tooth impressions as an aid to the determination o. age in deer.' *J. wildl. Manag.*, **22**, 442–3.

FOÀ, C. (1900). 'La greffe des ovaires en rélation avec quelques questions de biologie générale.' *Arch. ital. Biol.*, **34**, 43.
(1901). 'Sur la greffe des ovaires.' *Arch. ital. Biol.*, **35**, 364.

FORBES, G. S., and CRAMPTON, H. E. (1942). 'The effect of population density upon growth and size in *L. palustris*.' *Biol. Bull.*, **82**, 283–9.

FORSTER, A. (1945). 'Longevity.' *Brit. med. J.*, **ii**, 545.

FOSTER, T. D. (1932). 'Observations on the life history of a fingernail shell of the genus *Sphaerium*.' *J. Morph.*, **53**, 473–97.
(1936). 'Size of shell in land snails of the genus *Polygyra* with particular reference to major and minor varieties.' *Amer. midl. Nat.*, **17**, 978–82.

FRANK, F. (1956). 'Hohes Alter bei der Europaischen Feldspitzmaus *Crocidina l. leucodon*.' (Hermann, 1780). *Saugetierk. Mitt.*, **4**, 31.

FRASER, C. McL. (1931). 'Notes on the ecology of the cockle *Cardium corbis* Martyn.' *Trans. Roy. Soc. Canada*, **25**, 59.

FRETTER, V. (1947–8). 'The structure and life history of some minute prosobranchs of rock pools.' *J. mar. biol. Ass. U.K.*, **27**, 597–623.

FREUD, J., LEVIE, L. H., and KROON, D. B. (1939). 'Observations on growth (chorionotrophic) hormone and localization of its point of attack.' *J. Endocrin.*, **1**, 56.

FREUD, J., and UYLDERT, E. (1947). 'A new idea about senility.' *Acta brev. neerl. Physiol.*, **14**, 18.

FREUDENBERG, K. (1951). 'Die natürliche Lebensdauer des Menschen.' *Z. Altersforsch.*, **5**, 241.

FRIEDEL, E. (1880). 'Die lebenden Wasserthiere auf der Internationalen Fischerei-Ausstellung zu Berlin im Jahre 1880.' *Zool. Gart.*, **21**, 323.

FRIEDENTHAL, H. (1910). 'Über die Giltigkeit des Massenwirkung für den Energieumsatz der lebendigen Substanz; II.' *Zbl. f. Physiol.*, **24**, 321–7.

FRITSCH, R. H. (1953). 'Die Lebensdauer von *Daphnia* spec. bei verscheidener Ernährung usw.' *Z. wiss Zool.*, **157**, 35.
(1956). 'Drei Orthokolone von *Daphnia magna* Straus ohne Lansing-Effect.' *Pubbl. Stat. zool. Napoli*, **28**, 214–24.
(1959). 'Herzfrequenz, Häutungsstadien und Lebensdauer bei Männchen von *D. magna* Straus.' *Z. wiss. Zool.*, **161**, 266–76.

FRITSCH, R. H., and MEIJERING, M. P. D. (1958). 'Die Herzfrequenz-Kurve von *Daphnia magna* Straus innerhalb einzelner Häutungsstadien.' *Experientia*, Basle, **14**, 346–7.

FROHAWK, F. W. (1935). 'Feeding butterflies in captivity.' *Entomologist*, **68**, 184.

Bibliography

FROST, W. E. (1943). 'The natural history of the minnow, *Phoxinus phoxinus*.' *J. Anim. Ecol.*, **12**, 139.

—— (1954). 'The food of pike, *Esox lucius* L., in Windermere.' *J. Anim. Ecol.*, **23**, 339.

FROST, W. E., and KIPLING, C. (1949). 'The determination of the age and growth of the pike (*Esox lucius* L.) from scales and opercular bones.' *J. Cons. Exp. Mer.*, **24**, 314–41.

FROST, W. E., and SMYLY, W. J. P. (1952). 'The brown trout of a moorland fishpond.' *J. Anim. Ecol.*, **21**, 71.

FUKUDA, M., and SIBATANI, A. (1953). 'Biochemical studies on the numbers and composition of liver cells in post-natal growth of the rat.' *Jap. Biochem. J.*, **40**, 95.

FURTH, J., UPTON, A. C., CHRISTENBERRY, K. W., BENEDICT, W. H., and MOSHMAN, J. (1954). 'Some late effects in mice of ionizing radiation from an experimental nuclear detonation.' *Radiology*, **63**, 562–70.

GAILLARD, P. J. (1942). *Hormones regulating growth and development in embryonic explants*. Paris: Hermann.

GAIN, W. H. (1889). 'A few notes on the food and habits of slugs and snails.' *Naturalist*, pp. 55–9.

GALEA, P. H. (1936). 'Longevity of a mule.' *Field*, 1936, p. 1556.

GALTSOFF, P. S. (1952). 'Staining of growth rings in the vertebrae of Tuna (*Thynnus thynnus*).' *Copeia* (1952), 103.

GARDNER, G., and HURST, H. (1933). 'Life-tables for White Leghorn chickens in the State of Utah.' *Proc. Utah Acad. Sci.*, **10**, 149.

GARDNER, T. S. (1946). 'The effect of yeast nucleic acid on the survival time of 600 day old albino mice.' *J. Gerontol.*, **1**, 445.

GARDNER, T. S., and FORBES, F. B. (1946). 'The effect of sodium thiocyanate and yeast nucleic acid on the survival time of 700 day old albino mice.' *J. Gerontol.*, **1**, 453.

GARDNER, W. K. (1952). 'Some endocrinological aspects of ageing.' *J. Gerontol.*, **7**, 293.

GATES, W. H. (1926). 'The Japanese waltzing mouse.' *Publ. Carneg. Instn.*, **337**, 83.

GEISER, S. W. (1924–5), 'The differential death-rate of the sexes among animals.' *Wash. Univ. Stud.*, **12**, 73.

GELDIAY, R. (1957). 'Studies on local populations of the freshwater limpet *Ancylus fluviatilis* (Müller).' *J. anim. Ecol.*, **25**, 389–402.

GEORGIANA, M. (1949). 'Longevity of the parasitic wasp, *Habrobracon uglandis* Ashmead.' *Amer. Nat.*, **83**, 39.

Bibliography

GERKING, S. D. (1957). 'Evidence of aging in natural populations of fishes.' *Gerontologia*, **1**, 287–305.

(1959). 'Physiological changes accompanying ageing in fishes.' *CIBA Foundation Colloquia on Ageing*, **5**, 181–207.

GEY, G. O. (1952). 'Cellular gerontologic research.' *J. Gerontol.*, **7**, 294.

GEYER, D. (1909). *Die Weichtiere Deutschlands*. Stuttgart.

GILLMAN, T. In BOURNE, G. (1962), *Structural aspects of ageing*, Pitman Medical, London.

GLEY, E. (1922). 'Sénescence et endocrinologie.' *Bull. Acad. Méd. Paris*, **87**, 285.

GLEZINA, O. M. (1939). 'Age changes in oxidation-reduction processes in the muscle tissue of birds.' *Biokhim. Zh.*, **13**, 105.

GLINOS, A. D., and BARTLETT, E. G. (1951). 'The effect of regeneration on the growth potential *in vitro* of rat liver at different ages.' *Canc. Res.*, **11**, 164.

GLINOS, A. D., and GEY, G. O. (1952). 'Humoral factors involved in the induction of liver regeneration in the rat.' *Proc. Soc. exp. Biol. N.Y.*, **80**, 421.

GLOVER, J. W. (1921). *U.S. life tables, 1890, 1901, 1910 and 1901–10*, p. 301 (U.S. Bureau of Census).

GOETSCH, W. (1922). 'Lebensdauer und Geschlechtlige Fortpflanzung bei Hydra.' *Biol. Zbl.*, **42**, 231.

(1925). 'Beiträge zum Unsterblichkeitsproblem der Metazoen. V.' *Biol. Zbl.*, **45**, 192.

(1940). *Vergleichende Biologie der Insektenstaaten*. Leipzig.

GOLDSCHMIDT, J., HOFFMAN, R., and DOLJANSKY, L. (1937). 'Étude comparative sur la durée de la période de latence pour la croissance des tissus embryonnaires et adultes explantés *in vitro*.' *C.R. Soc. Biol., Paris*, **126**, 389.

GOLDSMITH, E. D. (1942). 'Sexuality in *Dugesia trigrina* (syn. *Planaria maculata*).' *Nature*, **150**, 351.

GOLDSMITH, E. D., NIGRELLI, R. F., GORDON, R. S., CHARIPPER, H. A., and GORDON, M. (1944). 'Effect of thiourea upon fish development.' *Endocrinol.*, **35**, 132.

GOLDZIEHER, J. W. (1949). 'The direct effect of steroids on the senile human skin.' *J. Gerontol.*, **4**, 104.

GOLDZIEHER, J. W., and GOLDZIEHER, M. A. (1950). 'Effect of steroids on the ageing skin.' *J. Gerontol.*, **5**, 385.

GONZALEZ, B. M. (1923). 'Experimental studies on the duration of life. VIII. The influence upon duration of life of certain mutant genes of *Drosophila melanogaster*.' *Amer. Nat.*, **57**, 289.

GOODBODY, I. (1962). 'The biology of *Ascida nigra* (Savigny); I. Survival and mortality in an adult population.' *Biol. Bull.*, **122**, 40–51.

Bibliography

GOULD, G. M., and PYLE, W. T. (1898). *Anomalies and curiosities of medicine*. London: Rebman.

GOULD, R. T. (1945). *Enigmas*. London: Bles (2nd edn.).

GOWEN, J. W. (1931). 'On chromosome balance as a factor in duration of life.' *J. gen. Physiol.*, **14**, 447.
    (1934). 'The gene in pathology.' *Cold Spr. Harb. Symp. quant. Biol.*, **2**, 128.

GOWER, J., and STADLER, J. (1956). 'Life-spans of different strains of mice as affected by acute irradiation with 100 PKV X-rays.' *J. exp. Zool.*, **132**, 133–56.

GRAD, B. (1953). 'Changes in oxygen consumption and heart rate of rats during growth and ageing; role of the thyroid gland.' *Amer. J. Physiol.*, **174**, 481.

GRAHAM, A., and FRETTER, V. (1946–7). 'The life history of *Patina pellucida* Linn.' *J. mar. biol. Ass. U.K.*, **26**, 590–601.

GRAHN, D., and HAMILTON, K. (1958). 'Survival of inbred mice under daily γ-irradiation as related to control survival and the genetic constitution.' *Rad. Res.*, **9**, 122–3.

GRAVE, B. H. (1928). 'Natural history of the shipworm, *Teredo navalis*, at Wood'sHole, Mass.' *Biol. Bull.*, **55**, 260–82.
    (1933). 'Rate of growth, age at sexual maturity and duration of life of certain sessile organisms at Wood's Hole, Mass.' *Biol. Bull.*, **65**, 375–86.

GREEN, J. (1954). 'Size and reproduction in *Daphnia magna*.' *Proc. zool. Soc., Lond.*, p. 535.
    (1957). 'The growth of *Scrobicularia plana* (da Costa) in the Gwendraeth estuary.' *J. mar. biol. Ass. U.K.*, **36**, 41–7.

GREENE, R. (1959). 'A remedy for ageing.' *Lancet*, **i**, 786.

GREENE, R., and PATERSON, A. S. (1943). 'Sudden senescence.' *Lancet*, **ii**, 158.

GREENWOOD, A. W. (1932). 'The value of progeny in relation to age of dam.' *Harper-Adams Util. Poult. J.*, **17**, 478.

GREENWOOD, M., and IRWIN, J. O. (1939). 'The biostatistics of senility.' *Hum. Biol.*, **11**, 1.

GREGERMAN, R. I. (1959). 'Adaptive enzyme responses in the senescent rat: tryptophan peroxidase and tyrosine transaminase.' *Am. J. Physiol.*, **197**, 63–4.

GREVILLE, T. N. E. (1946). *United States life tables and actuarial tables, 1939–1941*. Bureau of the Census, Washington.

GRIER, N. M. (1922). 'Observations on the rate of growth of the shell of the lake-dwelling freshwater mussels.' *Amer. midl. Nat.*, **8**, 129–48.

GRIFFIN, C. E. (1928). 'The life history of automobiles.' *Michigan Business Studies* (Univ. Mich.), vol. **1**.

Bibliography

GRIFFITHS, J. T., and TAUBER, O. E. (1942). 'Fecundity, longevity and parthenogenesis of the American roach (*Periplaneta americana* L.).' *Physiol. Zool.*, **15**, 196.

GRIMM, H. (1949). 'Wachstumsfördernde und wachstumshemmende Stoffe im menschlichen Blutserum.' *Z. Altersforsch.*, **5**, 197.

GRMEK, M. D. (1958). 'On ageing and old age—basic problems and historic aspects of gerontology and geriatrics.' *Monogr. Biol.*, **5**, No. 2.

GROBSTEIN, C. (1947). 'The role of androgen in the declining regenerative capacity during morphogenesis of the *Platypoecilus maculatus* gonopodium.' *J. exp. Zool.*, **106**, 313.

GROSS, J. (1925). 'Versuche und Beobachtungen über die Biologie der Hydriden.' *Biol. Zool.*, **45**, 192.

GROSS, J., and SCHMITT, F. O. (1948). 'The structure of human skin collagen as studied with the electron microscope.' *J. exp. Med.*, **88**, 555.

——— (1950). 'Connective tissue fine structure and some methods for its analysis.' *J. Gerontol.*, **5**, 343.

GROSS, J. In BOURNE, G. (1962), *Structural aspects of ageing*. Pitman Medical, London.

GRÜNEBERG, H. (1951). *The genetics of the mouse*. The Hague.

——— (1954). 'Variation in inbred lines of mice.' *Nature, Lond.*, **173**, 674.

GUBERLET, J. E. (1928). 'Observations on the spawning habits of *Melibe leonina* (Gould).' *Pub. Puget. Sd. Mar. Biol. Sta.*, **6**, 263–70.

GUDERNATSCH, J. F. (1912). 'Feeding experiments on tadpoles. I. The influence of certain organs given as food on differentiation.' *Arch. EntwMeck. Org.*, **35**, 57.

GUILBERT, H. R., and Goss, H. (1932). 'Some effects of restricted protein intake on the oestrous cycle and gestation in rats.' *J. Nutrit.*, **5**, 215.

GUMBELL, E. J. (1938). 'La durée extrême de la vie humaine.' *Actualités Sci. Indust.*, **520**, 1.

GURDON, J. B. (1962). 'Adult frogs derived from nuclei of single somatic cells.' *Devel. Biol.*, **4**, 256–73.

GURNEY, J. H. (1899). 'On the comparative ages to which birds live.' *Ibis*, pp. 19–42.

GUTHRIE, D. M. (1953). *Personal communication*.

GUTSELL, J. S. (1930). 'Natural history of the bay scallop.' *Bull. U.S. Bur. Fish.*, **46**, 569–632.

HAAS, F. (1941). 'Records of large freshwater mussels.' *Zool. Sci. Rep. Field Mus. Nat. Hist.*, **24**, 259–70.

HABERMAEHL, K. H. (1961). *Die Altersbestimmung bei Haustieren, Pelztieren und beim jagdbaren Wild*. Parey, Berlin and Hamburg.

HAEMMERLING, J. (1924). 'Die ungeschlechtliche Fortpflanzung und Regeneration bei *Aeolosoma lemprichii*.' *Zool. Jb.* (1 Abt.), **41**, 581.

Bibliography

von HAGEN, W. (1938). 'Contribution to the biology of *Nasutitermes* s.s.' *Proc. zool. Soc. Lond.*, **108**, A, 39.

HÄGGQVIST, G. (1948). 'Nervenfaserkaliber bei Tieren verschiedener Grösse.' *Anat. Anz.*, **96**, 398–412.

von HAHN, H. P., and VERZÁR, F. (1963). 'Age-dependent thermal denaturation of DNA from bovine thymus.' *Gerontologia*, **7**, 105–8.

HAKH, I. W. D., and WESTLING, E. H. (1934). 'A possible cause of old age.' *Science*, **79**, 231.

HALDANE, J. B. S. (1941). *New Paths in Genetics*. London.
    (1949). 'Paternal and fraternal correlations of fitness.' *Ann. Genet.*, **14**, 288.
    (1953). 'Some animal life-tables.' *J. Inst. Actu.*, **79**, 351.

HALL, G. O., and MARBLE, D. R. (1931). 'The relationship between the first year egg production and the egg production of later years.' *Poultry Sci.*, **10**, 194.

HAMAI, I. (1937). 'Some notes on relative growth, with specific reference to the growth of limpets.' *Sci. Rep. Tôhoku Imp. Univ. Biol.*, **12**, 71–95.

HAMBURGER, C. (1948). 'Normal urinary excretion of neutral 17-ketosteroids with special reference to age and sex variations.' *Acta endocrinol.*, **1**, 19.

HAMILTON, J. B. (1948). 'The role of testicular secretions as indicated by the effects of castration in man and by studies of pathological conditions and the short life span associated with maleness.' *Recent Prog. Hormone Res.*, **3**, 257.

HAMILTON, J. B., CATCHPOLE, H. R., and HAWKE, C. C. (1944). 'Titres of urinary gonadotropins in old eunuchs.' *Anat. Rec.*, **88**, 435.
    (1945). 'Titres of gonadotropins in urine of aged eunuchs.' *J. clin. Endocrinol.*, **5**, 203.

HAMILTON, J. B., and HAMILTON, H. B. (1948). 'Ageing in apparently normal men. I. Urinary titres of ketosteroids and of α- and β-hydroxyketosteroids.' *J. clin. Endocrinol.*, **8**, 433.

HAMILTON, J. B., HAMILTON, H. B., and MESTLER, G. E. (1954). 'Ageing in apparently normal men. II. Androgenic activity of urinary ketosteroids and of their alpha and beta fractions.' *J. clin. Endoc. Metab.*, **14**, 139.

HAMILTON, J. B., TERADA, H., and MESTLER, G. E. (1955). 'Studies of growth throughout the life-span in Japanese: growth and size of nails and their relationship to age, sex, heredity and other factors.' *J. Geront.*, **10**, 401–15.

HAMILTON, W. J. (1940). 'The biology of the smoky shrew (*Sorex fumeus fumeus* Miller).' *Zoologica, N.Y.*, **25**, 473.

HAMMOND, J., and MARSHALL, F. H. (1952). 'The life cycle.' In Marshall, *Physiology of Reproduction*. London: Longmans.

306

Bibliography

HANDLER, P. (1961). 'Biochemical consideration of relationships between effects of time and of radiation on living systems.' *Fed. Proc.*, **20**, Suppl. 8, 8–13.

HANSARD, S. L., COMAR, C. L., and DAVIS, G. K. (1954). 'Effects of age upon the physiological behaviour of calcium in cattle.' *Amer. J. Physiol.*, **177**, 383.

HANSEMANN, D. V. (1914). 'Über Alterserscheinungen bei *Bacillus rossii*.' *Sitzb. Nat. Fr. Berlin*, 187–91.

HARANGHY, L., BALÁSZ, A., and BURG, M. (1962). 'Histological and histochemical analysis in mussels (*Anodonta*) of the involution of the genitals.' Proc. 1st intl. Congr. Hungarian Gerontologists: Budapest, 1962.

HARMAN, D. (1955). *Aging—a theory based on free radical and information theory.* U.C.R.L. publ. 3078, Univ. of Calif.

— (1956). 'Aging—a theory based on free radical and radiation chemistry.' *J. Geront.*, **11**, 298–300.

— (1957). 'Prolongation of the normal life span by radiation-protection chemicals.' *J. Gerontol.*, **12**, 257.

HARMS, J. W. (1926). *Verjungung des Lebens.* Senckenberg-Bücher II. Berlin: Bermuhler.

— (1949). 'Altern und Somatod der Zellverbandstiere.' *Z. Altersforsch.*, **5**, 73.

HARMS, W. (1912). 'Beobachtungen über den naturlichen Tod der Tiere. I. Hydroides pectinata.' *Zool. Anz.*, **40**, 117.

HARRIS, J. A., and BENEDICT, F. G. (1921). 'A biometric study of basal metabolism in man.' *Carnegie Inst. Wash. Publ.*, **303**.

HARTLAUB, C. (1916). 'Über das Altern einer Kolonie von *Syncoryne*.' *Wiss. Meersuntersuch.*, **11**.

HARTLEY, W. G. (1958). 'The microscopical study of salmon scales.' *J. Queckett micr. Club*, **28**, 95–8.

HARTMANN, M. (1921). 'Untersuchungen über die Morphologie und Physiologie des Formwechsels der Phytomonadinen (Volvocales). III. Mitt. Die dauernd agame Zucht von *Eudorina elegans*: experimentelle Beiträge zum Befruchtungs- und Todproblem.' *Arch. Protistenk.*, **43**, 7.

HARTZELL, A. (1945). 'Thiourea (thiocarbamide)—adult life span feeding experiments in rats.' *Conts. Boyce Thompson Inst.*, **13**, 501.

HARVEY, P. A. In KOFOID, C. A. (1934), *Termites and termite control*, p. 227. Univ. California Press.

HASE, A. (1909). 'Über die deutschen Süsswasserpolypen *Hydra fusca*.' *Arch. f. Rassen- u. Gesellschafts-Biologie*, **6**, 721.

HAŠEK, M. (1953). 'Вегетативная гибридизация животных путем соединения кровообращения в течение эмбрионального развития.' (Vegetative hybridization in animals through embryo parabiosis.) *Česk. Biol.*, **2**, 267.

Bibliography

HASKELL, —. (1948–9). No title. *Ann. Rep. mar. Lab. Texas Game and Fish Commission*, 212–17.

HASKIN, H. H. (1955). 'Age determination in molluscs.' *Trans. N.Y. Acad. Sci.*, **16**, 300–4.

HAYFLICK, L., and MOORHEAD, P. S. (1961). 'The serial cultivation of human diploid cell strains.' *Exp. cell Res.*, **25**, 585–621.

HAZAY, J. (1881). 'Die Mollusken-Faune von Budapest.' *Malak. Blätt.*, **3**, 1–69, 160–82; **4**, 43–224.

HEATH, H. (1905). 'The breeding habits of chitons of the Californian coast.' *Zool. Anz.*, **29**, 390–3.

HEATH, O. V. S. (1957). 'Ageing in higher plants.' *Sympos. Inst. Biol.*, **6**, 9–20.

HECHT, S. (1916). 'Form and growth in fishes.' *J. Morph.*, **27**, 379.

HEILBRUNN, L. V. (1943). *An outline of general physiology.* 2nd Edn. Philadelphia and London: Saunders.

HENDERSON, W. R., and ROWLANDS, I. W. (1938). 'The gonadotrophic activity of the anterior pituitary gland in relation to increased intracranial pressure.' *Brit. med. J.*, **i**, 1094.

HERDAN, G. (1952). 'Causes of excess male mortality in man.' *Acta genet. Basel*, **3**, 351.

HERRICK, F. H. (1898). 'The American lobster.' *Bull. U.S. Fish Comm.*, **15**, 1.
(1911). 'Natural history of the American lobster.' *Bull. U.S. Bureau of Fisheries*, **29**, 149.

HERRINGTON, H. B. (1948). 'Further proof that *Sphaerium occidentale* does not attain full growth in one year.' *Canad. field Nat.*, **62**, 74–5.

HERTIG, A. T. (1944). 'The ageing ovary—a preliminary note.' *J. clin. Endocrin.*, **4**, 581.

HERTWIG, R. (1906). 'Über Knospung und Geschlechtentwicklung von *Hydra fusca.*' *Biol. Zbl.*, **26**, 489.

HERTZ, R., and HISAW, F. L. (1934). 'Effects of follicle-stimulating and luteinizing pituitary extracts on the ovaries of the infantile and juvenile rabbit.' *Amer. J. Physiol.*, **108**, 1.

HERVEY, G. F., and HEMS, J. (1948). *The goldfish.* London: Batchworth Press.

VON HESSLING, T. (1859). *Die Perlmuscheln und ihre Perlen.* Leipzig.

HEVESY, G. (1947). 'Report of XIth Intl. Congress, Pure and Applied Chemistry.' *Nature, Lond.*, **160**, 247.

HEVESY, G., and OTTESEN, J. (1945). 'Life cycle of the red corpuscles of the hen.' *Nature, Lond.*, **156**, 534.

HEWER, H. R. (1960). 'Age determination in seals.' *Nature, Lond.*, **187**, 959–60.

Bibliography

HEWITT, H. B., and WILSON, C. W. (1959). 'A survival curve for mammalian cells irradiated *in vivo*.' *Nature, Lond.*, **183**, 1060–1.

HILDEBRAND, S. F. (1932). 'Growth of diamond-backed terrapins: size attained, sex ratio and longevity.' *Zoologica, N.Y.*, **9**, 551.

HINTON, M. A. C. (1925). *Proc. Linn. Soc.*, **138**, 18.

(1926). *Monograph of the voles and lemmings.* London: British Museum.

HINTON, S. (1962). 'Longevity of fishes in captivity as of September 1956.' *Zoologica, N.Y.*, **47**, 105–16.

HODGE, C. F. (1894–5). 'Changes in human ganglion cells from birth to senile death. Observations on man and honey-bee.' *J. Physiol.*, **17**, 129.

HOFF, C. C. (1937). 'Studies on the Limnaeid snail *Fossaria parva* Lea.' *Trans. Illinois Acad. Sci.*, **30**, 303–6.

HOFFMAN, R. S., GOLDSCHMIDT, J., and DOLJANSKI, L. (1937). 'Comparative studies on the growth capacities of tissues from embryonic and adult chickens.' *Growth*, **1**, 228.

HOLDEN, M. J., and MEADOWS, P. S. (1962). 'The structure of the spine of the spur dogfish (*Squalus acanthias* L.) and its use for age determination.' *J. mar. Biol. Ass.*, **42**, 179–98.

HOLEČOVÁ, E., FABRY, P., and POUPA, O. (1959). 'Studies in the adaptation of metabolism—VIII: the latent period of explanted tissues of rats adapted to intermittent starvation.' *Physiol. Bohemoslov.*, **8**, 15–21.

HOLMGREN, N. (1909). 'Termitenstudien.' *Kon. Svensk. Vetensk. Akad. Handl.*, **44**.

HOPKINS, H. S. (1924). 'Respiration in the tissues of mollusks in relation to age.' *Anat. Rec.*, **29**, 91.

(1930). 'Age differences and the respiration of muscle tissue of mollusks.' *J. exp. Zool.*, **56**, 209.

HORNSEY, S. (1959). 'Fertility and life span of mice protected by hypothermia against total body irradiation.' *Gerontologia*, **3**, 128–36.

HORST, VAN DER. (1929). 'Lebensalter und Schälengrösse.' *Arch. Mollusk.*, **61**, 46.

HORST, K., MENDEL, L. B., and BENEDICT, F. G. (1934). 'The influence of previous diet, growth and age upon the basal metabolism of the rat.' *J. Nutr.*, **8**, 139.

HOWARD, L. O. (1939). 'Ageing of insects.' In Cowdry, E. V.: *Problems of ageing.* London: Baillière, Tindall and Cox.

HOWES, E. L., and HARVEY, S. C. (1932). 'Age factor in velocity of growth of fibroblasts in the healing wound.' *J. exp. Med.*, **55**, 577.

HRŮZA, Z., and FABRY, P. (1957). 'Some metabolic and endocrine changes due to long-lasting caloric under-nutrition.' *Gerontologia*, **1**, 279–87.

HRŮZA, Z., CHVAPIL, M., and KOBRLE, V. (1961). 'The effect of ageing and castration on the tensile strength, elasticity and swelling of rat collagen fibres.' *Physiol. Bohemoslov*, **10**, 291–5.

Bibliography

Hsu, T. C., and Pomerat, C. M. (1953). 'Mammalian chromosomes *in vitro*. III. On somatic aneuploidy.' *J. Morph.*, **93**, 301.

Hubendick, B. (1948). 'Über den Bau und des konzentrischen Opercular-typus bei Gastropoden.' *Arch. Zool.*, **40**, (A 10): 1–28.

Hufeland, C. W. (1798). *Makrobiotik, oder der Kunst das menschliche Leben zu verlängern.* Jena.
(1829). *The art of prolonging human life*, &c. London: Simpkin Marshall. (Eng. trans. of foregoing.)

Hummel, K. P., and Barnes, L. L. (1938). 'Calcification of the aorta, heart and kidneys of the albino rat.' *Am. J. Path.*, **14**, 121.

Hunerhoff, E. (1931). 'Über ein bisher unbekanntes Larvenorgan und die Regeneration bei *Apsilus vorax*.' *Zool. Anz.*, **92**, 327.

Hunt, T. E. (1942). 'Mitotic activity in the anterior hypophysis of female rats.' *Anat. Rec.*, **82**, 263.
(1943). 'Mitotic activity in the anterior hypophysis of mature female rats of different age groups and at different periods of the day.' *Endocrinology*, **32**, 334.
(1947). 'Mitotic activity in the anterior hypophysis of ovariectomized rats after injection of oestrogens.' *Anat. Rec.*, **97**, 127.

Hunter, W. R. (1953). 'On the growth of the freshwater limpet, *Ancylus fluviatilis* Müll.' *Proc. zool. Soc. Lond.*, **123**, 623–6.
(1961). 'Annual variations in growth and density in natural populations of freshwater snails in the West of Scotland.' *Proc. zool. Soc. Lond.*, **136**, 219–53.

Hursh, J. B. (1957). 'The effect of ionising radiation on longevity.' *AEC report*, UR-506.

Hutt, F. B. (1949). *Genetics of the fowl.* New York: McGraw-Hill.

Huxley, A. (1937). *After many a summer.* London: Chatto and Windus.

Huxley, J. S. (1932). *Problems of relative growth.* London: Methuen.
(1942). *Evolution: the modern synthesis.* London: Allen and Unwin.

Huxley, J. S., and de Beer, G. R. (1923). 'Studies in dedifferentiation—IV. Resorption and differential inhibition in *Obelia* and *Campanularia*.' *Quart. J. micr. Sci.*, **67**, 473.

Huxley, T. H. (1880). *The Crayfish.* London: Kegan Paul.

Hvass, H. (1938). *Zool. Gärten, Lpz.*, **10**, 229.

Hyman, L. H. (1951). *The Invertebrates.* Vol. III. London and New York: McGraw-Hill Co.

Ingle, L. (1933). 'Effects of environmental conditions on longevity.' *Science*, **78**, 511.

Ingle, L., Wood, T. R., and Banta, A. M. (1937). 'A study of the longevity, growth, reproduction and heart rate in *Daphnia longispina* as influenced by limitations in quantity of food.' *J. exp. Zool.*, **76**, 325.

310

Bibliography

IRIE, T. (1957). 'On the forming season of annual rings in the otoliths of several marine teleosts.' *J. Fac. Fish and amin. Husb.*, Hiroshima Univ., **1**, 311–17.

ISELY, F. B. (1931). 'A 15-year growth record in freshwater mussels (*Quadrula*).' *Ecology*, **12**, 616–18.

ISHIYAMA, R. (1951). 'Studies on the rays and skates belonging to the family *Rajidae* found in Japan and adjacent regions.' (In Japanese–English summary). *Bull. Jap. Soc. Sci. Fish.*, **16**, 112–18, 119–24.

ISRAEL, W. (1913). *Biologie der Süsswassermuscheln.* Stuttgart.

IZUMI, N. (1956). 'Effect of the atomic bomb on school children in Urakami district, Nagasaki.' *Rep. Jap. Soc. prom. Sci.*, 1701–7.

JACKSON, C. H. N. (1940). 'The analysis of a tsetse fly population.' *Ann. Eugen., Lond.*, **10**, 332.

JACKSON, C. M. (1936). 'Recovery in rats upon re-feeding after prolonged suppression of growth by dietary deficiency in protein.' *Amer. J. Anat.*, **58**, 179.

JACOBS, P. A., BROWN, W. M. C., and DOLL, R. (1961). 'Distribution of human chromosome counts in relation to ageing.' *Nature, Lond.*, **191**, 1178–80.

JALAVISTO, E. (1950). 'The influence of parental age on the expectation of life.' *Rév. Med. Liège*, **5**, 719.

JANET, C. (1904). *Observations sur les fourmis.* Limoges.

JANISCH, E. (1924). 'Über die experimentelle Beeinflussung der Lebensdauer und des Alterns schädlicher Insekten.' *Arb. Biol. Reichsart. f. Land.- u. Fortwirtschaft.*, **13**, 173.

JARVIK, L. F., and FALEK, A. (1963). 'Intellectual stability and survival in the aged.' *J. Gerontol.*, **18**, 173–6.

JAYNE, E. P. (1953). 'Cytology of the adrenal gland of the rat at different ages.' *Anat. Rec.*, **115**, 459.

JENNINGS, H. S. (1945). '*Paramecium bursaria*: life history. V. Some relations of external conditions, past or present, to ageing and to mortality of exconjugants, with summary of conclusions on age and death.' *J. exp. Zool.*, **99**, 15.

JENNINGS, H. S., and LYNCH, R. S. (1928). 'Age, mortality, fertility and individual diversity in the Rotifer *Proales sordida* Gorse. II.' *J. exp. Zool.*, **51**, 339.

JHINGRAN, V. G. (1957). 'Age determination of the Indian major carp (*Cirrhina mrigala* Ham) by means of scales.' *Nature, Lond.*, **179**, 468–9.

JICKELI, C. F. (1902). *Die Unvolkommenheit des Stoffwechsels als Veranlassung für Vermehrung usw.* Friedländer: Berlin.

OEDICKE, P. (1919), 'Ein Beitrag zum eunuchoiden Riesenwuchs.' *Z. ges. Neurol. Psychiat.*, **44**, 385.

Bibliography

JOHN, D. D. (1937). 'Antarctic whales.' *J. Soc. Pres. Fauna Emp.*, **31,** 15.

JONES, D. B. (1951). 'Sex differences in the growth of young rats and the survival of adult rats fed protein-deficient diets.' *J. Nutrit.*, **44,** 465–75.

JONES, E. C., and KROHN, P. (1959). 'Influence of the anterior pituitary on the aging process in the ovary.' *Nature, Lond.*, **183,** 1155–8.

— (1960a). 'The effect of unilateral ovariectomy in the reproductive life span of mice.' *J. Endocr.*, **20,** 129–34.

— (1960b). 'Orthotopic ovarian transformation in mice.' *J. Endocr.*, **20,** 135–46.

— (1961). 'The effect of hypophysectomy on age changes in the ovaries of mice.' *J. Endocr.*, **21,** 497–509.

JONES, H. B. (1955). 'A special consideration of the aging process, disease and life expectancy.' *Adv. biol. med. Physics*, **4,** 281–337.

JONES, J. W., and HYNES, H. B. N. (1950). 'The age and growth of *Gastrosteus aculeatus, Pygosteus pungitius* and *Spinachia vulgaris* as shown by their otoliths.' *J. anim. Ecol.*, **19,** 59–73.

JOSEPHINA, (SISTER) C. S. J. (1955). 'Longevity of religious women.' *Review for Religious*, **14,** 29–30.

JURCZÝK, C. (1926). 'Zur Regeneration bei *Stephanocerus.*' *Zool. Anz.*, **67,** 333.

— (1927). 'Beiträge zur Morphologie, Biologie und Regeneration von *Stephanocerus fimbriatus* Goldfuss.' *Z. wiss. Zool.*, **129,** 103.

KALLMAN, F. J., and SANDER, G. (1948). 'Twin studies on ageing and longevity.' *J. Hered.*, **39,** 349.

— (1949). 'Twin studies in senescence.' *Amer. J. Psychiat.*, **106,** 29.

KASSOWITZ, M. (1899). *Allgemeine Biologie*. Vienna.

KELLEY, R. B. (1939). 'Female aspects of relative fertility in sheep.' *Aust. vet. J.*, **15,** 184.

KENYON, A. T. (1942). 'The comparative metabolic influences of testicular and ovarian hormones in man.' *Biol. Sympos.*, **9,** 11.

KERSHAW, W. E., LAVOIPIERRE, M. M. J., and CHALMERS, T. A. (1953). 'Studies on the intake of microfilariae by their insect vectors, their survival, and their effect on the survival of their vectors. I. *Dirofilaria immitis* and *Aedes aegypti.*' *Ann. trop. Med. Parasitol.*, **47,** 207.

KEVAN, D. K. McE. (1934). '*Limapontia depressa* (A. and H.) var. nov. in Scotland.' *J. Conchol.*, **20,** 16–24.

— (1939). 'Further notes on *Limapontia depressa* var. *pellucida* Kevan.' *J. Conchol.*, **21,** 160–2.

— (1941). 'Notes on *Limapontia depressa* var. *pellucida* kept under artificial conditions.' *J. Conchol.*, **21,** 301–2.

KEYS, A. B. (1928). 'The weight-length relation in fishes.' *Proc. nat. Acad. Sci., Wash.*, **14,** 922.

Bibliography

KING, H. D. (1915). 'Growth and variability in body weight of the albino rat.' *Anat. Rec.*, **9**, 751.

(1939). 'Life processes in gray Norway rats during 14 years in captivity.' *Amer. anat. Mem.*, **17**, 1.

KING, J. T., and VISSCHER, M. B. (1950). 'Longevity as a function of diet in the C_3H mouse.' *Feder. Proc.*, **9**, 70.

KING, W. G. (1911). *Census of England and Wales*, **7**, 46.

KINSELL, L. W. (1953). 'Hormonal regulation of human growth.' In *Protein metabolism, hormones and growth*. New Jersey: Rutgers Univ. Press.

KINSEY, A. C., POMEROY, W. B., MARTIN, C. E., and GEBHARD, P. H. (1953). *Sexual behaviour in the human female*. Saunders, Philadelphia.

KIRK, E., and KVORNING, S. A. (1949). 'Quantitative measurement of the elastic properties of the skin and subcutaneous tissue in young and old individuals.' *J. Geront.*, **4**, 273.

KIRK, J. E. (1948). 'The acid phosphatase concentration of the prostatic fluid in young, middle-aged and old individuals.' *J. Geront.*, **3**, 98.

(1949). 'The effect of testosterone administration on the acid phosphatase concentration of the prostatic exprimate in old men.' *Urol. cutan. Rev.*, **53**, 683.

(1949). 'The urinary excretion of neutral 17-ketosteroids in middle-aged and old men.' *J. Geront.*, **4**, 34.

(1951). 'Steroid hormones and ageing.' A review. *J. Geront.*, **6**, 253.

KIRKLAND, H. T. (1928). 'A case of schistosomiasis presenting some unusual features.' *J. trop. Med. Hyg.*, **31**, 78.

KISÉ, Y., and OCHI, T. (1934). 'Basal metabolism of old people.' *J. Lab. clin. Med.*, **19**, 1073.

KLEBANOW, D., and HEGNAUER, H. (1949). 'Die germinative Insuffizienz der alternden Frau.' *Z. Altersforsch.*, **5**, 157.

KNABE, K. (1932). 'Beitrag zur Dauer von Filarieninfektion.' *Arch. f. Sch. u. Tropenhyg.*, **36**, 496.

KNOBLOCH, M. (1951). 'Fingernagelwachstum und Alter.' *Z. Altersforsch.*, **5**, 357.

KOBOZIEFF, N. (1931). 'Mortalité et âge limite chez la souris.' *C.R. Soc. Biol., Paris*, **106**, 704.

KOCH, C. (1952). 'Von meinen ältesten Urodelen.' *Aquar. Terrar. Z.*, **5**, 9.

KOCHAKIAN, C. D. (1937). 'Testosterone and testosterone acetate and the protein and energy metabolism of castrate dogs.' *Endocrinology*, **21**, 750.

KOCHAKIAN, C. D., and MURLIN, J. R. (1931). 'The effect of male hormone on the protein and energy metabolism of castrate dogs.' *J. Nutrit.*, **10**, 439.

KOHN, R. R., and ROLLERSON, E. (1960). 'Aging of human collagen in relation to susceptibility to the action of collagenase.' *J. Gerontol.*, **15**, 10–15.

Bibliography

KOLISKO, A. (1938). 'Lebensgeschichte der Rädertiere auf Grund von Individualzuchten.' *Arch. Hydrobiol.*, **33**, 165.

KOPACZEWSKI, W. (1938). 'Problème de vieillissement: recherches sur les colloïdes.' *Protoplasma*, **30**, 291.

KOPEČ, S. (1924). 'Studies on the influence of inanition on the development and duration of life in insects.' *Biol. Bull. Wood's Hole*, **46**, 1.

— (1928). 'On the influence of intermittent starvation on the longevity of the imaginal stage of *Drosophila melanogaster*.' *Brit. J. exp. Biol.*, **5**, 204.

KORENCHEVSKY, V. (1942). 'Natural relative hyperplasia and the process of ageing.' *J. Path. Bact.*, **54**, 13.

— (1947). 'The longest span of life found in the records of centenarians in England and Wales.' *Brit. med. J.*, **ii**, 14.

— (1948). 'Effect of sex and thyroid hormones on the process of ageing in female rats.' *Brit. med. J.*, **i**, 728.

— (1949). 'The problem of ageing. Basic difficulties of research.' *Brit. med. J.*, **i**, 66.

— (1961). *Physiological and pathological ageing*. Karger, Basle.

KORENCHEVSKY, V., and JONES, V. E. (1947). 'The effects of androsterone, oestradiol, and thyroid hormone on the artificial premature "climacteric" of pure gonadal origin produced by ovariectomy in rats. III. Effects on histologic structure of vagina, uterus, adrenals and thyroid.' *J. Gerontol.*, **2**, 116.

— (1948). 'The effects of androsterone, oestradiol, and thyroid hormone on the artificial premature "climacteric" of pure gonadal origin produced by ovariectomy in rats.' *J. Gerontol.*, **3**, 21.

KORENCHEVSKY, V., PARIS, S. K., and BENJAMIN, B. (1950). 'Treatment of senescence in female rats with sex and thyroid hormones.' *J. Gerontol.*, **5**, 120.

— (1953). 'Treatment of senescence in male rats with sex and thyroid hormones and desoxycorticosterone acetate.' *J. Gerontol.*, **8**, 415.

KORSCHELT, E. (1908). 'Versuche an Lumbriciden und deren Lebensdauer im Vergleich mit andern wirbellösen Tieren.' *Verh. deutsch. zool. Ges.*, p. 113.

— (1914). 'Über Transplantationsversuche, Ruhezustände und Lebensdauer der Lumbriciden.' *Zool. Anz.*, **43**, 537.

— (1922). *Lebensdauer, Altern und Tod*. Fischer, Jena.

— (1925). In *Leben, Altern, Tod*. Senckenberg-bücher II. Berlin: Bermühler-Verlag.

— (1931). 'Über das vermutliche Alter der Riesenschildkröten.' *Zool. Anz.* **96**, 113.

KORTLANDT, A. (1942). 'Levensloop, samenstelling en structuur der Nederlandse aalscholver bevolking.' *Ardea*, **31**, 175.

KOTSOVSKY, D. (1929). 'The origin of senility.' *Amer. J. Physiol.*, **90**, 419.

— (1931). 'Allgemeine vergleichende Biologie des Alters.' *Ergeb. Physiol.*, **31**, 132.

Bibliography

KOUNTZ, W. B. (1950). 'Restoration of body function in the aged.' *J. Gerontol.*, **5**, 385.

KRAAK, W. K., RINKEL, G. L., and HOOGERHEIDE, J. (1940). 'Oecologische bewerking van de Europese ringgegevens van de Kievit (*Vanellus vanellus* L.).' *Ardea*, **29**, 151.

KRAUS, A. S., and LILIENFELD, A. M. (1959). 'Some epidemiological aspects of the high mortality rate in the young widowed group.' *J. chronic Dis.*, **10**, 207–17.

KRISTENSEN, I. (1957). 'De groeisnelheid van het Tafelmesheft (*Ensis siliqua.*' *Lev. Natuur*, **60**, 93.

(1957). 'De Artemisschelp (*Dosinia exoleta*).' *Lev. Natuur*, **59**, 82–4.

(1957). 'Differences in density and growth in a cockle population in the Dutch Wadden Sea.' (Ph.D. Thesis, University of Leiden.)

KROHN, P. L. (1955). 'Tissue transplantation techniques applied to the problem of the ageing of the organs of reproduction.' *CIBA Foundation Colloquia on Ageing*, **1**, 141.

(1962). 'Heterochronic transplantation in the study of ageing.' *Proc. Roy. Soc. (B).*, **157**, 128–47.

KRULL, W. H. (1931). 'Importance of laboratory raised snails in helminthology with life-history notes on *Gyraulus Parvus*.' *Occ. Pap. Mus. Zool. Univ. Mich.*, **226**, 1–10.

KRUMBHAAR, E. B., and LIPPINCOTT, S. W. (1939), 'Postmortem weight of "normal" human spleens at different ages.' *Amer. J. med. Sci.*, **197**, 344–58.

KRUMBIEGEL, I. (1929a). 'Lebensdauer, Altern und Tod in ihren Beziehungen zur Fortpflanzung.' *S.B. Ges. naturf. Fr. Berl.*, **94**, 1928 (1929).

(1929b). 'Untersuchungen über die Einwirkung auf Altern und Lebensdauer der Insekten ausgefuhrt an *Carabus* und *Drosophila*.' *Zool. Jb.* (2 Abt.), **51**, 111.

KUBO, I., and KONDO, K. (1953). 'Age determination of the *Babylonia japonica* (Reeve), an edible marine gastropod, basing on the operculum.' *J. Tokyo Univ. Fish.*, **39**, 199–207.

KUNDE, M. M., and NORLUND, M. (1927). 'Inactivity and age as factors influencing the basal metabolic rate of dogs.' *Amer. J. Physiol.*, **80**, 681.

KÜNKEL, K. (1908). 'Vermehrung und Lebensdauer der *Limnaea stagnalis* L.' *Nachrbl. deutsch. Malak. Ges.*, **40**, 70–7.

(1908). 'Vermehrung und Lebensdauer der Nacktschnecken.' *Verh. deutsch. zool. Ges.*, **18**, 153–61.

(1916). *Zur Biologie der Lungenschnecken*. Heidelberg, pp. 316 sq.

(1928). 'Zur Biologie von *Eulota fruticum* Müller.' *Zool. Jb.* (*Zool.*), **45** 317–42.

(1929). 'Experimentelle Studie über *Vitrina brevis* Fer.' *Zool. Jb.* (*Zool.*), **46**, 575–626.

KUNZE, —. (1933). Cited by Burger, M. (1954).

Bibliography

KURBATOV, A. D. (1951). Курбатов, А.Д.: 'Изменения наследственности и повышение жизненности потомства путем трансплантации яйчных клеток между породами кроликов.' (Alteration of heredity and increased vigour of progeny after ovum transplantation between strains of rabbit.) *Adv. mod. Biol. Moscow*, **31**, 2.

KURTZ, E. B., and WINFREY, R. (1931). 'Life-characteristics of physical property.' *Bull. Iowa Engineering Exp. Station*, No. 103.

KURZROK, R., and SMITH, P. E. (1938). 'The pituitary gland.' *Proc. Assn. Nervous and Mental Diseases*, **17**, chap. xvii.

LABITTE, A. (1916). 'Longévité de quelques insectes en captivité.' *Bull. Mus. Hist. nat. Paris*, **22**, 105.

LACK, D. (1943a). *The life of the robin*. London: Witherby.
—— (1943b). 'The age of blackbirds.' *Brit. Birds*, **36**, 166.
—— (1943c). 'The age of some more British birds.' *Brit. Birds*, **36**, 193, 214.
—— (1946). 'Do juvenile birds survive less well than adults?' *Brit. Birds*, **39**, 258.
—— (1950). 'Population ecology in birds.' A review. *Proc. Xth Int. Ornith. Congr.*
—— (1954). *The natural regulation of animal numbers*. Oxford: University Press.

LAMOTTE, M. (1951). 'Recherches sur la structure génétique des populations naturelles de *Cepaea nemoralis* (L.).' *Bull. Biol. France, Suppl.*, **35**, 1–238.

LAMY, E. (1933). 'Quelques mots sur la durée de la vie chez les Mollusques.' *J. Conchyl.*, **77**, 483–502.

LANDAHL, H. D. (1959). In BIRREN, J. E., *Handbook of aging and the individual*. University of Chicago Press.

LANDAUER, W., and LANDAUER, A. B. (1931). 'Chick mortality and sex ratios in the domestic fowl.' *Amer. Nat.*, **65**, 492.

LANE, P. W., and DICKIE, M. M. (1958). 'The effect of restricted food intake on the life span of genetically obese mice.' *J. Nutrit.*, **64**, 549–54.

LANG, A. (1896). 'Kleine biologische Beobachtungen über die Weinberg-schnecke (*Helix pomatia* L.).' *Vierteljahr. Ges. Zurich*, **61**, 488.
—— (1904). 'Über Vorversuche zu Untersuchungen über die Varietäten-bildung von *Helix hortensis* und *Helix nemoralis*.' *Denkschr. d. Med. Naturwiss. Ges. Jena*, **ii**, 437–505.
—— (1908). *Über die Bastarde von Helix hortensis und Helix nemoralis. Eine Untersuchung zu experimentelle Vererbungslehre.* Jena: G. Fischer.

LANSING, A. I. (1942). 'Some effects of hydrogen ion concentration, total salt concentration, calcium and citrate on longevity and fecundity in the rotifer.' *J. exp. Zool.*, **91**, 195.
—— (1947a). 'Evidence for ageing as a consequence of growth cessation.' *Anat. Rec.*, **99**, 579.
—— (1947b). 'A transmissible, cumulative and reversible factor in ageing.' *J. Gerontol.*, **2**, 228.

Bibliography

LANSING, A. I. (1948). 'The influence of parental age on longevity in rotifers.' *J. Gerontol.*, **3**, 6.

— (1951). 'Some physiological aspects of ageing.' *Physiol. Rev.*, **31**, 274.

— (1952). *Problems of ageing* (ed.). New York: Williams and Wilkins.

LANSING, A. I., ROBERTS, E., RAMASARMA, G. B., ROSENTHAL, T. B., and ALEX, M. (1951). 'Changes with age in aminoacid composition of arterial elastin.' *Proc. Soc. exp. Biol. N.Y.*, **76**, 714.

LANSING, A. I., ROSENTHAL, T. B., and KAMEN, M. D. (1949). 'Effect of age on calcium binding in mouse liver.' *Arch. Biochem.*, **20**, 125.

LANSING, A. I., and WOLFE, J. M. (1942). 'Changes in the fibrillar tissue of the anterior pituitary of the rat associated with advancing age.' *Anat. Rec.*, **83**, 355.

LATTER, O. H. (1935). 'Unusual length of life and curious site of larva of *Cossus ligniperda*.' *Proc. r. ent. Soc., Lond.*, **10**, 41.

LAUER, A. R. (1952). *Age and sex in relation to accidents* in 'road users' characteristics'. *Nat. Acad. Sci. N.R.C. Highway res. Bd. Bull.*, **60**.

LAUSON, H. D., GOLDEN, J. B., and SEVERINGHAUS, E. L. (1939). 'The gonadotrophic content of the hypophysis throughout the life cycle of the normal female rat.' *Amer. J. Physiol.*, **125**, 396.

LAWS, R. M. (1952). 'A new method of age determination for mammals.' *Nature, Lond.*, **169**, 972.

— (1953). 'The elephant seal (*Mirounga leonina* L.). I. Growth and age.' *Falkland Ids. Dependencies Survey Sci. Rep.*, No. 8.

LAWS, R. M., and PURVES, P. E. (1956). 'The earplug of the *Mysticeti* as an indication of age, with special reference to the North Atlantic Fin Whale (*Balaenoptera physalus* Linn).' *Norsk Hvålfangstid*, **45**, 413–25.

LAWSON, T. C. (1939). 'Echinococcus cysts of the liver of 56 years' duration.' *J. Amer. Med. Ass.*, **112**, 1331.

LAZOVSKAYA, L. N. (1942). 'Age modifications of respiration of blood vessels.' *Biul. Eksp. Biol. Med.*, **14**, 46.

— (1943). 'The change in respiration of blood vessels with age.' *Biokhimia*, **8**, 171.

LEATHEM, J. H. (1949). 'The antihormone problem in endocrine therapy.' *Rec. Prog. Hormone Res.*, IV, 115.

LEBEAU, A. (1953). 'L'âge du chien et celui de l'homme.' *Bull. Acad. Vet., France*, **26**, 229–32.

LEBLOND, C. P., and WALKER, B. E. (1956). 'Renewal of cell populations.' *Physiol. Rev.*, **36**, 255–76.

LEDERER, G. (1941). 'Zur Haltung des China-alligators (*Alligator sinensis* Fauvel).' *Zool. Gärt., Lpz.*, **13**, 255.

LEFEIRE, G., and CURTIS, W. C. (1912). 'Studies on the reproduction and artificial propagation of freshwater mussels.' *Dept. Comm. Lab. Bull. Bureau Fish.*, **30**, 105.

317

Bibliography

LEHMAN, H. C. (1943). 'The longevity of the eminent.' *Science*, **98**, 270.

LEHMENSICK, R. (1926). 'Zur Biologie, Anatomie und Eireifung der Rädertiere.' *Z. wiss. Zool.*, **128**, 37.

LEMBERG, R., and LEGGE, J. W. (1949). *Hematin compounds and bile pigments.* New York: Interscience Publications.

LEOPOLD, A. C. (1961). 'Senescence in plant development.' *Science*, **134**, 1727–32.

LEPESCHKIN, W. W. (1931). 'Death and its causes.' *Quart. Rev. Biol.*, **6**, 167.

LESHER, S., FRY, R. J. M., and KOHN, H. I. (1961). 'Aging and the generation cycle of intestinal epithelial cells in the mouse.' *Gerontologia*, **5**, 176–81.

LESLIE, P. H., and RANSON, R. M. (1940). 'The mortality, fertility and rate of natural increase of the vole (*Microtus agrestis*) as observed in the laboratory.' *J. Anim. Ecol.*, **9**, 27.

LEVI, W. M. (1957). *The Pigeon.* Sumter, South Carolina.

LIEBERS, R. (1937). 'Beiträge zur Biologie der Rädertiere: Untersuchungen an *Euchlanis dilatata* und *Proales decipiens.*' *Z. wiss. Zool.*, **150**, 206.

LILLY, M. M. (1953). 'The mode of life and the structure and functioning of the reproductive ducts of *Bythinia tentaculata* (L).' *Proc. malac. Soc. Lond.*, **30**, 87–110.

LINDOP, P. J., and ROTBLAT, J. (1959). 'Aging effects of ionising radiation.' *Prog. Nucl. Energy*, **6**, (2), 58–69.

—— (1959). 'Shortening of life-span of mice as a function of age at irradiation.' *Gerontologia*, **3**, 122–7.

—— (1961). 'Shortening of life and causes of death in mice exposed to a single whole body dose of radiation.' *Nature, Lond.*, **189**, 645–8.

—— (1961). 'Long term effects of a single whole-body exposure of mice to ionizing radiations.' *Proc. Roy. Soc.* (*B*), **154**, 332–49 and 350–68.

LINDSAY, E. (1940). 'The biology of the silverfish, *Ctenolepisma longicaudata* Esch. with particular reference to its feeding habits.' *Proc. Roy. Soc. Victoria*, **52**, 35.

LINSLEY, E. G. (1938). 'Longevity in the Cerambycidae.' *Pan-Pacif. Ent.*, **14**, 177.

LIPSCHUTZ, A. (1915). *Allgemeine physiologie des Todes.* Fr. Vieweg, Braunschweig.

LOBBAN, M. C. (1952). 'Structural variations in the adrenal cortex of the cat.' *J. Physiol.*, **118**, 565.

LOEB, J. (1908). 'Über den Temperaturkoeffizienten für die Lebensdauer kaltblütiger Thiere usw.' *Pflugers Arch.*, **124**, 411.

LOEB, J., and NORTHROP, J. H. (1917). 'On the influence of food and temperature on the duration of life.' *J. biol. Chem.*, **32**, 103.

LOEB, L. (1944). *Hormones and the process of ageing. Harvey Lecture*, **36**, 228.

318

Bibliography

LONG, J. A., and EVANS, H. M. (1922). 'The estrous cycle in the rat and its associated phenomena.' *Mem. Univ. Calif.*, **6**.

LONGSTAFF, J. (1921). 'Observations on the habits of *Cochlitoma zebra* var. *fulgurata* Pfr. and *obesa* Pfr. in confinement.' *Proc. zool. Soc. Lond.*, 379–87.

LORAND, A. (1904). 'Quelques considérations sur les causes de la sénilité.' *C.R. Soc. Biol., Paris*, **57**, 500.

—— (1929). 'La rôle de l'autointoxication intestinale dans la production de la vieillesse.' *Clinique, Paris*, **24**, 205.

LORD, R. D. (1961). 'Potential life span of Cottontails.' *J. Mammal.*, **42**, 99.

LORENZ, T. W., and LERNER, I. (1946). 'Inheritance of sexual maturity in male chickens and turkeys.' *Poult. Sci.*, **25**, 188.

LOWRY, O. H., and HASTINGS, A. B. (1952). 'Quantitative histochemical changes in ageing.' In COWDRY, E. V., *Problems of Ageing*. Williams and Wilkins Co.

LUK'YANOV, V. S. (1952). Лукьянов, В.С.: 'О сохранение здоровья и работоспособности.' (The preservation of health and work-capacity.) Medgiz, Moscow.

LUPIEN, P. J., and McCAY, C. M. (1960). 'Thermic contraction of and elasticity in the Chinchilla tendon fiber as influenced by age.' *Gerontologia*, **4**, 90–103.

LYEPESCHINSKAYA, O. B. (1950). Лепесчинская, О.Б.: 'Произхождение клеток из живого вещества и роль живого вещества в организме.' (Production of cells from living matter and the role of living matter in the organism.) Acad. Med. Sci. USSR. Moscow. 2nd edn.

LYNCH, R. S., and SMITH, H. B. (1931). 'A study of the effects of modification of the culture medium upon length of life and fecundity in a Rotifer (*Proales sordida*), etc.' *Biol. Bull. Wood's Hole*, **60**, 30.

MACARTHUR, J. W., and BAILLIE, W. H. T. (1926). 'Sex differences in mortality and metabolic activity in *Daphnia magna*.' *Science*, **64**, 229.

—— (1929a). 'Metabolic activity and duration of life. I. Influence of temperature on longevity in *Daphnia magna*.' *J. exp. Zool.*, **53**, 221.

—— (1929b). 'Metabolic activity and duration of life. II. Metabolic rates and their relation to longevity in *Daphnia magna*.' *J. exp. Zool.*, **53**, 243.

—— (1932). 'Sex differences of mortality in Abraxas-type species.' *Quart. Rev. Biol.*, **7**, 313.

McCANCE, R. A., and WIDDOWSON, A. M. (1955). 'A fantasy on ageing and the bearing of nutrition upon it.' *CIBA Foundation Colloquia on Ageing*, **1**, 186.

McCAY, C. M. (1952). In Lansing, A. I. (Ed.), *Problems of ageing*. Baltimore: Williams and Wilkins Co.

319

Bibliography

McCay, C. M., and Crowell, M. F. (1934). 'Prolonging the life-span.' *Sci. Mon.*, **39**, 405.

McCay, C. M., Maynard, L. A., Sperling, G., and Barnes, L. L. (1939). 'Retarded growth, life span, ultimate body size and age changes in the albino rat after feeding diets restricted in calories.' *J. Nutrit.*, **18**, 1.

McCay, C. M., Maynard, L. A., Sperling, G., and Osgood, H. S. (1941). 'Nutritional requirements during the latter half of life.' *J. Nutrit.*, **21**, 45.

McCay, C. M., Pope, F., and Lunsford, W. (1956). 'Experimental prolongation of the life span.' *Bull. N.Y. Acad. Med.*, **32**, 91–101.

McCay, C. M., Pope, F., Lunsford, W., Sperling, G., and Samvhavapol, P. (1957). 'Parabiosis between old and young rats.' *Gerontologia*, **1**, 7–17.

McCay, C. M., Sperling, L. S., and Barnes, L. L. (1943). 'Growth, ageing and chronic diseases and life span in the rat.' *Arch. Biochem.*, **2**, 469.

McCullough, E. P., and Renshaw, J. F. (1934). 'The effects of castration in the adult male.' *J. Amer. med. Ass.*, **103**, 1140.

Macdonnell, W. R. (1913). 'On the expectation of life in ancient Rome and in the provinces of Hispania and Lusitania, and Africa.' *Biometrika*, **9**, 366.

McDowell, E. C., Taylor, M. T., and Broadfort, T. (1951). *Carnegie Inst. Wash. Year Book*, **50**, 200.

McGavack, T. H. (1951). 'Endocrine patterns during aging.' *Amer. J. Int. Med.*, **35**, 961.

McIlhenny, E. A. (1940). 'Sex ratio in wild birds.' *Auk*, **57**, 85.

McIlwain, H. (1946). 'The magnitude of microbial reactions involving vitamin-like compounds.' *Nature, Lond.*, **158**, 898.
— (1949). 'Metabolic changes which form the basis of a microbiological assay of nicotinic acid.' *Proc. Roy. Soc. (B)*, **136**, 12.

McLaren, A., and Michie, D. (1954). 'Are inbred strains suitable for bioassay?' *Nature, Lond.*, **173**, 686.

McMillan, N. F. (1947). 'The ecology of *Limapontia capitata* (Müller). *J. Conchol.*, **22**, 277–85.

Madigan, F. C. (1959). 'A life table for religious priests, 1953–1957.' *Review for Religious*, **18**, 225–31.

Magnus-Levy, H., and Falk, E. (1899). 'Der Lungengaswechsel der Menschen in den verscheidenen Alterstugen.' *Pflugers. Arch. ges. Physiol.* (Physiol. Suppl.), 314.

Malpas, A. H. (1933). 'Further observations of the age and growth rate of the Ceylon pearl oyster, *Margaritifera vulgaris*.' *Bull. Ceylon Fisheries*, **5**, 21–48.

Mandl, M., and Zuckerman, S. (1952). 'Factors influencing the onset of puberty in albino rats.' *J. Endocrinol.*, **8**, 357.

Manschot, W. A. (1940). 'Een geval van progero-nanie (Progeria von Gilford).' *Nederl. Tijdschr. Geneesk*, **84**, 3374.

Bibliography

MANSCHOT, W. A. (1940). *Over Progeronanie*. Amsterdam: Van Gorcum & Co.

(1950). *Acta Paediatr. Stockh.*, **39**, 158.

MANSFIELD, A. W., and Fisher, H. D. (1960). 'Age determination in the harbour seal, *Phoca vitulina* L.' *Nature, Lond.*, **186**, 92–3.

MANVILLE, R. H. (1958). 'Concerning platypuses.' *J. Mammal.*, **130**, 582–3.

MARIANI, T., MARTINEZ, C., SMITH, J. M., and GOOD, R. A. (1960). 'Age factor and induction of immunological tolerance to male skin iso-grafts in female mice subsequent to the neonatal period.' *Ann. N.Y. Acad. Sci.*, **87**, 93–105.

MARINESCO, G. (1934). 'Nouvelle contribution à l'étude du mécanisme de la vieillesse.' *Bull. Acad. Med. Paris*, **111**, 761.

(1934). 'Études sur le mécanisme de la vieillesse.' *Rev. Soc. argent. Biol.*, **10**, 355.

MARKUS, H. C. (1934). 'Life history of the blackhead minnow. (*Pimephales promelas*).' *Copeia*, 116–22.

MARSHAK, A. (1936). 'Growth differences in reciprocal hybrids and cytoplasmic influence on growth in mice.' *J. exp. Zool.*, **72**, 497.

MARSHAK, A., and BRYON, R. L. (1945). 'The use of regenerating liver as a method of assay.' *Proc. Soc. exp. Biol., N.Y.*, **59**, 200.

MARSHALL, H. (1947). 'Longevity of the American herring gull.' *Auk*, **64**, 188.

MARSHALL, J. T. (1898). 'Additions to British Conchology.' *J. Conchol.*, **9**, 120–38.

MARZOLF, R. C. (1955). 'Use of pectoral spines and vertebrae for determining age and rate of growth of the Channel Catfish.' *J. Wildl. Manag.*, **19**, 243–9.

MASON, K. E., and WOLFE, J. M. (1930). 'The physiological activity of the hypophyses of rats under various experimental conditions.' *Anat. Rec.*, **45**, 232.

MASTERS, W. H. (1952). 'The female reproductive system.' In COWDRY, E. V., *Problems of ageing*. Williams and Wilkins Co.

MATHESON, C. (1950). 'Longevity in the grey seal.' *Nature, Lond.*, **166**, 73.

MATTESON, M. R. (1948). 'Life history of *Elliptio complanatus* (Dillw.).' *Amer. midl. Nat.*, **40**, 690–723.

MATTHES, E. (1951). 'Der Einfluss der Fortpflanzung auf die Lebensdauer eines Schmetterlings (*Fumea crassiorella*).' *Z. vergl. Physiol.*, **33**, 1.

MAUPAS, E. (1883). 'Contribution à l'étude morphologique et anatomique des Infusoires ciliés.' *Arch. Zool. exp. gen. S. 2*, **1**.

(1886). 'Recherches expérimentales sur la multiplication des Infusoires ciliés.' *Arch. Zool. exp. gen. S. 2*, **6**.

Bibliography

MAURIZIO, A. (1946). 'Beobachtungen über die Lebensdauer und den Futterverbrauch gefangen gehaltener Bienen.' *Beih. Schweiz. Beinenztg.*, **2,** 1.

— (1950). 'Untersuchungen über den Einfluss der Pollennahrung und Brutpflege auf die Lebensdauer und den physiologische Zustand von Bienen.' *Schweiz. Beinenztg.*, **73,** 58.

— (1959). 'Factors influencing the life span of bees.' *CIBA Foundation Colloquia on Ageing*, **5,** 231–43.

MAYER, J. (1949). 'Definition and quantitative expression of ageing.' *Growth*, **13,** 97.

MAYNARD SMITH, J. (1958a). 'The effects of temperature and of egglaying on the longevity of *Drosophila subobscura*.' *J. exp. Biol.*, **35,** 832–42.

— (1958b). 'Prolongation of the life of *Drosophila subobscura* by a brief exposure of adults to a high temperature.' *Nature, Lond.*, **181,** 496–7.

— (1959a). 'A theory of ageing.' *Nature, Lond.*, **184,** 956–8.

— (1959b). 'Sex limited inheritance of longevity in *Drosophila subobscura*.' *J. Genet.*, **56.**

— (1959c). 'Rate of ageing in *Drosophila subobscura*.' *CIBA Foundation Colloquia on Ageing*, **5,** 269–81.

— (1962). 'The causes of ageing.' *Proc. Roy. Soc.* (*B*), **157,** 115–27.

MAYNARD SMITH, J., and MAYNARD SMITH, S. (1954). 'Genetics and cytology of *Drosophila subobscura*. VIII. Heterozygosity, viability and rate of development.' *J. Genet.*, **52,** 152.

MEAD, A. D., and BARNES, E. W. (1904). 'Observations on the soft-shelled clam.' *34th Rep. Comm. Inland Fish.*, *Rhode Island*.

MEDAWAR, P. B. (1940). 'The growth, growth-energy and ageing of the chicken's heart.' *Proc. Roy. Soc.* (*B*), **129,** 332.

— (1942). 'Discussion of growth and new growth.' *Proc. Roy. Soc. Med.*, **35,** 500.

— (1945). 'Old age and natural death.' *Modern Quart.*, **1,** 30.

— (1952). *An unsolved problem of biology*. London: H. K. Lewis.

MEDCOF, J. C. (1940). 'On the life cycle and other aspects of the snail *Campeloma* in the Speed River.' *Canad. J. Res.*, **18**D, 165–72.

MEIJERING, M. P. D. (1958). 'Herzfrequenz und Lebensablauf von *Daphnia magna* Straus.' *Z. f. wiss. Zool.*, **161,** 239–65.

— (1960). 'Herzfrequenz und Herzschlagzahlen zwischen Häutung und Eiablage bei Cladoceren.' *Z. f. wiss. Zool.*, **164,** 127–42.

MELLEN, I. (1939). *A practical cat book for amateurs and professionals*. Scribner, N.Y.

— (1940). *The Science and Mystery of the Cat*. Scribner, N.Y.

METALNIKOV, S. (1936). 'L'évolution de la mort dans le règne animal.' *Rév. gen. Sci.*, 31 Jan. 1936.

— (1937). *La lutte contre la mort*. Paris: Gallimard.

Bibliography

METCHNIKOFF, E. (1904). *The Nature of Man*. London: Heinemann.

(1907). *The prolongation of life—optimistic studies*. London: Heinemann.

(1915). 'La mort du papillon du murier—un chapitre de thanatologie.' *Ann. Inst. Pasteur.* (1915), p. 477.

MEYERS, G. S. (1952). 'Annual fishes.' *Aquarium J.*, **23**, 125.

MIESCHER, K. (1955). 'The problem of ageing.' *Experientia*, **11**, 417–40.

MILDVAN, A. S., and STREHLER, B. L. (1960). 'A critique of theories of mortality.' *AIBS Symposium*, 'The Biology of Aging'. Publ. No. 6, 216–35.

MILLER, H. M. (1931). 'Alternation of generations in the rotifer *Lecane inermis* Bryce. I. Life histories of the sexual and non-sexual generations.' *Biol. Bull. Wood's Hole*, **60**, 345.

MILLER, M. C. (1962). 'Annual cycles of some Manx nudibranchs.' *J. anim. Ecol.*, **31**, 545–69.

MINER, R. W. (1954). Editor. 'Parental age and characteristics of the offspring.' *Ann. N.Y. Acad. Sci.*, **57**, 451.

MINOT, C. S. (1908). *The problem of age, growth and death; a study of cytomorphosis, based on lectures at the Lowell Institute, March 1907*. London.

(1913). *Moderne Probleme der Biologie*. Jena.

MISHAIKOV, D. (1929). (Title unknown.) *Trimesechno Spisanie Glavnata Direkt. Statist.*, **1**, 153, 174.

MITCHELL, P. C. (1911). 'On longevity and relative viability in mammals and birds, with a note on the theory of longevity.' *Proc. zool. Soc.*, **1**, 425.

MOHLER, S. R. (1961). 'General biology of senescence.' *Postgrad. Med.*, **30**, 527–38.

MOHR, E. (1951). 'Lebensdauer einiger Tiere in Zoologischen gärten.' *Zool. Gärt., Lpz.*, **18**, 60.

MOLE, R. H. (1957). 'Shortening of life by chronic irradiation—the experimental facts.' *Nature, Lond.*, **180**, 456–68.

MOLE, R. H., and THOMAS, A. M. (1961). 'Life shortening in female CBA mice exposed to daily irradiation for limited periods of time.' *Int. J. Radiation Biol.*, **3**, 493–508.

MOLISCH, H. (1938). *The longevity of plants*. New York: N.Y. Botanical Garden.

MOLTONI, E. (1947). 'Fringuello vissuto in schiavitù per ben 29 anni.' *Riv. ital. Orn.*, **17**, 139.

MONTGOMERY, T. H. (1906). 'On reproduction, animal life cycles and the biological unit.' *Trans. Tex. Acad. Sci.*, **9**.

MOON, H. D., SIMPSON, M. E., LI, C. H., and EVANS, H. M. (1952). 'Effects of pituitary growth hormone in mice.' *Cancer Res.*, **12**, 448.

MOORE, C. R., and SAMUELS, L. T. (1931). 'Action of testis hormone in correcting changes induced in rat prostate and seminal vesicles by vitamin B deficiency or partial inanition.' *Amer. J. Physiol.*, **96**, 278.

Bibliography

MOORE, D. (1924). 'Note on the longevity of *Clonorchis sinensis*.' *U.S. Public Health Reports*, **39,** 1802.

MOORE, H. B. (1934). 'The biology of *Balanus balanoides*. I. Growth rate in relation to size, season and tidal level.' *J. mar. Biol. Ass. U.K.,* **19,** 851.

—— (1935). 'A comparison of the biology of *Echinus esculentus* in different habitats.' *J. mar. Biol. Ass. U.K.,* **20,** 109.

—— (1938–9). 'The biology of *Purpura lapillus*: (Part III): Life history and relation to environmental factors.' *J. mar. Biol. Ass. U.K.,* **23,** 67–74.

—— (1957). 'The biology of *Littorina littorea*. I. Growth of shell and tissues, spawning, length of life and mortality.' *J. mar. Biol. Ass. U.K.,* **21,** 721–42.

MORANT, G. M. (1950). 'Secular changes in the heights of British people.' *Proc. Roy. Soc. (B),* **137,** 443.

MORTIMER, R. K., and JOHNSTON, J. R. (1959). 'Life span of individual yeast cells.' *Nature, Lond.,* **183,** 1751–2.

MORTON, J. E. (1954). 'Notes on the ecology and annual cycle of *Carychium tridentatum* at Box Hill.' *Proc. malac. Soc. London,* **31,** 30–45.

MOSKOVLJEVIĆ, V. (1939). *Bee World,* **20,** 83; **21,** 39–41.

MOYSEY, F. E. (1963). 'A tale of two tortoises.' *Trans. Proc. Torquay nat. Hist. Soc.,* **13,** 7–12.

MUHLBOCK, O. (1959). 'Factors influencing the life span of inbred mice.' *Gerontologia,* **3,** 177–83.

MUHLMANN, M. S. (1900). *Über die Ursache des Alters.* Wiesbaden: Bergman.

—— (1911). 'Das Altern und der physiologische Tod.' *Samml. anat. physiol. Vortr.,* **1,** 455.

—— (1924). 'Meine Theorie des Alterns und des Todes; zugleich zur Abwehr.' *Virchows Arch.,* **253,** 225.

—— (1927). 'Wachstum, Altern und Tod. Über die Ursache des Alterns und des Todes.' *Ergeb. Anat. EntwGesch.; Anat. Abt.,* **27,** 1.

MULINOS, M. G., and POMERANTZ, L. (1941). 'Hormonal influences on weight of adrenal in inanition.' *Amer. J. Physiol.,* **132,** 368.

MURIE, A. (1944). *The wolves of Mount McKinley.* U.S. Dep. Int. Nat. Park Service, Washington.

MURRAY, J. (1910). 'Antarctic Rotifera.' *British Antarctic Expedition, 1907–1909,* **1** (3), 41.

MURRAY, W. S. (1934). 'The breeding behaviour of the dilute brown stock of mice (Little *dba*).' *Amer. J. Cancer,* **20,** 573.

MURRAY, W. S., and HOFFMANN, J. G. (1941). 'Physiological age as a basis for the comparison of strains of mice subject to spontaneous mammary carcinoma.' *Cancer Res.,* **1,** 298.

NAGORNYI, A. V. (1948). Нагорный, А. Б.: 'Старение и продление жизни.' (Old age and the prolongation of life.) Sovietskaya Nauka, Moscow.

NASCHER, I. (1920). 'A noted case of longevity—John Shell, centenarian.' *Amer. Med.,* **15,** 151.

Bibliography

NAYAR, K. N. (1955). 'Studies on the growth of the wedge clam *Donax* (*Latona*) *cuneatus* Linn.' *Indian J. Fish.*, **2**, 325–49.

NEARY, G. J., MUNSON, R. J., and MOLE, R. N. (1957). *Chronic irradiation of mice by fast neutrons.* Pergamon Press.
   (1960). 'Ageing and radiation.' *Nature, Lond.*, **187**, 10–18.

NEEDHAM, A. E. (1950). 'Growth and regeneration rates in relation to age in Crustacea.' *J. Geront.*, **5**, 5.

NEEDHAM, J. (1942). *Biochemistry and morphogenesis.* Cambridge: University Press.

NEUBERGER, A., and SLACK, H. G. B. (1953). 'The metabolism of collagen from liver, bone, skin and tendon in the normal rat.' *Biochem. J.*, **53**, 47.

NEUHAUS, W. (1957). 'Hohes Alter einer Waldmaus (*Apodemus sylvaticus* L, 1758).' *Saügetierek. Mitt.*, **5**, 171–2.

NEWCOMBE, C. L. (1935). 'Growth of *Mya arenaria* in the Bay of Fundy region.' *Canad. J. Res. Ottawa*, **13**, 97–137.
   (1936). 'Validity of concentric rings of *Mya arenaria* L. for determining age.' *Nature, Lond.*, **137**, 191–2.

NEWMAN, G. (1959). [Communication to 12th Annual Meeting of the Gerontological Society of America.] *J. Gerontol.*, **14**, 491–515.

NICHOLS, J. T. (1939). 'Data on size, growth and age in the box turtle, *Terrapene carolina.*' *Copeia*, **14**.

NIKITIN, V. N. (1954). Никитин, Б.Н.: 'Долголетие'' (Longevity.) *Sci. & Life, Moscow*, (8) 27.
   (1958). Отечественные работы по возрастной физиологии, биохимии и морфологии (Russian studies of age, physiology, biochemistry and morphology.) Kharkov: University Press.
   (1960). Влияние продолжительного калорийнонедостаточного питания на длительность жизни, метаболизм и эндокринные железы крыс. [Influence of prolonged calorie-deficient feeding on longevity, metabolism and endocrine glands in rats.] In *ВОПРОСЫ ГЕРОНТОЛОГИИ И ГЕРИАТРИЯ* (Questions of Gerontology and Geriatrics). Leningrad: State Medical Publishing Ho.

NIWA, N. (1950). 'Life of *Viviparus malleatus.*' *Bull. Jap. Soc. sci. Fish.*, **16**, 108–10.

NOBLE, G. K. (1931). *The Biology of the Amphibia.* New York: McGraw-Hill.

NOLAND, L. E., and CARRIKER, M. R. (1946). 'Observations on the biology of the snail *Limnaea stagnalis appressa* during 20 generations in laboratory culture.' *Amer. midl. Nat.*, **36**, 467–93.

NORRIS, J. L., BLANCHARD, J., and POLOVNY, C. (1942). 'Regeneration of rat liver at different ages.' *Arch. Path.* (*Lab. Med.*), **34**, 208.

Bibliography

NORRIS, M. J. (1933). 'Contributions toward the study of insect fertility. II. Experiments on the factors influencing fertility in *Ephestia kuhniella* Z.' *Proc. zool. Soc. Lond.*, 903.

(1934). 'Contributions toward the study of insect fertility. III. Adult nutrition, fecundity and longevity in the genus *Ephestia*.' *Proc. zool. Soc. Lond.*, 334.

NORTHROP, J. (1917). 'The effect of prolongation of the period of growth on the total duration of life.' *J. biol. Chem.*, **32**, 123.

DU NOUŸ, P. L. (1916). 'Cicatrization of wounds.' *J. exp. Med.*, **24**, 461.

(1932). 'Une mesure de l'activité physiologique.' *C.R. Soc. Biol., Paris*, **109**, 1227.

(1936). *Biological Time*. Methuen, London.

NOVÁK, E. (1921). *Menstruation and its disorders*. New York: Appleton.

(1944). 'The constitutional type of precocious female puberty, with a report of nine cases.' *Amer. J. Obst. Gynec.*, **47**, 20.

NOYES, B. (1922). 'Experimental studies on the life history of a rotifer reproducing parthenogenetically (*Proales decipiens*).' *J. exp. Zool.*, **35**, 222.

OHSUMI, S., NISHIWAKI, M., and HIBIYA, T. (1958). 'Growth of fin whales in the northern part of the N. Pacific.' *Sci. Rep. Whales Res. Inst.*, **13**, 97–133.

OLDHAM, C. (1930). 'Fecundity of *planorbis corneus*.' *Naturalist*, 177.

(1931). 'Note on *V(iviparus) contectus*.' *J. Conchol.*, **19**, 179.

(1942a). 'Autofecundation and duration of life in *Limax cinereoniger*.' *Proc. malac. Soc. Lond.*, **25**, 9.

(1942b). 'Notes on *Geomalacus maculosus*.' *Proc. malac. Soc. Lond.*, **25**, 10.

OLIFF, W. D. (1953). 'The mortality, fecundity and intrinsic rate of natural increase of the multimammate mouse (*Rattus (Mastomys) natalensis* Smith) in the laboratory.' *J. Anim. Ecol.*, **22**, 217.

OLIVER, J. A. (1935). 'Young Billy Johnson's old box turtle.' *Animal Kingdom*, **56**, 154.

OLSEN, W. W. (1944). 'Bionomics of the lymnaeid snail *Stagnicola bulimoides techella*, the intermediate host of the liver fluke in southern Texas.' *J. agric. Res.*, **69**, 389–403.

ORTON, J. H. (1928). 'On rhythmic periods of shell growth in *Ostrea edulis* with a note on fattening.' *J. mar. Biol. Ass. U.K.*, **15**, 365.

(1929). 'Reproduction and death in invertebrates and fishes.' *Nature, Lond.*, **123**, 14.

ORTON, J. H., and AMURTHALINGAM, C. (1930). 'Giant English Oysters.' *Nature, Lond.*, **126**, 309.

Bibliography

OSBORNE, T. B., and MENDEL, L. B. (1914). 'The suppression of growth and the capacity to grow.' *J. biol. Chem.*, **18**, 95.

— (1916). 'The resumption of growth after long-continued failure to grow.' *J. biol. Chem.*, **23**, 439.

— (1916). 'Acceleration of growth after retardation.' *Amer. J. Physiol.*, **40**, 16.

PAI, S. (1928). 'Die Phasen des Lebenzyklus der *Anguillula aceti* Ehr. und ihre experimentellmorphologische Beeinflussung.' *Z. wiss. Zool.*, **131**, 293.

— (1934). 'Regenerationsversuche an Rotatorien.' *Sci. Rep. Univ. Chekiang*, **1**.

PANNIKKAR, N. K. (1938). 'Recent researches on *Trochus*.' *Current Sci.*, *Bangalore*, **6**, 552–3.

PARHON, C. I. (1955). *Biologia Vîrstelor—cercetari clinici și exerimentale.* Bucharest: Acad. R.P.R.

PARHON, C. I., PITIS, M., STAN, M., and PETRESCO, S. (1961). 'Étude physiologique de la fibre collagène du rat blanc thyréo-gonadectomisé.' *Gerontologia*, **6**, 118–25.

PARK, T. (1945). 'Life tables for the black flour-beetle, *Tribolium madens* Charp.' *Amer. Nat.*, **79**, 436.

PARKER, G. H. (1926). 'The growth of turtles.' *Proc. Nat. Acad. Sci. Wash.*, **12**, 422.

— (1929). 'The growth of the loggerhead turtle.' *Amer. Nat.*, **63**, 367.

PARKER, W. R. (1933). 'Pelorus Jack.' *Proc. Linn. Soc.*, 1933, p. 2.

PARKES, A. S. (1929). 'Note on the growth of young mice suckled by rats.' *Ann. Appl. Biol.*, **16**, 171.

— (1942–4). 'Induction of superovulation and superfecundation in rabbits.' *J. Endocrinol.*, **3**, 268.

PARKES, A. S., and SMITH, A. U. (1953). 'Regeneration of rat ovarian tissue grafts after exposure to low temperatures.' *Proc. Roy. Soc.* (B), **140**, 455.

PARSONS, P. A. (1962). 'Maternal age and developmental variability.' *J. exp. Biol.*, **39**, 251–60.

PARSONS, R. J. (1936). In *Medical papers dedicated to H. A. Christian.* Baltimore.

PAYNE, F. (1949). 'Changes in the endocrine glands of the fowl with age.' *J. Geront.*, **4**, 193.

— (1952). 'Cytological changes in the cells of the pituitary, thyroids, adrenals and sex [glands of the ageing fowl.' In LANSING, *Problems of ageing.*

PEABODY, F. E. (1958). 'A Kansas drouth recorded in growth zones of a bull snake.' *Copeia* (1958), 91–4.

— (1961). 'Annual growth zones in living and in fossil vertebrates.' *J. Morph.*, **108**, 11–62.

Bibliography

PEARCE, J. M. (1936). 'Age and tissue respiration.' *Amer. J. Physiol.*, **114**, 255.

PEARCE, L., and BROWN, W. H. (1960). 'Hereditary premature senescence in the rabbit.' *J. exp. Med.*, **111**, 485–516.

PEARL, R. (1927). 'On the distribution of differences of vitality among individuals.' *Amer. Nat.*, **61**, 113.

— (1928). *The rate of living.* New York: Knopf.

— (1940). *Introduction to medical biometry and statistics*, 3rd edn. Pennsylvania: W. B. Saunders Co.

PEARL, R., and DOERING, C. R. (1923). 'A comparison of the mortality of certain lower organisms with that of man.' *Science*, **57**, 209.

PEARL, R., and MINER, J. R. (1935). 'Experimental studies in the duration of life. XIV. The comparative mortality of certain lower organisms.' *Quart. Rev. Biol.*, **10**, 60.

— (1936). 'Life tables for the pecan-nut case bearer (*Acrobasis caryae*, Grote).' *Mém. Mus. Hist. nat. Belg.*, **3**, 169.

PEARL, R., PARK, T., and MINER, J. R. (1941). 'Experimental studies on the duration of life. XVI. Life-tables for the flour beetle *Tribolium confusum* Duval.' *Amer. Nat.*, **75**, 5.

PEARL, R., and PARKER, S. L. (1924). 'Experimental studies on the duration of life. IX. New life-tables for *Drosophila*.' *Amer. Nat.*, **58**, 71.

— (1922). 'Experimental studies in the duration of life. II. Hereditary differences in duration of life in line-bred strains of *Drosophila*.' *Amer. Nat.*, **56**, 174.

PEARL, R., and PEARL, R. de W. (1934). *The ancestry of the long-lived.* London: H. Milford.

— (1943). 'Studies on human longevity. VI. Distribution and correlation of variation in the total immediate ancestral longevity of nonagenarians and centenarians in relation to inheritance factor in the duration of life.' *Hum. Biol.*, **6**, 98.

PEARSON, K. (1895). 'Mathematical contributions to the theory of evolution. II. Skew variations in homogeneous material.' *Phil. Trans. Roy. Soc.*, **186**, Ser. A, 343.

PEARSON, K., and ELDERTON, E. M. (1913). 'On the hereditary character of general health.' *Biometrika*, **9**, 320.

PEARSON, O. P. (1945). 'Longevity of the short-tailed shrew.' *Amer. Midl. Nat.*, **34**, 531.

PEARSON, O. P., and BALDWIN, P. H. (1953). 'Reproduction and age structure of a mongoose population.' *J. Mammal.*, **34**, 436.

PEASE, M. (1947). 'How long do poultry breeding stock live?' *J. Ministr. Agric.*, **54**, 263.

PEASE, M. S. (1928). 'Experiments on the inheritance of weight in rabbits.' *J. Genet.*, **20**, 261.

Bibliography

PELSENEER, P. (1894). 'Introduction à l'étude des mollusques.' *Mém. Soc. roy. Malac. Belg.*, **37** (1892), 31–243 (p. 54).

—— (1932). 'Un moyen de déterminer la durée de la vie des mollusques.' *C.R. Ass. franc. Av. Sci.*, **56**, 289.

—— (1934). 'La durée de la vie et l'âge de la maturité sexuelle chez certains mollusques.' *Ann. Soc. zool. Belge*, **64**, 93.

—— (1935). *Essai d'Éthologie Zoologique.* Bruxelles.

PENFOLD, W. J., PENFOLD, H. B., and PHILLIPS, M. (1936). 'A survey of the incidence of *Taenia saginata* infestation in the population of the State of Victoria, etc.' *Med. J. Australia*, 23rd Year, I, **283**.

PERKINS, C. B. (1948). 'Longevity of snakes in captivity in the U.S.' *Copeia*, 217.

PERKS, W. (1932). 'On some experiments in the graduation of mortality statistics.' *J. Inst. Actu.*, **63**, 12–57.

PERRONE, J. C., and SLACK, H. G. B. (1952). 'The metabolism of collagen from skin, bone and liver in the normal rat.' *Biochem. J.*, **49**, lxxii.

PERRY, J. S. (1953). 'The reproduction of the African elephant, *Loxodonta africana*.' *Phil. Trans. Roy. Soc. (B)*, **237**, 93.

PERRY, R. (1953). 'Some results of bird ringing.' *New Biol.*, **15**, 58.

PETROVA, M. K. (1946). Петрова, М.К.: 'О роли фунпиональной ослабленной коры головного мозга в возниковеннии различных патологических процессов.' (Functional weakening of the cerebral cortex in the aetiology of various disease states.) Moscow.

PETTER-ROUSSEAUX, A. (1953). 'Recherches sur la croissance et le cycle d'activité testiculaire de *Natrix natrix helvetica* (Lacépède).' *Terre et Vie*, **100**, 175–223.

PFLUGFELDER, O. (1948). 'Volumetrische Untersuchungen an den corpora allata der Honigbiene (*Apis mellifica*).' *Biol. Zbl.*, **67**, 223.

PICADO, T. C. (1930). 'Effets des injections de serum homologue sur la taille et croissance des animaux.' *Ann. Inst. Pasteur*, **44**, 584.

PICADO, T. C., and ROTTER, W. (1936). 'Précipitines anti-glandes endocrines et longévité chez quelques espèces de vertébrés.' *C.R. Soc. Biol.*, Paris, **123**, 869.

PIEPHO, H. (1938). 'Über die Auslösbarkeit überzähliger Haütungen und vorzeitiger Verpuppung an Hautstücken bei Kleinschmetterlingen.' *Naturwiss.*, **26**, 841.

PIERSON, B. F. (1938). 'Relation of mortality after endomixis to the prior interendomitotic interval in *Paramecium aurelia*.' *Biol. Bull. Wood's Hole*, **74**, 235.

PINCUS, G. (1950). 'Measures of stress responsivity in younger and older men.' *Psychosom. Med.*, **12**, 225.

PITT, F. (1945). 'Breeding of the harvest mouse in captivity.' *Nature, Lond.*, **155**, 700.

Bibliography

PIXELL-GOODRICH, H. (1920). 'Determination of age in honey bees.' *Quart. J. micr. Sci.*, **64,** 191.

PLATE, L. (1886). 'Beiträge zur Naturgeschichte der Rotatorien.' *Jena Z. f. Naturwiss.*, **19,** 1.

POLEŽAIEV, L. V., and GINSBURG, G. I. (1939). 'Studies by the method of transplantation on the loss and restoration of the regenerative power in the tailless amphibian limbs.' *C.R. Acad. Sci. U.R.S.S.*, **23,** 733.

PONTECORVO, G. (1946). 'Microbiology, biochemistry and the genetics of microorganisms.' *Nature, Lond.*, **157,** 95.

PORTER, A. (1958). 'A venerable gander.' *Country Life*, 30/10/58, 1010.

POSGAY, J. A. (1954). In HASKINS, H. H. (1955).

PRUITT, W. O. (1954). 'Ageing in the masked shrew, *Sorex cinereus cinereus* Kerr.' *J. Mammal.*, **35,** 35.

PRZIBRAM, H. (1909). *Experimental-Zoologie*. Vienna. Vol. II, p. 126.

PUCK, T. T. (1961). 'Cellular aspects of irradiation and aging in animals.' *Fed. Proc.*, **20,** Suppl. 8, 31–4.

PULLMAN, B., and PULLMAN, A. (1962). 'Electronic delocalization and biochemical evolution.' *Nature, Lond.*, **196,** 1137–42.

PÜTTER, A. (1921). 'Die ältester Menschen.' *Naturwiss.*, **9,** 875.

QUAYLE, D. B. (1952). 'The rate of growth of *Venerupis pullastra* (Montagu) at Millport, Scotland.' *Proc. Roy. Soc. Edinb.*, (B), **64,** 384–406.

QUICK, H. E. (1924). 'Length of life of *Paludestrina ulvae*.' *J. Conchol.*, **17,** 169.

RABB, G. B. (1960). 'Longevity record for mammals at the Chicago Zoological park.' *J. Mammal.*, **41,** 113–14.

RABEN, M. S., and WESTERMEYER, V. W. (1952). 'Differentiation of growth hormone from the pituitary factor which produces diabetes.' *Proc. Soc. exp. Biol.*, **80,** 83.

RABES, O. (1901). 'Über Transplantations-Versuche an Lumbriciden.' *Biol. Zbl.*, **21,** 633.

RAFFEL, D. (1932). 'The occurrence of gene mutations in *Paramecium durelia*.' *J. exp. Zool.*, **63,** 371.

RAHM, P. G. (1923). 'Beiträge zur Kenntnis der Moosfauna.' *Z. allg. Physiol.*, **20,** 1.

RANKIN, N. (1957). 'A goose nearly 50 years old.' *Country Life*, 7/2/1957.

RAO, H. S. (1937). 'On the habitat and habits of *Trochus niloticus* Linn. in the Andaman seas.' *Rec. Ind. Mus., Calcutta*, **39,** 47–82.

RAPSON, A. M. (1952). 'The Toheroa, *Amphidesma ventricosum* Gray (Eulamellibranchiata): development and growth.' *Amer. J. marine freshw. Res.*, **3,** 170–98.

Bibliography

RASQUIN, P., and HAFTER, E. (1951). 'Age changes in the testis of the teleost, *Astyanax americanus*.' *J. Morph.*, **89**, 397.

RAU, P. (1924). 'The biology of the roach, *Blatta orientalis* Linn.' *Trans. Acad. Sci. St. Louis*, **25**, 57.

RAU, P., and RAU, N. (1914). 'Longevity in saturnid moths and its relation to the function of reproduction.' *Trans. Acad. Sci. St. Louis*, **23**, 1.

v. REDEN, K. A. (1960). 'Sterblichkeitsmaxima bei *Daphnia magna* Straus.' *Z. f. wiss. Zool.*, **164**, 119–26.

REDFIELD, A. C. (1939). 'The history of and population of *Limacina retroversa* during its drift across the Gulf of Maine.' *Biol. Bull.*, **76**, 26–47.

REECE, R. P., and TURNER, C. W. (1937). 'The lactogenic and thyrotropic hormone content of the anterior lobe of the pituitary gland.' *Univ. Missouri Agr. Exp. Sta. Res. Bull.*, **266**, 1.

REGAN, W. M., MEAD, S. W., and GREGORY, P. W. (1947). 'The relation of inbreeding to calf mortality.' *Growth*, **11**, 101.

REICHENBACH, M., and MATHERS, R. A. (1959). In BIREN, J. E. *A handbook of aging and the individual*. Univ. Chicago Press.

REINER, J. M. (1947). 'The effect of age on the carbohydrate metabolism of tissue homogenates.' *J. Gerontol.*, **2**, 315.

RENSCH, B. (1954). 'The relation between the evolution of the central nervous functions and the body-size of animals.' In HUXLEY, J., HARDY, A. C., and FORD, E. B. *Evolution as a Process*. Allen & Unwin, London.

REY, P. (1936). 'La longévité des *Galleria* adultes, mâles et femelles.' *C.R. Soc. Biol.*, **121**, 1184.

RIBBANDS, C. R. (1950). 'Changes in the behaviour of honey-bees following their recovery from anaesthesia.' *J. exp. Biol.*, **27**, 302.
—— (1952). 'Division of labour in the honey-bee community.' *Proc. Roy. Soc. (B)*, **140**, 32.
—— (1953). *The behaviour and social life of honey bees*. London: Bee Research Association Ltd.

RIBBERT, H. (1908). *Der Tod aus Altersschwäche*. Bonn: Cohen.

RICHARDS, O. W. (1953). *The Social Insects*, p. 188. London: Macdonald.

RICKER, W. E. (1945). 'Natural mortality among Indiana blue-gill sunfish.' *Ecology*, **26**, 111.
—— (1948). 'Methods of estimating vital statistics of fish populations.' *Indiana Univ. Publ. Sci. Ser.*, **15**, 1.

RIESEN, W. H., HERBST, E. J., WALLIKER, C., and ELVEHJEM, C. A. (194–). 'The effect of restrictive calorie intake on the longevity of rats.' *Amer. J. Physiol.*, **148**, 614–17.

RILEY, W. A. (1919). 'The longevity of the fish tapeworm of man, *Diphyllobothrium latum*.' *J. Parasitol.*, **5**, 193.

RISBEC, J. (1928). 'De la durée d'évolution chez *Aeolidia amoena* Risb.' *C.R. Acad. Sci., Paris*, **191**, 278–80.

Bibliography

RIZET, G. (1953). 'Sur l'impossibilité d'obtenir la multiplication vegetative ininterrompue et illimitée de l'Ascomycète *Podospora anserina.*' *C.R. Acad. Sci.*, **237**, 828.

ROBERTSON, F. W., and REEVE, E. C. R. (1952). 'Heterozygosity, environmental variation, and heterosis.' *Nature, Lond.*, **170**, 286.

ROBERTSON, O. H., DRUPP, M. A., THOMAS, S. F., FAVOM, C. B., HANE, S., and WEXLER, B. C. (1961). 'Hyperadrenocorticism in spawning migratory and non-migratory Rainbow Trout (*Salmo gairdnerii*); comparison with Pacific Salmon (*Genus Oncorhynchus*).' *Endocrinol.*, **1**, 473–84.

ROBERTSON, O. H., and WEXLER, B. C. (1959). 'Hyperplasia of the adrenal cortical tissue in Pacific salmon and Rainbow trout accompanying sexual maturation and spawning.' *Endocrinol.*, **65**, 225–38.

—— (1962). 'Histological changes in the organs and tissues of senile castrated Kokanee Salmon.' *Gen. compar. Endocrinol.*, **2**, 458–72.

ROBERTSON, T. B. (1923). *The chemical basis of growth and senescence.* Philadelphia.

ROBERTSON, T. B., DAWBARN, M. C., WALTERS, J. W., and WILSON. J. D. O. (1933). 'Experiments on the growth and longevity of the white mouse, II.' *Aust. J. exp. Biol. med. Sci.*, **11**, 219.

ROBERTSON, T. B., MARSTON, H. K., and WALTERS, J. W. (1934). *Aust. J. exp. Biol. and Sc.*, **12**, 33.

ROBERTSON, T. B., and RAY, L. A. (1919). 'Experimental studies on growth, XI. The influence of pituitary gland tissue, tethelin, egg lecithin, and cholesterol upon the duration of life in the white mouse.' *J. biol. Chem.*, **37**, 427.

—— (1920). 'Experimental studies on growth. XV. On the growth of relatively long-lived compared with that of relatively short-lived animals.' *J. biol. Chem.*, **42**, 71.

ROBSON, J. M. (1947). *Recent advances in sex and reproductive physiology.* London: Churchill.

ROCKSTEIN, M. (1950). 'The relation of cholinesterase activity to change in cell number with age in the brain of the adult worker honey bee.' *J. cell. comp. Phys.*, **35**, 11.

—— (1953). 'Some aspects of physiological aging in the adult worker honey bee.' *Biol. Bull.*, **105**, 154–9.

—— (1958). 'Heredity and longevity in the animal kingdom.' *J. Gerontol.*, **13**, suppl. 2, 7–12.

—— (1959). 'The biology of aging in insects.' *CIBA Foundation Colloquia on Ageing*, **5**, 247–63.

ROCKSTEIN, M., and GUTFREUND, D. E. (1961). 'Age changes in adenine nucleotides in flight muscles of male house fly.' *Science*, **133**, 1476–7.

ROCKSTEIN, M., and LIEBERMAN, H. M. (1958). 'Survival curves for male and female house flies (*Musca domestica* L.).' *Nature, Lond.*, **181**, 787–8.

Bibliography

ROGERS, J. B. (1950). 'The development of senility in the guinea pig.' *Anat. Rec.*, **106**, 286.

ROKHLINA, M. L. (1951). Рохлина, М.Л.: 'Путь с долголетию.' (The road to longevity.) Pravda, Moscow.

ROLLINAT, R. (1934). 'La vie des reptiles de la France centrale.' Paris.

ROSENTHAL, O., BOWIE, M. A., and WAGONER, G. (1940). 'Metabolism of cartilage (bovine) with particular reference to the effects of ageing.' *J. Amer. med. Ass.*, **115**, 2114.

—— (1941). 'Studies in the metabolism of articular cartilage. I. Respiration and glucolysis of cartilage in relation to age.' *J. cell. comp. Physiol.*, **17**, 221.

—— (1942). 'The dehydrogenetic ability of bovine articular cartilage in relation to its age.' *J. cell. comp. Physiol.*, **19**, 333.

ROSS, M. H. (1961). 'Length of life and nutrition in the rat.' *J. Nutrit.*, **75**, 197–210.

ROTHSCHILD, A., and ROTHSCHILD, M. (1939). 'Some observations on the growth of *Peringia ulvae* (Penn) in the laboratory.' *Novit. Zool.*, **41**, 240–7.

ROTHSCHILD, M. (1935). 'Gigantism and variation in *Peringia ulvae* Penn, caused by infection with larval trematodes.' *J. mar. Biol. Ass. U.K.*, **20**, 537.

—— (1941–3). 'The effect of trematode parasites on the growth of *Littorina neritoides* (L.).' *J. mar. Biol. Ass. U.K.*, **25**, 69–78.

ROUX, W. (1881). *Der Kampf der Teile im Organismus.* Leipzig.

RUBBEL, VON A. (1913). 'Beobachtungen über das Wachstum von *Margaritana margaritifera*.' *Zool. Anz.*, **41**, 156–62.

RUBIN, B. L., DORFMAN, R. I., and PINCUS, G. (1955). '17-ketosteroid excretion in ageing subjects.' *CIBA Foundation Symposia on Ageing*, **1**, 126.

RUBNER, M. (1908). 'Probleme des Wachstums und der Lebensdauer.' *MittGes. inn. Med., Wien*, **7**, 58.

RUDZINSKA, M. (1951). 'The influence of amount of food on the reproduction rate and longevity of a Suctorian (*Tokophrya infusionum*).' *Science*, **113**, 10–11.

—— (1952). 'Overfeeding and life-span in *Tokophyra infusionum*.' *J. Gerontol.*, **7**, 544.

RUGH, R., and WOLFF, J. (1958). 'Increased radioresistance through heterosis.' *Science*, **127**, 144–5.

RUSSELL, W. L. (1957). 'Shortening of life in the offspring of mice exposed to neutron radiation from an atomic bomb.' *Proc. nat. Acad. Sci. U.S.*, **43**, 324.

RUTGERS, A. J. (1953). 'Mortality by cancer as a function of age.' *Experientia*, **12**, 470.

Bibliography

RUTMAN, R. J. (1950). 'A maternal influence on the incorporation of methionine into liver protein.' *Science*, **112**, 252.

— (1951). 'The inheritance of rates of methionine uptake by rat liver protein and relations to growth.' *Genetics*, **36**, 59.

RUUD, J. T., JONSGARD, A., and OTTESTAD, P. (1950). 'Age studies in blue whales.' *Hvalråd. Skr.*, **33**, 1.

RŮŽÍČKA, V. (1924). 'Beiträge zum Studium der Protoplasmahysteretischen Vorgänge (Zur Kausalität des Alterns).' *Arch. mikr. Anat.*, **101**, 459.

— (1929). 'Beiträge zum Studium der Protoplasmahysteresis, etc. (Zur Kausalität des Alterns).' *Arch. EntwMeck. Org.*, **116**, 104.

SACHER, G. A. (1956). 'On the statistical nature of mortality, with especial reference to chronic radiation mortality.' *Radiology*, **67**, 250–7.

— (1957). 'Dependence of acute radiosensitivity on age in adult female mouse.' *Science*, **125**, 1039–40.

— (1958). 'Reparable and irreparable injury.' In *Radiation Biology and Medicine* (ed. W. D. Claus). Addison-Wesley Co., Reading, Mass.

— (1958). 'Entropic contributions to mortality and aging.' In *Symposium on Informn Theory Biology*, Pergamon Press.

— (1959). 'Relation of life span to brain and body weight in mammals.' *CIBA Foundation Colloquia on Ageing*, 115–33, 1959.

SACHER, G. A., GRAHN, D., HAMILTON, K., GURIAN, J., and LESHER, S. (1958). 'Survival of LAF mice exposed to Co^{60} γ rays for the duration of life at dosages of 6–20,000 r/day.' *Radiat. Res.*, **9**, 175–6.

SACHER, G. A., and TRUCCO, E. (1962). 'A theory of the improved performance and survival produced by small doses of radiations and other poisons.' In *Biological Aspects of Aging*. London & New York: Columbia Univ. Press.

SALDAU, M. P. (1939), Салдау, М.П.: Темп роста промысловых моллюсков некоторых районов европейской части СССР. (Growth rate of commercially valuable molluscs in some districts of the European part of the USSR.) *Bull. Inst. freshw. Fish., Leningr.*, **22**, 244–69.

SALMON, T. N. (1941). 'Effect of pituitary growth substance on the development of rats thyroidectomised at birth.' *Endocrinology*, **29**, 291.

SAMUELS, L. T. (1946). 'The relation of the anterior pituitary hormones to nutrition.' *Rec. Prog. Hormone Res.*, **1**, 147.

SANDERSON, W. A. (1949). [Report of British Association Symposium on social and psychiatric aspects of ageing.] *Nature, Lond.*, **163**, 221.

SANDGROUND, J. H. (1936). 'On the potential longevity of various helminths, with a record from a species of *Trichostrongylus* in man.' *J. Parasit.*, **22**, 464.

SAVORY, T. H. (1927). *The biology of spiders*. London: Sidgwick and Jackson.

Bibliography

Sawin, P. B. (1954). In Miner, R. W. (Ed.) 'Parental age and characteristics of the offspring.' *Ann. N.Y. Acad. Sci.*, **57**, 451.

Saxton, J. A. (1945). 'Nutrition and growth and their influence on longevity in rats.' *Biol. Sympos.*, **11**, 177.

Saxton, J. A., and Kimball, G. C. (1941). 'Relation of nephrosis and other diseases of albino rats to modifications of diet.' *Arch. Path., Chicago*, **32**, 951.

Saxton, J. H., and Greene, H. S. N. (1939). 'Age and sex differences in hormone content of the rabbit hypophysis.' *Endocrinology*, **24**, 494.

Schäfer, H. (1953). 'Untersuchungen zu Ökologie von *Bithynia tentaculata*.' *Arch. Molluskenk.*, **82**, 67–70.

Schaffer, V. B. (1950). 'Growth layers on the teeth of Pinnipedia as an indication of age.' *Science, N.Y.*, **112**, 309.
   (1958). 'Long life of a River Otter.' *J. Mammal.*, **39**, 591.

Schloemer, C. L. (1936). 'The growth of the muskellunge, *Esox masquinongy immaculatus* (Garrard) in various lakes and drainage areas of Northern Wisconsin.' *Copeia*, **185**.

Schlomka, G., and Kersten, E. (1952). 'Über Möglichkeiten einer statistischen Altenscharakteristik auf Grund von Morbiditätszahlen.' *Z. Altersforsch.*, **6**, 306.

Schlottke, E. (1930). 'Zellstudien an *Hydra*. I. Altern und Abbau von Zellen und Kernen.' *Z. mikr.-anat. Forsch.*, **22**, 493.

Schmalhausen, I. (1928). 'Das Wachstumsgesetz und die Methode der Bestimmung der Wachstumskonstante.' *Arch. EntwMeck. Org.*, **113**, 462.
   (1929). 'Zum Wachstumstheorie.' *Arch. EntwMeck. Org.*, **116**, 5677.

Schmidt, H. (1923). 'Über den Alterstod der Biene.' *Jena Z. f. Naturwiss.*, **59**, 343.

Schmidt, W. J. (1952). 'Einiges über das altern der Tiere.' *Z. Altersforsch.*, **6**, 344.

Schneider, K. M. (1932). 'Zum Tode des Leipzigen Riesensalamanders.' *Zool. Gärt., Lpz.*, **5**, 142.

Schulze-Röbbecke, G. (1951). 'Untersuchungen über Lebensdauer, Altern, und Tod bei Anthropoden.' *Zool. Jb.*, **62**, 366.

Scow, R. O., and Marx, W. (1945). 'Response to pituitary growth hormone of rats thyroidectomized on the day of birth.' *Anat. Rec.*, **91**, 227.

Sebesta, F. (1935). 'Beobachtungen über das Alter der Raniden.' *Blätt. Aq. Terrar.*, **46**, 115.

Sekera, E. (1926). 'Beiträge zur Kenntnis der Lebensdauer bei einigen Turbellarien und Süsswassernemertinen.' *Zool. Anz.*, **66**, 307.

Seltger, R., and Sartwell, P. E. (1958). 'Ionising radiation and the longevity of physicians.' *J. Amer. med. Ass.*, **166**, 585–7.

Bibliography

SELYE, H. (1946). 'General adaptation syndrome and diseases of adaptation.' *J. clin. Endocrin.*, **6**, 117.

— (1962). *Calciphylaxis.* Univ. Chicago Press.

SELYE, H., and ALBERT, S. (1942). 'Age factor in responsiveness of pituitary and adrenal folliculoids.' *Proc. Soc. exp. Biol.*, *N.Y.*, **50**, 159.

SENNING, W. C. (1940). 'A study of age determination and growth of *Necturus maculosus* based on the parasphenoid bone.' *Am. J. Anat.*, **66**, 483.

SERGEEV, A. (1937). 'Some materials to the problem of the reptile post-embryonic growth.' *Zool. Zh.*, **16**, 723.

— (1939). [? title]. *Probl. Ecol. Biotsen.*, *Leningr.*, **4**, 276.

SESHAIYA, R. V. (1927). 'On the breeding habits and fecundity of the snail *Limnaea luteola* Lk.' *J. Bombay nat. Hist. Soc.*, **32**, 154.

SETTE, O. E. (1943). 'Biology of the Atlantic mackerel (*Scomber scombrus*) of North America. I. Early life history including the growth, drift and mortality of the egg and larval population.' *Bull. U.S. Fish. Wildl. Serv. Fish.*, **50**, 147.

SEVERTSOV, A. N. (1939). Северцов, А.Н.: 'Морфологические закономерности Зволюционного процесса.' (Morphological laws of the evolutionary process.) *Sorena*, **3**, 23.

SEWELL, R. B. S. (1924). 'Observations on growth in certain molluscs and on the changes correlated with growth in the radula of *Pyrazus palustris*.' *Rec. Ind. Mus. Calcutta*, **27**, 529–48.

SEYMOUR, F. I., DUFFY, C., and KOERNER, A. (1935). 'A case of authenticated fertility in a man aged 94.' *J. Amer. med. Ass.*, **105**, 1423.

SHANKLIN, W. M. (1953). 'Age changes in the histology of the human pituitary.' *Acta anat.*, Basel, **19**, 290.

SHARP, D. (1883). 'Longevity in a beetle.' *Entom. monthly Mag.*, **19**, 260.

SHARP, W. M. (1958). 'Aging gray squirrels by the use of tail pelage characteristics.' *J. wildl. Manag.*, **22**, 39–44.

SHAW, R. F., and BERCAW, B. L. (1962). 'Temperature and life span in poikilothermous animals.' *Nature, Lond.*, **196**, 454–7.

SHELDON, J. H. (1949). *Social medicine of old age.* Oxford University Press.

SHELDON, W. G. (1949). 'Reproductive behaviour of foxes in New York State.' *J. Mammal.*, **30**, 236.

SHEMIN, D., and RITTENBERG, D. (1944). 'Some interrelationships in general nitrogen metabolism.' *J. biol. Chem.*, **153**, 401.

SHEPS, M. C. (1961). 'Marriage and mortality.' *Am. J. pub. Health*, **51**, 547–55.

SHERMAN, H. C., and CAMPBELL, H. L. (1935). 'Rate of growth and length of life.' *Proc. Nat. Acad. Sci.*, **21**, 235.

Bibliography

SHOCK, N. W. (1942). 'Standard values for basal oxygen consumption in adolescence.' *Amer. J. Dis. Childhood*, **64**, 19.

(1948). 'Metabolism in old age.' *Geriatrics*, **1**, 232.

(1951). *A classified bibliography of gerontology and geriatrics*. U.S.A.: Stanford University Press.

SHOCK, N. W., WATKIN, D. M., and YIENGST, M. J. (1954). 'Age changes in renal function and basal oxygen consumption as related to total body water.' *Fed. Proc.*, **13**, 136.

SHULOV, A. (1939–40). 'On the biology of *Latrodectes* spiders in Palestine.' *Proc. Linn. Soc., Lond.*, **309**.

SILBERBERG, M., and SILBERBERG, R. (1951). 'Diet and life-span.' *Physiol. Rev.*, **35**, 347–62.

(1954). 'Factors modifying the life span of mice.' *Amer. J. Physiol.*, **177**, 23.

SIMMONDS, L. W. (1945). *The role of the aged in primitive society*. Yale University Press.

(1946). 'Attitudes toward ageing and the aged: primitive societies.' *J. Geront.*, **1**, 72.

SIMMONDS, M. (1914a). 'Über embolische Prozesse in der Hypophysis.' *Arch. f. path. Anat.*, **217**, 226.

(1914b). 'Zur Pathologie der Hypophysis.' *Verh. dtsch. path. Ges.*, **17**, 808.

SIMMS, H. S. (1936). 'The effect of physiological agents upon adult tissues in vitro.' *Science*, **83**, 418.

(1958). 'Aging and longevity of rats under favourable conditions.' *Publ. Hlth. Rep. U.S. Public Health Service*, **73**, 1115–16.

SIMMS, H. S., and STILLMAN, N. P. (1936). 'Substances affecting adult tissue *in vitro*. II. A growth inhibitor in adult tissue.' *J. gen. Physiol.*, **20**, 621.

(1937). 'Substances affecting adult tissue *in vitro*. III. A stimulant (the "A" factor) in serum ultrafiltrate involved in overcoming adult tissue dormancy.' *J. gen. Physiol.*, **20**, 649.

SIMONSEN, M., ENGELBRETH-HOLM, J., JENSEN, E., and POULSEN, H. (1958), 'A study of the graft-versus-host reaction in transplantation to embryos. F_1 hybrids, and irradiated animals.' *Ann. N.Y. Acad. Sci.*, **73**, 834–9.

SINCLAIR, H. M. (1955). 'Too rapid maturation in children as a cause of ageing.' *CIBA Foundation Colloquia on Ageing*, **1**, 194.

SINEX, F. M. (1957). 'Aging and the lability of irreplaceable molecules.' *J. Geront.*, **12**, 190–8.

SIVERTSEN, E. (1941). 'On the biology of the Harp Seal, *Phoca groenlandica* Ersel.' *Hvalråd. Skr., Oslo*, No. 26.

SLEPTZOV, M. M. (1940). 'Détermination de l'âge chez *Delphinus delphis* L.' *Bull. Soc. Nat. Moscow*, **49**, 43.

Bibliography

SLONAKER, J. R. (1912). 'The normal activity of the albino rat from birth to natural death, its rate of growth and the duration of life.' *J. Anim. Behav.*, **2**, 20.

—— (1930). 'The effect of the excision of different sexual organs on the development, growth and longevity of the albino rat.' *Am. J. Physiol.*, **93**, 307.

SMALLWOOD, W. M., and PHILIPS, R. L. (1916). 'The nuclear size in the nerve cells of bees during the life cycle.' *J. comp. Neurol.*, **27**, 69.

SMART, I., and LEBLOND, C. P. (1961). 'Evidence for the division and transformations of neuroglia cells in the mouse brain as derived from radioautography after injection of thymidine-H³.' *J. comp. Neurol.*, **116**, 349–66.

SMITH, M. (1951). *The British amphibians and reptiles.* London: Collins.

SMITH, P. E., and DORTZBACH, C. (1929). 'The first appearance in the anterior pituitary of the developing pig foetus of detectable amounts of the hormones stimulating ovarian maturity and general body growth.' *Anat. Rec.*, **43**, 277.

SMYTH, N. (1937). 'Longevity in horses.' *Cavalry J.*, **27**, 101.

SOLLAUD, E. (1916). 'Recherches sur la biologie des "Palemonides" des côtes de la France.' *Rec. Fonds Bonaparte*, **1**, 69.

SOLOMON, D. R., and SHOCK, N. W. (1950). 'Studies of adrenal cortical and anterior pituitary function in elderly men.' *J. Gerontol.*, **5**, 302.

SONDÉN, K., and TIGERSTEDT, R. (1895). 'Die Respiration und der Gesammtstoffwechsel des Menschen.' *Skand. Arch. Physiol.*, **6**, 1.

SONNEBORN, T. M. (1930). 'Genetic studies on *Stenostomum incaudatum* n.sp. I. The nature and origin of differences in individuals formed during vegetative reproduction.' *J. exp. Zool.*, **57**, 57.

—— (1938). 'The delayed occurrence and total omission of endomixis in selected lines of *Paramecium aurelia*.' *Biol. Bull. Wood's Hole*, **74**, 76.

—— (1960). 'The human early foetal death rate in relation to the age of father.' Publ. No. 6 *The Biology of Aging*, p. 288. AIBS, Washington.

SONNEBORN, T. M., and SCHNELLER, M. (1960a). 'Physiological basis of aging in *Paramecium*.' *Ibid.*, 283–4.

—— (1960b). 'Age induced mutations in *Paramecium*.' *Ibid.*, 286–7.

SOROKINA, M. I. (1950). Сорокина, М.И.: 'Об изменчивости хромосомного комплекса в тканевых клетах теплокровных животных.' (Variability of the chromosome complex in tissue cells of warm-blooded animals.) *Bull. Acad. Sci. U.R.S.S.*, **6**, 97.

SOSNOVSKI, I. P. (1957). 'On the longevity of animals in the Moscow Zoo.' *Priroda*, **9**, 119–20.

SPARROW, A. H., and SCHAIVER, L. A. (1958). 'The radioresistance of high polyploids.' *Radiat. Res.*, **9**, 187.

SPEAR, F. G. (1928). 'The effect of low temperature on mitosis *in vitro*.' *Arch. exp. Zellforsch.*, **1**, 484.

Bibliography

SPECTOR, W. S. (1956). *Handbook of biological data*. Saunders.

SPEMANN, F. W. (1924). 'Über Lebensdauer, Altern und andere Fragen der Rotatorien-biologie.' *Z. wiss. Zool.*, **123**, 1.

SPENSER, R. R., and MELROY, M. B. (1949). 'Studies of survival of unicellular species. I. Variations in life expectancy of a paramecium under laboratory conditions.' *J. nat. Cancer Inst.*, **10**, 1.

SPIEGELMAN, S., BARON, L. S., and QUASTLER, H. (1951). 'Enzymatic adaptation in non-viable cells.' *Fed. Proc.*, **10**, 130.

STEARNS, R. E. C. (1877). 'On the vitality of certain land molluscs.' *Amer. Nat.*, **11**, 100–2.

STEBBINS, R. C. (1948). 'Additional observations on home ranges and longevity in the lizard *Sceleporus graciosus*.' *Copeia*, **20**.

STEBBINS, R. C., and ROBINSON, H. B. (1946). 'Further analyses of a population of the lizard *Sceleporus graciosus gracilis*.' *Univ. Calif. Publ. Zool.*, **48**, 149.

STEINMETZ, C. H. (1954). 'Some effects of thyroxine and antithyroid compounds on tadpoles and their relation to hormonal control of growth.' *Physiol. Zool.*, **27**, 28.

STEPHAN, H. (1954). 'Die Anwendung der Snell'schen Formel $h = k^s.p$ auf die Hirn-Korpergewichtsbeziehungen bei verschiedenen Hunderassen.' *Zool. Anz.*, **153**, 15–27.

STEPHEN, A. C. (1931). 'Notes on the biology of certain lamellibranchs on the Scottish coast.' *J. mar. Biol. Ass. U.K.*, **17**, 277–300.

STEPHENSON, R. A. (1935). *British sea anemones*. London: The Ray Society.

STEVENSON, J. A. (1932). 'Growth in the giant scallop squid (*Loligo pealii*) at St. Andrews N.B.' *Ann. Rep. Biol. Bd. Ottawa*, pp. 37–8.

STEWART, D. C., and KIRK, P. L. (1954). 'The liquid medium in tissue culture.' *Biol. Revs.*, **29**, 119.

STOKES, B. (1958). 'The worm-eating slugs *Testacella scutulum* Sow. and *T. haliotidea* Drap. in captivity.' *Proc. malac. Soc. Lond.*, **33**, 11–20.

STOLČ, A. (1902). 'Über den Lebenszyklus der niedrigsten Süsswasserannulaten und über einiger sich anschliessende biologische Fragen.' *Bull. intern. Acad. Sci. Bohème*, 1902.

STOLTE, H. A. (1924). 'Altersveränderung bei limicolen Oligochäten.' *Verhand. Deutsch. Zool. Ges.*, **29**, 43.

— (1927). 'Studien zur Histologie des Altersprozesses.' *Z. wiss. Zool.*, **129**, 1.

— (1937). 'Gestaltung, Zeichnung und Organabbau unter dem Einfluss normaler und "alternden" gonaden bei *Polyophthalmus pictus* (Polychaeta).' *Z. wiss. Zool.*, **150**, 107.

STORER, J. B. (1959). 'Rate of recovery from radiation damage and its possible relation to life-shortening in mice.' *Radiat. Res.*, **10**, 180–5.

Bibliography

STREHLER, B. L. (1959). 'Origins and comparisons of the effects of time and high energy radiations on living systems.' *Quart. Rev. Biol.*, **34**, 117–42.

— (1961). 'Aging in coelenterates.' In LENHOFF, H. M., and LOOMIS, W. F., *Biology of Hydra and other Coelenterates*. Univ. Miami Press, Coral Gables.

— (1962). *Time, cells and aging.* Academic Press, London and New York.

— (1962). 'Further studies on the thermally-induced aging of *Drosophila melanogaster*.' *J. Gerontol.*, **17**, 347–52.

STRONG, L. C. (1936). 'Production of CBA strain inbred mice: long life associated with low tumour incidence.' *Brit. J. exp. Path.*, **17**, 60.

STRONG, L. C., and SMITH, G. M. (1936). 'Benign hepatomas in mice of the CBA strain.' *Amer. J. Cancer*, **27**, 279.

SUMMERS, F. M. (1938). 'Form regulation in *Zoothamnion alternans*.' *Biol. Bull. Wood's Hole*, **74**, 130.

SUNTZEFF, V., COWDRY, E. V., and HIXON, B. B. (1962). 'Possible maternal influence on longevity of offspring in mice.' *Biological Aspects of Aging*. New York & London: Columbia Univ. Press.

SUZUKI, S. (1935). 'On the age and growth of *Nerita japonica* Dunken.' *Sci. Rep. Imp. Tôhoku Univ.*, **10**, 247–56.

SUZUKI, Y. (1926). 'A study of the resistance of animals by the tissue culture method.' *Mitt. allg. Path. Sendai*, **2**, 191.

SWIFT, D. R. (1954). 'Influence of mammalian growth hormone on rate of growth of fish.' *Nature, Lond.*, **173**, 1096.

SWYER, G. I. M. (1954). *Reproduction and sex.* London: Routledge.

SZABÓ, I. (1931a). 'The three types of mortality curves.' *Quart. Rev. Biol.*, **6**, 462.

— (1931b). 'Absterben und Entwicklung.' *Biol. generalis*, **7**, 163.

— (1932a). *Elettartam és örëgedës.* Budapest.

— (1932b). 'Das Alterspigment bei einigen Schnecken, untersucht an überlebenden Ganglienzellen.' *Arb. ung. Biol. Forsch. Inst.*, **5**, 38.

— (1935). 'Senescence and death in invertebrate animals.' *Riv. Biol.*, **19**, 377.

SZABÓ, I., and SZABÓ, M. (1929). 'Lebensdauer, Wachstum und Altern, studiert bei der Nacktschneckenart *Agriolimax agrestis*.' *Biol. generalis*, **5**, 95–118.

— (1930a). 'Todesursachen und pathologische Erscheinungen bei Pulmonaten.' *Arch. f. Mollusk.*, **62**, 123.

— (1930b). 'Vorläufige Mitteilung über die an der Nacktschnecke *Agriolimax agrestis* beobachteten Altersveränderungen.' *Arb. Ungar. Biol. Forschungsinst.*, **3**, 350–7.

— (1931a). 'Todesursachen und pathologische Erscheinungen bei Pulmonaten. II. Hautkrankheiten bei Nacktschnecken.' *Arch. Molluskenk*, **63**, 156–60.

Bibliography

Szabó, I., and Szabó, M. (1931b). 'Histologische Studien über den Zusammenhang der verschiedenen Alterserscheinungen bei Schnecken. I and II.' *Z. vgl. Physiol.*, **15**, 329 and 345.

—— (1931c). 'Lebenszyklen der Nacktschnecke *Limax flavus* L.' *Zool. Anz.*, **96**, 35–8.

—— (1934a). 'Alterscheinungen und Alterstod bei Nacktschnecken.' *Biol. Zbl.*, **54**, 471–7.

—— (1934b). 'Lebensdauer und Körpergrösse einiger Nacktschnecken.' *Zool. Anz.*, **106**, 106–11.

—— (1936). 'Histologische Untersuchungen über den Zusammenhang zwischen Langlebigkeit und Fortpflanzung.' *Zool. Anz.*, **113**, 143–53.

Szabó, M. (1935a). 'Pathologische Erscheinungen bei Schnecken.' *Allattani Közl. T.*, **32**, 132.

—— (1935b). 'On a culture method for the rotifer *Lecane inermis* Bv. together with some notes on the biology of this animal.' *Arb. ung. Biol. Forsch. Inst.*, **8**.

Szilard, L. (1959). 'On the nature of the aging process.' *Proc. Nat. Acad. Sci.*, **45**, 30–45.

—— (1960). 'Dependence of the sex ratio at birth on the age of the father.' *Nature, Lond.*, **186**, 649–50.

Tack, E. (1940). 'Die Ellritze (*Phoxinus laevis* Bg.): eine monographische Bearbeitung.' *Arch. Hydrobiol.*, **37**, 321.

Tainter, M. L. (1936). 'Dinitrophenol in diet, on growth and duration of life of the white rat (*sic*).' *Proc. Soc. exp. Biol.*, **31**, 1161.

—— (1938). 'Growth, life-span and food intake of white rats fed dinitrophenol throughout life.' *J. Pharmacol.*, **63**, 51.

Tanaka, T. (1951). 'A study of the somatic chromosomes in various organs of the white rat (*Rattus norvegicus*) especially in regard to the number and its variation.' *Res. Genet.*, **2**, 39.

—— (1953). 'A study of the somatic chromosomes of rats.' *Cytologia*, **18**, 343.

Tang, S. F. (1941). 'The breeding of the escallop *Pecten maximus* (L) with a note on the growth rate.' *Proc. Lpool. biol. Soc.*, **54**, 9–28.

Tannenbaum, A. (1947). 'Effects of varying caloric intake upon tumor incidence and tumor growth.' *Ann. N.Y. Acad. Sc.*, **49**, 6–17.

Tanner, J. M. (1955). *Growth at Adolescence.* Oxford: Blackwell.

Tannreuther, G. (1919). 'Studies on *Asplanchnia ebbesborni* with special reference to the male.' *Biol. Bull. Wood's Hole*, **37**, 194.

Taylor, J. W. (1894–1924). *Monograph of the land and freshwater mollusca of the British Isles.* Taylor, Leeds.

Taylor, M. (1958). 'Longevity of *Proteus* group of amoebae.' *Nature, Lond.*, **182**, 1245.

Bibliography

TAYLOR, R. H. (1959). 'Age determination in wild rabbits.' *Nature, Lond.*, **184,** 1158–9.

TEGGE, M. S. (1936). 'Length of life of a rabbit.' *Science*, **84,** 575.

TEISSIER, G. (1934). 'Recherches sur le vieillissement et sur les lois de la mortalité. II. Essai d'interpretation générale des courbes de survie.' *Ann. Physiol. Phys-chim. biol.*, **10,** 260–84.

TERAO, A. (1931). 'Change of vitality with age as based on the living unit of the organism. I. Oxygen consumption in the daphnid *Simocephalus exspinosus.*' *Proc. Imp. Acad. Tokyo*, **7,** 23.

—— (1932). 'Duration of life in the water flea *Moina macropa* Straus, with special reference to rate of living.' *J. Imp. Fish. Inst.*, **27,** 63.

TERAO, A., and TANAKA, T. (1930). 'Duration of life in the water flea *Moina macropa* Straus in relation to temperature.' *J. Imp. Fish. Inst.*, **25,** 67.

TERESCHENKO, K. K. (1917). 'La brême (*Abramis brama*) de la région du Volga et de la mer Caspienne.' *Trav. Lab. Ichthyol. Astrakhan*, **4,** 2.

THANNHAUSER, S. J. (1945). 'Werner's syndrome (progeria of the adult) and Rothmund's syndrome: 2 types of closely related heredofamilial atrophic dermatoses with juvenile cataracts and endocrine features; a critical study with 5 new cases.' *Ann. int. Med.*, **23,** 559.

THEORELL, H., BÉZNAK, M., BONNICHSEN, R., PAUL, K. G., and ÅKESON, A. (1951.) 'Distribution of injected radioactive iron in guinea pigs and its rate of appearance in some hemoproteins and feuritins.' *Acta chem. Scand.*, **5,** 445.

THERMAN, E., and TIMONEN, S. (1951). 'Inconstancy of the human somatic chromosome complement.' *Hereditas*, **37,** 266.

THOMPSON, D'ARCY W. (1942). *On growth and form.* New ed., p. 199. Cambridge University Press.

THOMS, W. J. (1873). *The longevity of man: its facts and fictions.* London.

THOMSON, J., and FORFAR, J. O. (1950). 'Progeria (Hutchinson-Gilford syndrome). Report of a case and review of the literature.' *Arch. Dis. Childhood*, **25,** 224.

THÜMMEL, E. (1938). 'Lebensdauer einer Blindschleiche.' *Zool. Gärten., Lpz.*, **10,** 153.

THUNG, P. J. In BOURNE, G. (1962). 'Structural aspects of ageing.' Pitman Medical, London.

THURINGER, J. M. and KATZBERG, A. A. (1959). 'The effect of age on mitosis in the human epidermis.' *J. Invest Derm.*, **33,** 35–9.

TILL, J. E., and McCULLOCH, E. A. (1961). 'In vivo radiosensitivity of bone marrow.' *Radiat. Res.*, **14,** 213.

TIMONEN, S., and THERMAN, E. (1950). 'Variation of the somatic chromosome number in man.' *Nature, Lond.*, **166,** 995.

Bibliography

TODOROV, I. N. (1959). (Тодоров N. H.—Некоторые возрастные особенности в действии соматотрофного гормона гипофиза на обмен нуклейновых кислот.) 'Some age effects of pituitary somatotrophin on nucleic acid metabolism.' *Biochimiya*, **24**, 1010–19.

TOMILIN, M. I. (1936). 'Death of the oldest chimpanzee in captivity.' *Science*, **83**, 103.

TOMILIN, S. A. (1938). Томилин, С.А.: Статистика долговечности. (The statistics of longevity.) *Proc. Conf. Probl. Old Age, Kiev*, p. 247.

TOWNSEND, C. H. (1931). 'Growth and age in the giant tortoise of the Galapagos.' *Zoologica, N.Y.*, **9**, 469.

— (1937). 'Growth of the Galapagos tortoise, *Testudo vicina*, from 1928 to 1937.' *Zoologica, N.Y.*, **22**, 289.

TOWNSEND, F. (1946). 'Ageing processes in the endocrine glands.' *J. Geront.* **1**, 278.

TURNER, C. W., and CUPPS, P. T. (1938). 'The thyrotropic hormone of the pituitary in albino rats during growth, pregnancy and lactation.' *Endocrinology*, **24**, 650.

TURNER, C. W., and KEMPSTER, H. L. (1948). 'Mild hypothyroidism maintains egg production with advancing age.' *Poult. Sci.*, **27**, 453.

TYLER, A. (1953). 'Prolongation of the life span of sea urchin spermatozoa and improvement of the fertilization reaction, by treatment of sperm and eggs with metal chelating agents.' *Biol. Bull. Wood's Hole*, **104**, 224.

— (1960). 'Clues to the etiology, pathology and therapy of cancer provided by analogies with transplantation disease.' *J. nat. Cacu. Inst.*, **25**, 1197–1229.

UBISCH, L. (1926). 'Untersuchungen über Bau, Funktion, Entwicklung und Regeneration der Rense des Weibchens von *Stephanoceros eichorni*.' *Z. wiss. Zool.*, **127**, 590.

ULMER, F. A. (1960). 'A longevity record for the Mindanao Tarsier.' *J. Mammal.*, **41**, 512.

UNGAR, G. (1944). 'The inhibition of histamine release by a pituitary-adrenal syndrome.' *J. Physiol.*, **103**, 333–43.

UPTON, A. C. (1957). 'Ionizing radiation and the aging process.' *J. Gerontol.*, **12**, 306–13.

— (1960). 'Ionizing radiation and aging.' *Gerontologia*, **4**, 162–76.

UPTON, A. C., KIMBALL, A. W., FURTH, J., CHRISTENBERRY, K. W., and BENEDICT, W. H. (1960). 'Some delayed effects of atom-bomb radiations in mice.' *Cancer Res.*, **20**, 1–62.

UPTON, A. C., McDONALD, T. P., CHRISTENBERRY, K. W., and GUDE, W. D. (1961). 'Delayed somatic effects of radiometric agents and X-rays.' *Biol. Div. Semiannual Progress Rep., Feb. 15, 1961*. (Oak Ridge Nat. Lab. Publ., **3095**), p. 84.

Bibliography

VALLOIS, H. V. (1937). 'La durée de vie chez l'homme fossile.' *C.R. Acad. Sci.*, **204**, 60.

VAN CLEAVE, H. J. (1934). 'Length of life-span as a factor in regulating populations.' *Ecology*, **15**, 17.

— (1935). 'The seasonal life history of an amphibious snail, *Fossaria modicella*, living on sandstone cliffs.' *Ecology*, **16**, 101.

VAN CLEAVE, H. J., and ALTRINGER, D. A. (1937). 'Studies in the life cycle of *Campeloma rufum*, a freshwater snail.' *Amer. Nat.*, **71**, 167–84.

VAN CLEAVE, H. J., and CHAMBERS, R. (1935). 'Studies in the life history of a snail of the genus *Lioplax*.' *Amer. Midl. Nat.*, **16**, 913.

VAN CLEAVE, H. J., and LEDERER, L. C. (1932). 'Studies on the life cycle of the snail *Viviparus contectoides*.' *J. Morph.*, **53**, 499.

VAN CLEAVE, H. J., and MARKUS, H. C. (1929). 'Studies on the life cycle of the blunt-nosed minnow.' *Amer. Nat.*, **63**, 530.

VANE, F. R. (1946). 'Longevity of mayflies.' *Northw. Nat.*, **21**, 252.

VAN HEERDT, P. F., and SLUITER, J. W. (1955). 'Longevity in bats.' *Natuurhist. Maandbl.*, **44**, 35.

VARLEY, G. C. (1947). 'The natural control of population balance in the knapweed gall-fly (*Urophora jaceana*).' *J. Anim. Ecol.*, **16**, 139.

VASNETZOFF, V. V. (1934). 'Versuch einer vergleichenden Erforschung des Wachstums der Cypriniden.' *Zool. Zh.*, **13**, 540.

VENGE, O. (1953). 'Studies of the maternal influence on the growth in rabbits.' *Acta agric. Scand.*, **3**, 243.

VERZÁR, F. (1955). 'Veränderung der thermoelastischen Eigenschaften von Sehnenfasern beim Altern.' *Experientia*, **11**, 230.

— (1957). 'Aging of connective tissue.' *Gerontologia*, **1**, 363–78.

— (1959a). 'Influence of ionizing radiation on the age reaction of collagen fibres.' *Gerontologia*, **3**, 163–70.

— (1959b). 'Note on the influence of procain (Novocain) para-amino-benzoic acid or diethylethanolamin on the ageing of rats.' *Gerontologia*, **3**, 351–8.

VETUKHIV, M. (1957). 'Longevity of hybrids between geographic populations of *Drosophila pseudoobscura*.' *Evolution*, **11**, 348–60.

VICTOR, J., and POTTERS, J. S. (1935). 'Studies in mouse leukaemia: pre-leukaemic changes in lymphoid metabolism.' *Brit. J. exp. Path.*, **16**, 243.

VIGNAL, L. (1919). 'Observations sur les *Rumina decollata*.' *Bull. Soc. Zool. Fr.*, **44**, 115.

— (1923). 'De la durée de la vie chez l'*Helix spiriplana* Olivi.' *J. Conchyl.*, **67**, 262.

VISCHER, A. L. (1947). *Old age, its compensations and rewards*. London: Allen and Unwin.

Bibliography

VISSCHER, M. B., KING, J. T., and LEE, Y. C. P. (1952). 'Further studies of the influence of age and diet upon reproductive senescence in strain A female mice.' *Amer. J. Physiol.*, **170**, 72–6.

VOGT, C., and VOGT, O. (1946). 'Age changes in neurones.' *Nature, Lond.*, **158**, 304.

VOGT, W. (1949). *The road to survival.* London and New York.

WALFORD, R. L. (1962). 'Autoimmunity and aging.' *J. Gerontol.*, **17**, 281–5.

WALKER, B. E., and BOOTHROYD, E. R. (1953). 'Chromosome numbers in somatic tissues of mouse and man.' *Genetics*, **39**, 210.

WALKER, D. G., ASLING, C. W., SIMPSON, M. E., LI, C. H., and EVANS, H. M. (1952). 'Structural alterations in rats hypophysectomised at six days of age and their connection with growth hormone.' *Anat. Rec.*, **114**, 19.

WALNE, P. R. (1961). 'Observations on the mortality of *Ostrea edulis*.' *J. mar. biol. Ass. U.K.*, **41**, 113–22.

WALOFF, N., NORRIS, M. J., and BROADHEAD, E. C. (1947). 'Fecundity and longevity of *Ephestia elutella* Hubner.' *Proc. r. ent. Soc., Lond.*, **99**, 245.

WALTER, E. (1922). 'Über die Lebensdauer der freilebenden Süsswasser-cyclopiden und andere Fragen ihrer Biologie.' *Zool. Jb.* (Syst. Abt.), **44**, 375.

WALTERSTOFF, W. (1928). '*Triton (Cynops) pyrrhogaster* 25 Jähre.' *Blätt. Aquar. Terrar. Kde.*, **39**, 183.

WALTON, C. L., and HONES, W. W. (1926). 'Further observations on the life history of *Limnaea truncatula*.' *Parasitology*, **18**, 144–7.

WARDLE, R. A., and McLEOD, J. A. (1952). *The zoology of tapeworms.* Minneapolis: Univ. Minnesota Press.

WARREN, S. (1956). 'Longevity and causes of death from irradiation in physicians.' *J. Amer. med. Ass.*, **162**, 464–8.

WARTHIN, A. S. (1929). *Old age, the major involution; the physiology and pathology of the ageing process.* New York: Hoeber.

WATKIN, E. E. (1941). 'The yearly life cycle of the amphipod *Corophium volutator*.' *J. Anim. Ecol.*, **10**, 77.

WEBER, R. (1942). 'Höhes Alter verscheidenen Tiere im Düsseldorfer Zoologischen Garten.' *Zool. Gärt.*, **14**, 208.

WEIDENREICH, F. (1939). 'The duration of life of fossil man in China and the pathological lesions found in his skeleton.' *China med. J.*, **55**, 34.

WEISMANN, A. (1882). *Über die Dauer des Lebens.* Jena.
  —— (1891). 'The duration of life.' In *Essays upon heredity.* Oxford.

WEISS, J., and LANSING, A. I. (1953). 'Age changes in the fine structure of anterior pituitary of the mouse.' *Proc. Soc. exp. Biol., N.Y.*, **82**, 460.

WEISS, P. (1950). 'Perspectives in the field of morphogenesis.' *Quart. Rev. Biol.*, **25**, 177–98.

Bibliography

WELCH, R. (1901). 'Longevity of land molluscs.' *Irish Nat.*, **10**, 145.

WELLENSIEK, U. (1953). 'Die Allometrie verhältnisse und Konstruktions-änderung bei dem kleinsten Fisch im Vergleich mit etwas grösseren verwandten Formen.' *Zool. Jb. (Anat.)*, **73**, 187.

WENDT, A. (1934). 'Verjügung eines Marmormolches.' *Blätt. Aquar. Terrar.*, **45**, 281.

WERNER, C. W. O. (1904). *Über Katarakt in Verbindung mit Sklerodermie.* Inaugural Dissertation, Kiel.

WESTOLL, T. S. (1950). 'Some aspects of growth studies in fossils.' *Proc. Roy. Soc. (B)*, **137**, 490–509.

WEYER, F. (1931). 'Cytologische Untersuchungen am Gehirn alternden Bienen und die Frage nach dem Alterstod.' *Z. Zellforsch.*, **14**, 1–54.

WEYMOUTH, F. W., (1923). 'The life history and growth of the Pismo clam.' *Fish. Bull.*, **7**, State of Calif. Fish and Game Commission, Sacramento. (1931). 'The relative growth-rate and mortality of the Pacific razor clam (*Siliqua patula* Dixon) and their bearing on the commercial fishery.' *Bull. U.S. Bur. Fish.*, **46**, 543.

WEYMOUTH, F. W., and McMILLIN, H. C. (1931). 'The relative growth and mortality of the Pacific razor clam (*Siliqua patula* Dixon) and their bearing on the commercial fishery.' *Bull. U.S. Bureau Fish.*, **46**, 543–67.

WEYMOUTH, F. W., and THOMPSON, S. H. (1930). 'The age and growth of the Pacific cockle (*Cardium corbis* Martyn).' *Bull. U.S. Bur. Fish.*, *Washington*, **46**, 633–41.

WHEELER, J. F. G. (1934). 'On the stock of whales at South Georgia.' *Discovery Rep.*, **9**, 251.

WHEELWRIGHT, O. M. (1951). 'Life span of foxes.' *Field, Lond.*, **197**, 438.

WHITNEY, J. E., BENNET, L. L., LI, C. H., and EVANS, H. M. (1948). 'Effect of growth hormone on the N_2 excretion and body weight of adult female rats.' *Endocrinology*, **43**, 237.

WIDDOWSON, E. M., and KENNEDY, G. C. (1962). 'Rate of growth, mature weight, and life-span.' *Proc. Roy. Soc. (B)*, **156**, 96–108.

WIESNER, B. P. (1932). 'The experimental study of senescence.' *Brit. med. J.*, **ii**, 585.

WIESNER, B. P., and SHEARD, N. M. (1934). 'The duration of life in an albino rat population.' *Proc. roy. Soc. Edinb.*, **55**, 1.

WIESNER, B. P., and YUDKIN, J. (1952). 'Inhibition of oestrus by cultivated gromwell.' *Nature, Lond.*, **170**, 474.

WIGGLESWORTH, V. B. (1934). 'Physiology of ecdysis in *Rhodnius prolixus* (Hemiptera). II. Factors controlling moulting and metamorphosis.' *Quart. J. micr. Sci.*, **76**, 269. (1945). 'Transpiration through the cuticle of insects.' *J. exp. Biol.*, **21**, 97.

346

Bibliography

WIGGLESWORTH, V. B. (1953a). 'The thoracic gland in *Rhodnius prolixus* (Hemiptera) and its role in moulting.' *J. exp. Biol.*, **29**, 561.

(1953b). 'Hormone balance and the control of metamorphosis in *Rhodnius prolixus* (Hemiptera). *J. exp. Biol.*, **29**, 620.

WILKINS, G. L. (1948). 'Prolonged dormancy of *Planorbis corneus* L. and *Limnaea peregra* Müller.' *J. Conchol.*, **22**, 303.

WILL, L. C., and McCAY, C. M. (1943). 'Ageing, basal metabolism and retarded growth.' *Arch. Biochem.*, **2**, 481.

WILLIAMS, C., MOORHEAD, L. V., and PULIS, J. F. (1959). 'Juvenile hormone in thymus, human placenta and other mammalian organs.' *Nature, Lond.*, **183**, 405.

WILLIAMS, L. W. (1910). *The anatomy of the common squid (Loligo pealii* Leseur). E. J. Brill, Leiden.

WILSON, D. P. (1949). 'Notes from the Plymouth aquarium.' *J. mar. Biol. Ass. U.K.*, **28**, 345.

WILSON, M. A. (1950). 'Duration of life in *Rana temporaria* Linn.' *Brit. J. Herpetol.*, **3**, 66.

WIMPENNY, R. S. (1953). *The plaice*. London: Arnold.

WINSOR, C. P., and WINSOR, A. A. (1935). 'The longevity and fertility of the pond-snail *Limnaea columella*.' *J. Wash. Acad. Sci.*, **25**, 302–7.

WITSCHI, E. (1952). 'Gonadotropins of the human hypophysis, particularly in old age.' *J. Gerontol.*, **7**, 307.

WOLFE, J. M. (1941). 'Effects of testosterone propionate on the structure of the anterior pituitaries of old male rats.' *Endocrinol.*, **29**, 969.

(1943). 'The effects of advancing age in the structure of the anterior hypophysis and ovaries of female rats.' *Amer. J. Anat.*, **72**, 361.

WOODRUFFE, G. E. (1951). 'A life-history of the brown house moth, *Hofmannsphila pseudospretella* Faint.' *Bull. ent. Res.*, **41**, 529.

WOOLEY, G. W., and LITTLE, C. C. (1946). 'Prevention of adrenal cortical carcinoma by diethylstilboestrol.' *Proc. nat. Acad. Sci. Wash.*, **32**, 239.

WOOLLEY, G. (1946). In HAMILTON, J. B. (1948). *Rec. Prog. Hormone Res.*, **3**, 257.

WRIGHT, E. A., and SPINK, J. M. (1959). 'A study of the loss of nerve cells in the central nervous system in relation to age.' *Gerontologia*, **3**, 377–87.

WRIGHT, M. N. (1936). 'The oldest jennet?' *Field*, 1936, p. 1556.

WRIGHT, S. (1926). 'Effect of age of parents upon characteristics of the guinea pig.' *Amer. Nat.*, **60**, 552.

WURMBACH, H. (1951). 'Über Wachstum und Altern der Fische.' *Z. Altersforsch.*, **5**, 277.

WYATT, H. V. (1961). 'The reproduction, growth and distribution of *Calyptraea Chinensis* (L.).' *J. anim. Ecol.*, **30**, 283–302.

Bibliography

YACOB, M., and SWAROOP, S. (1945). 'Longevity and old age in the Punjab.' *Brit. med. J.*, **2**, 433.

YIENGST, M., BARROWS, C., and SHOCK, N. (1959). 'Age changes in the chemical composition of muscle and liver in the rat.' *J. Gerontol.*, **14**, 400–4.

YONGE, C. M. (1962). 'On the biology of the mesogastropod *Trichotropis cancellata* Hinds, a benthic indicator species.' *Biol. Bull.*, **122**, 160–81.

YOUNG, F. G. (1953). 'Growth hormone and diabetes.' *Rec. Prog. Hormone Res.*, **VIII**, 471.

YOUNG, T. E. (1899). *On centenarians and the duration of the human race.* London: Layton.

ZANNAS, E., and AUBOYER, J. (1960). *Khajurāho.* Mouton, The Hague.

ZELINKA, C. (1891). 'Studien über Rädertiere—III.' *Z. wiss. Zool.*, **53**, 323.

ZONDEK, B., and ASCHHEIM, S. (1927). 'Hypophysenvorderlappen und Ovarium.' *Arch. Gynaek.*, **130**, 1.

ZUCKERMAN, S. (1951). 'The number of oocytes in the mature ovary.' *Rec. Prog. Hormone Res.*, **6**, 63.

GENERAL INDEX

Abkhasians, longevity, 88f
absenteeism, 37
acceleration: negative, of growth, 13; of senescence, in mammals, 207f
accidents, road, deaths in, 25, 27
accumulation, 47, 91, 127, 135
acrogeria, 184
acromegaly, 250, 251
actinians, 80, 116, 148, 150
activity, and longevity, 139, 273
adaptation, senescence as evolved, 11, 49
adrenal, 221, 238ff, 250; mitosis in, 222
adrenaline, 238
adrenocorticotropic hormone, 238, 241
adrenopause, 236
age: chimaeras, 278; determination, 63; evidence of, 65, 86; maternal, effects, 125f, 169f; in molluscs, 77; parental, and longevity, 169ff; paternal, 172; specific, 5, 34, 49, 97, 98, 193, 217;——in mammals, 199;—— in man, 278;—— inheritance, 165
ageing, see senescence
aggregation, in rotifers, 128
agouti, 66
albatross, 154
alchemists, 3
alligator, see crocodile
America, centenarians, 90, 91
amphibia, 215, 231; age determination, 63; growth in, 94; longevity, 72f; senescence in, 113, 115, 247
Amphineura, 82
Amphipoda, 157

anabolic hormones, see hormones
analogies, mechanical, 5
androgens, 180, 242f
aneuploidy, somatic, 18, 163, 216, 232, 233
Annelids, 80, 120
antibodies, 225
ants, 81, 128
arthropods: longevity in, 80f; senescence in, 128ff
ascidians, 156
Ascomycetes, 160
asexual reproduction, 119, 160
ass, 66, 68
atresia, follicular, 245
Aurora, 2
autocatalytic reaction, 12, 44, 188
autoimmunity, 185, 227ff, 233
axolotl, 247

baboons, 52, 66
Bacon, Francis, 5, 10, 16, 18, 56, 64f, 74, 86, 115
bacteria, 10, 218
baldness, 184
bats, 66
bdelloids, 220
bears, 66
beaver, 66
Bécquerel, A. C., 4
bees, 18, 50, 136ff, 157, 194, 221
beetles, 75, 81, 133f
Belloc, Hilaire, 92
beluga, 73
Bernard, Claude, 17
Bidder, G. P., 13–16, 51, 93, 99, 108, 116
bilharzia, 205
biochemical criteria, of senescence, 40

349

INDEX OF GENERIC NAMES IN THE TEXT

361

Index of Generic Names in the Text